Macrophage Plasma Membrane Receptors: Structure and Function

Monocytes are constitutively recruited from blood to many normal tissues where they adopt a common stellate morphology as they differentiate into mature macrophages. Extensive arborization of plasma membrane processes occurs in brain (microglia) and epidermis (Langerhans cells). Drawn from mouse tissue sections after immunocytochemical demonstration of a mouse macrophage specific antigen, F4/80. See chapter by Gordon *et al.* for further details.

Macrophage Plasma Membrane Receptors: Structure and Function

Proceedings of a meeting in Oxford, March 1987

Organized and edited by

Siamon Gordon

(Sir William Dunn School of Pathology, University of Oxford)

SUPPLEMENT 9   1988
JOURNAL OF CELL SCIENCE
Published by THE COMPANY OF BIOLOGISTS LIMITED, Cambridge

Typeset, Printed and Published by
THE COMPANY OF BIOLOGISTS LIMITED
Department of Zoology, University of Cambridge, Downing Street,
Cambridge CB2 3EJ

© The Company of Biologists Limited 1988

ISBN: 0 948601 13 2

JOURNAL OF CELL SCIENCE SUPPLEMENTS

This volume is the latest in a continuing series on important topics in cell and molecular biology. All supplements are available free to subscribers to *Journal of Cell Science* or may be purchased separately from The Biochemical Society Book Depot, PO Box 32, Commerce Way, Colchester CO2 8HP, UK.

PREFACE

Recent progress has made it opportune to review current knowledge of macro-phage plasma-membrane receptor structure and function. The importance of specific surface receptors in innate and immune host defence has been appreciated for some time, since they play a key role in phagocytic recognition and the destruction of foreign organisms and infected target cells. We now know that macrophage receptors also help to control cell growth, differentiation and activation, recruitment and adhesion in tissues and interactions with numerous ligands on other host cells and in the extracellular milieu. Thus, they contribute to macrophage functions within the normal host and during many disease processes involving tissue injury, inflammation, remodelling and repair throughout the body, including the arterial wall and central nervous system.

An international symposium took place in Oxford on March 31, 1987 to review selected aspects of macrophage receptor biochemistry and cell biology. The meeting was sponsored by The Company of Biologists Limited and this volume provides a more detailed review of the field, completed in January 1988, which places the recent research in perspective. The contributions cover a range of cellular activities in which macrophage receptors contribute to haematopoietic growth and malignancy (CSF receptors), opsonization and phagocytosis (Fc and CR3), lectin-like interactions with microbial and cellular targets, and atherosclerosis (lipoprotein receptors). Signal transduction in macrophages is considered with reference to protein myristoylation and the actin cytoskeleton. Finally, the role of novel non-phagocytic macrophage receptors is considered in relation to haematopoietic cell growth and differentiation. An introductory general review of macrophage distribution and receptor expression has been added to guide readers unfamiliar with the heterogeneity and adaptability of the macrophage and to draw attention to other less well-studied receptors.

I would like to thank Elwena Gregory and Stan Buckingham for their help with the manuscripts and photography and Dr Robert Johnson for his editorial advice. Apart from The Company of Biologists Limited, I gratefully acknowledge financial support for the symposium from the following companies: Sandoz, Squibb, May & Baker, Celltech, Ciba–Geigy, Glaxo, Dako, Koch Light, Scientific Supplies, Serotec, B.D.H. and Du Pont.

Oxford
March 1988

Siamon Gordon
University of Oxford

MACROPHAGE PLASMA MEMBRANE RECEPTORS: STRUCTURE AND FUNCTION

CONTENTS

J. Cell Sci. Suppl. 9, 1–26 (1988)
Printed in Great Britain © The Company of Biologists Limited 1988

Plasma membrane receptors of the mononuclear phagocyte system

SIAMON GORDON[1], V. HUGH PERRY[2], STEPHEN RABINOWITZ,
LAP-PING CHUNG AND HUGH ROSEN

[1]*Sir William Dunn School of Pathology* and [2]*Experimental Psychology, South Parks Road, Oxford, OX1 3RE*

Summary

Plasma membrane receptors control macrophage activities such as growth, differentiation and activation, migration, recognition, endocytosis and secretion. They are therefore important in a wide range of physiological and pathological processes including host defence, inflammation and repair, involving all systems of the body including the arterial wall and nervous system. The versatile responsiveness of these cells to various stimuli depends on their ability to express a large repertoire of receptors, some restricted to macrophages and closely related cells, others common to many cell types.

This volume contains reviews of the macrophage receptors that are best characterized and deals with aspects of signal transduction and function of the actin cytoskeleton. Our introduction is designed to place these topics in perspective. We summarize features of constitutive and induced mononuclear phagocyte distribution within the body and consider receptor expression and macrophage responses in the context of cell heterogeneity associated with its complex life history. We classify receptors discussed in detail in other chapters, list ligand-binding properties that are not as well defined, and briefly review general features of receptor function in macrophages. An understanding of macrophage receptor biology should bring insights into the contribution of these cells to physiology and disease and result in an improved ability to manipulate activities within the mononuclear phagocyte system.

Introduction

The first macrophage receptors to be identified were those for Fc fragments of immunoglobulins (FcR) (Berken & Benacerraf, 1966) and for cleavage products of the third component of complement (CR) (Lay & Nussenzweig, 1968). Over the past 20 years there has been a great deal of work on the role of these receptors in opsonin-mediated phagocytosis and cytotoxicity, notably by Rabinovitch, Silverstein, Cohn, Bianco, Michl, Griffin, Wright and Nathan. (For general reviews of mononuclear phagocytes see volumes edited by van Furth (1980, 1985) and for reviews of endocytosis see Silverstein *et al.* 1977 and Steinman *et al.* 1983.) The isolation of specific monoclonal antibodies (mAb) for an FcR by Unkeless (1979) and for CR3 by Springer *et al.* (1979) and Beller *et al.* (1982) initiated a period of receptor characterization. These studies defined the synthesis, turnover and function of the FcR, which was purified and reconstituted in artificial lipid bilayers (for reviews see Unkeless *et al.* 1981, 1988; Mellman *et al.* (1988) this volume). Recently three groups have isolated cDNA clones for FcR (Lewis *et al.* 1986; Ravetch *et al.* 1986; Hibbs *et al.* 1986), established that FcR are members of the immunoglobulin (Ig) superfamily (Williams, 1987) and begun to define the molecular basis of FcR heterogeneity. Receptors for C3 were also shown to be heterogeneous and CR3 was found to be part of a family of related leukocyte heterodimers (LFA/Mac-1/p150, 95) (Springer *et al.* 1984). These contain a common β chain, which is homologous with the integrin family of adhesion receptors present also in non-haematopoietic cells such as fibroblasts (Hynes, 1987; Ruoslahti & Pierschbacher, 1987).

Over the past decade it has become clear that macrophages express specific receptors for many other ligands including carbohydrate structures (Stahl *et al.* 1976, 1978), growth factors (Guilbert & Stanley, 1980), lymphokines such as τ interferon, and for plasma proteins that transport and clear lipid, Fe^{2+} and proteinases. Molecular studies of these receptors are in progress. Receptors for transferrin and lipoproteins have been well studied in other cells, but it is not known if their structure in macrophages is identical. Sherr *et al.* (1985) and Sacca *et al.* (1986) recently discovered that a macrophage-specific growth factor receptor (CSF-1 R, c-*fms*) is the cellular counterpart of a viral oncogene (v-*fms*) and further studies have established a central role for these molecules in normal and aberrant growth of macrophages (reviewed by Rettenmier *et al.* (1988) this volume). Receptors restricted to tissue macrophages in bone marrow (Crocker & Gordon, 1986) enable macrophages to regulate growth and differentiation of other haematopoietic lineages and have brought home the importance of non-phagocytic cell-adhesion molecules in macrophage functions (reviewed by Crocker *et al.* (1988) this volume).

Lymphoid surface glycoproteins, which play a role in immune cellular interactions, can also be expressed by macrophages. These include class I and class II molecules of the major histocompatibility complex (MHC) and CD4 antigens (Crocker *et al.* 1987), potential receptors for human immunodeficiency virus (HIV) entry. The normal ligands and receptor-like functions of these recognition molecules have not been defined. It is likely that several surface glycoproteins collaborate to promote specific, stable adhesion between macrophages and other cells in both phagocytic and non-phagocytic interactions. Receptors for complement and carbo-hydrate structure (Ezekowitz *et al.* 1984) or for complement and immunoglobulin (Ehlenberger & Nussenzweig, 1977) can synergize in the binding and ingestion of microorganisms and other particulate ligands by macrophages, and receptor interactions with matrix components such as fibronectin further modulate phagocytosis (see Wright & Detmers (1988) this volume). However, we have little understanding of these complex receptor interactions or of the molecular and signalling mechanisms that determine the resultant responses of the macrophage.

To place the cellular and biochemical aspect of macrophage receptor biology in perspective it is necessary to appreciate the complex life history of macrophages and their resultant considerable heterogeneity.

The mononuclear phagocyte system

Constitutive distribution of resident macrophages

Macrophages are normally present in many tissues of the mammalian host, including the central nervous system (CNS), endocrine organs, gut and kidney, in addition to their well-known distribution in liver (Kupffer cells), spleen and other haematopoietic and lymphoid tissues. (For reviews see Gordon, 1986; Perry & Gordon, 1988.) Most of the macrophages that are resident in adult tissues derive from blood monocytes and thus from progenitors in the bone marrow, although local production of cells may continue in sites such as spleen and lung (alveolar macrophages) in the absence of an overt inflammatory stimulus. Monocytes first invade many of these sites during development, as production shifts from yolk sac to foetal liver and then bone marrow, and contribute to tissue remodelling during organogenesis, e.g. during naturally occurring death of neurones and axons in the CNS (Perry *et al.* 1985). Recruitment from bone marrow continues throughout adult life at a relatively low level in the steady state, and can be considerably enhanced by infection or injury. Mature resident macrophages in tissues are relatively long-lived (weeks, rather than days) compared with cells transiently recruited in inflamed tissues, and perform ill-defined trophic and homeostatic functions within the host, rather than the cytocidal activities vital for immune defence (Gordon *et al.* 1986*a*).

Evidence for the constitutive, widespread migration of macrophages has come from immunocytochemical studies with appropriate macrophage-restricted mAb, which extended earlier morphological observations. In liver, skin, bone marrow and spleen, the phenotype *in situ* has been correlated with that of cells isolated from these organs. Unlike the loosely or non-adherent macrophages, which can be readily lavaged from alveolar spaces or serosal cavities, resident macrophages are often deeply embedded within tissues, thus requiring collagenase digestion for isolation, with care to avoid destruction of delicate plasma membrane processes (Crocker & Gordon, 1985). In the mouse, the macrophage-specific antigen (Ag) defined by a rat mAb, F4/80, has been particularly useful for the recognition of cells belonging to the mononuclear phagocyte system (MPS) (Gordon *et al.* 1986*b*). The F4/80 epitope is present on a 160K (K = $10^3 M_r$) integral plasma membrane molecule of unknown function. The Ag is stable to perfusion-fixation of tissues with glutaraldehyde or paraformaldehyde and, because of its plasma membrane localization, immunocyto-chemistry has made it possible to define the extent of macrophage processes and of their contacts with adjacent cells. These features are illustrated in Figs 1–3, which bring out the characteristic stellate morphology of resident macrophages in different tissues.

F4/80$^+$ macrophages are often associated with vascular endothelium or epithelium, in addition to their interstitial location. Thus, cells either line sinusoids as in liver (Fig. 1C,D) or in the adrenal gland (Fig. 2E,F), or surround capillaries, as in the lamina propria of the gut (Fig. 2A) and in highly vascularized interstitium of the ovary at particular phases of the reproductive cycle (Fig. 2D). Macrophage plasma membrane processes lie beneath the basement membrane of renal medullary epithelium (Fig. 2B), or penetrate a simple epithelium, as in the choroid plexus (Fig. 3B) or the submaxillary gland (Fig. 3D). Cells are found in skin (Fig. 3C,E) and throughout the transitional epithelium of bladder (Fig. 3F). Extensively arborized macrophages can form regular arrays in the basal layer of murine epidermis

(Langerhans cells) (Fig. 3C,E), in other stratified epithelia, e.g. oesophagus, cervix (Hume *et al*. 1984*a*) and within the plexiform layers of the retina (Fig. 3A). Processes of macrophages in bone marrow stroma (Fig. 1A) and in epidermis (Fig. 3C) make numerous contacts with neighbouring cells, which display a high rate of proliferation and turnover, a finding suggestive of growth regulation of haemato-poietic and epithelial cells by the centrally located macrophages.

Studies have revealed F4/80$^+$ macrophages in lymph nodes and the red pulp of spleen (Fig. 1B), but no labelling is seen in the white pulp, a region associated with T lymphocytes. Similar observations have been made with several anti-macrophage mAb, but it is likely that F4/80$^-$ macrophages are also present in these areas, as judged by other Ag markers. Additional heterogeneity in macrophage phenotype has been observed in the marginal zone of spleen (Humphrey & Grennan, 1981). These findings are of interest because of the obscure lineage interrelationship between macrophages and other 'accessory' cells that play a role in the induction of immune responses, especially primary T cell activation (Steinman *et al*. 1986). Steinman–Cohn dendritic cells, veiled cells and interdigitating cells are F4/80$^-$, are present in T cell regions and express novel Ag (Kraal *et al*. 1986). Langerhans cells share properties with these accessory cells and macrophages, but lose their F4/80 Ag when isolated from skin and acquire the ability to stimulate a mixed leukocyte reaction upon cultivation *in vitro* (Schuler & Steinman, 1985). The macrophage phenotype therefore varies depending on the microenvironment in which they are found and on the conditions of culture after cell isolation. Present evidence is that macrophages consist of a single lineage of bone-marrow-derived cells, which displays considerable heterogeneity as a result of regional differentiation and modulation, but which does not represent distinct subsets determined during development.

Induced recruitment and accumulation in tissues in response to injury

Macrophages are present at most portals of entry and body interfaces and are well placed to form a first line of defence. In skin, lung, liver and spleen they are often the first host cells encountered by an invading organism or antigen, and, by releasing various mediators, macrophages are able to initiate an acute inflammatory reaction before endothelial permeability is increased and circulating leukocytes are recruited

Fig. 1. F4/80 immunocytochemistry of resident and BCG-activated macrophages in sections of murine lymphohaematopoietic organs. All figures show brown peroxidase reaction product after glutaraldehyde-perfusion fixation and avidin–biotin–complex staining. Controls without F4/80 antibody were unlabelled throughout. For further details see Hume *et al*. (1983*a*). A. Bone marrow. Stellate stromal macrophages are found in haematopoietic cell clusters, associated with F4/80$^-$ cells of the myeloid and erythroid series. Occasional rounded monocytes are also F4/80$^+$. B. Spleen. Intense staining of macrophages in red pulp, with little staining in white pulp except associated with penetrating vessel. C,D. Normal liver at higher (C) and (D) lower magnification shows sinus-lining F4/80$^+$ Kupffer cells. Hepatic endothelium and hepatocytes are F4/80$^-$. E,F. Liver containing granulomata of mainly F4/80$^+$ activated macrophages at lower (E) and higher magnification (F). Occasional polymorphonuclear leukocytes (PMN) and T lymphocytes in lesions are F4/80$^-$. Note F4/80$^+$ Kupffer cells between granulomata and reactive macrophages in adjacent sinuses, reflecting increased traffic through organ (S. Rabinowitz, unpublished).

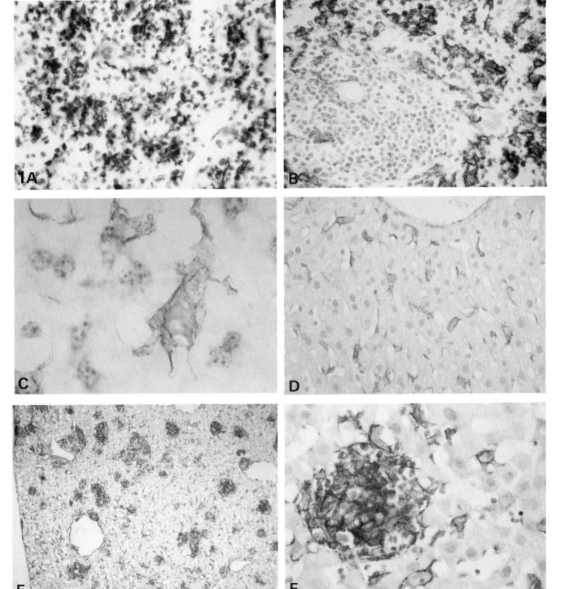

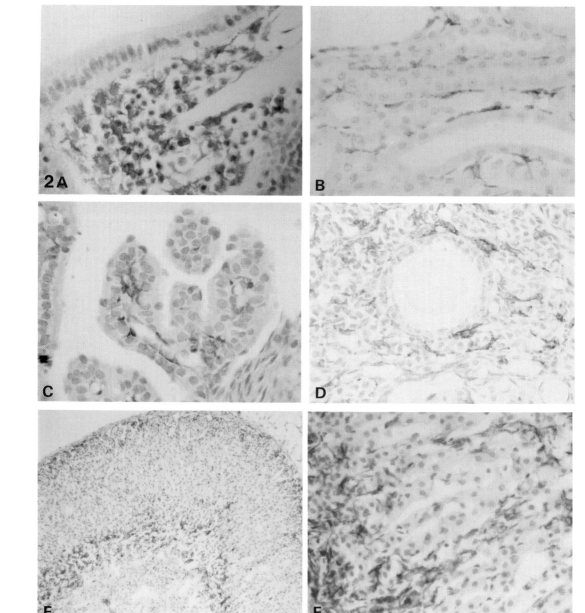

to an extravascular site of inflammation. Macrophages can recognize many foreign substances directly, without the help of plasma opsonins such as antibody and complement. This general ability to discriminate non-self from normal self predates the evolution of antigen-specific immune responses and may be related to the cells' ability to recognize effete or damaged cells. Whether macrophages are able to distinguish alterations induced by viral infection or malignant transformation of target cells is not yet clear.

If the resident, relatively quiescent macrophages found in most tissues cannot contain an invader, increased numbers of monocytes are recruited to the site of injury, together with other blood cells, especially polymorphonuclear leukocytes, and plasma-derived molecules. The inflammatory reaction results in enhanced production of myelomonocytic cells, their recruitment from the circulation and increased turnover in haematopoietic tissues and locally. Macrophages elicited in response to sterile stimuli such as thioglycollate broth differ from those induced by infectious and other agents such as Bacillé Calmette Guerin (BCG), which recruit and activate macrophages by antigen-specific T-lymphocyte-dependent mechanisms. Although the elicited or immunologically activated macrophages can be distinguished by their expression of MHC II antigens and differential cytotoxicity (Ezekowitz *et al.* 1981) both types of newly recruited macrophages display common induced activities. These include an enhanced ability to undergo a respiratory burst and to generate toxic oxygen products, and production of extracellular proteinase activities such as plasminogen activator (urokinase), elastase and collagenase, which contribute to fibrinolysis and connective tissue catabolism during tissue injury and repair (Gordon & Ezekowitz, 1985). Resident macrophages do not produce these secretory activities and, in the case of Kupffer cells and certain other tissue macrophage populations, may be unable to generate a respiratory burst (Ding & Nathan, 1988). Defence against rapidly proliferating organisms such as *Listeria monocytogenes* therefore depends on the ability of the host to recruit circulating monocytes rapidly to local sites of infection such as liver, where resident macrophages are unable to contain the infection (Lepay *et al.* 1985). Recruitment of monocytes after injury within the peripheral, but not the central, nervous system may contribute to differential degeneration and repair within these sites (Perry *et al.* 1985).

The defence capacity of resident and recruited macrophages is augmented by other elements of the immune response such as specific antibodies and complement, which

Fig. 2. F4/80 labelling of macrophages in adult mouse tissues. A. Small intestine shows F4/80$^+$ macrophages confined to lamina propria, closely surrounding capillaries which are distended by perfusion-fixation. B. Kidney. Stellate processes of macrophages lie beneath epithelium in renal medulla. C. Fallopian tube. Macrophage processes lie mainly beneath epithelium. D. Ovary. Numerous F4/80$^+$ cells in highly vascularized interstitial tissue surrounding developing follicle. E,F. Adrenal gland. E. F4/80$^+$ cells are prominent in outer cortex and at cortico-medullary junction. F. Outer cortex at higher magnification. Note network of macrophage processes between steroid-secreting cells (zona glomerulosa at left of picture), frequent association of labelled cells with capillaries and cells in inner cortex spread along the walls of radiating vascular sinuses. For further details see Hume & Gordon (1983); Hume *et al.* (1984*b*).

mediate FcR- and CR-dependent uptake and destruction of targets. Antigen-stimulated CD4$^+$ as well as CD8$^+$ T lymphocytes produce lymphokines that activate macrophages, especially τ interferon, and haematopoietic growth factors such as interleukin-3 (IL-3), granulocyte macrophage colony stimulating factor (GM-CSF), IL-4 and IL-5 (Chervinski *et al.* 1987; Kelso & Gough, 1987; Yokota *et al.* 1988). T lymphocytes therefore increase the numbers of macrophages both in haematopoietic tissues and locally, prime their respiratory burst capacity and enhance their killing potential towards extracellular as well as intracellular pathogens. Recruited, activated macrophages accumulate in tissues within granulomatous foci after mycobacterial infection of liver (Fig. 1E,F), or are diffusely distributed throughout haematopoietic organs, as in murine malaria (Lee *et al.* 1986). Unlike resident macrophages, which show considerable regional heterogeneity, elicited and immunologically activated macrophages display a similar phenotype in different sites. Heterogeneity in phenotype and receptor expression between recruited and resident macrophages can be ascribed to differences in cell maturity and their modulation by lymphokines and other regulating agents.

Not all responses to injury involve recruitment of both myeloid and monocytic cells and the manifestation of other typical features of inflammation. Monocytes/macrophages accumulate in the arterial wall in atherosclerosis, in lymphohaematopoietic and other tissues in other 'metabolic' or storage diseases, and in some malignant tumours in the absence of neutrophils and an obvious inflammatory response. Little is known about monocyte-restricted chemotactic agents or the properties of these more selectively recruited macrophages.

Overall, production, migration and distribution of macrophages in tissues is precisely controlled in the steady state and after injury, although the mechanisms involved are still poorly understood. Surface receptors play an important role in all these processes including macrophage responses to chemotactic and other stimuli, adhesion to vascular endothelium, migration through tissues, interactions with other cells and resultant modulation of effector functions.

Diversity of macrophage plasma membrane receptors

Given the wide distribution of macrophages and variety of macrophage functions and potential ligands, it is perhaps not surprising that macrophages are able to express a

Fig. 3. F4/80 labelling of microglia and macrophages associated with epithelia. A. Retina. Microglia extend fine F4/80$^+$ crenellated processes in outer plexiform layer to form a mosaic pattern. B. Choroid plexus. F4/80$^+$ macrophages are prominent beneath and among F4/80$^-$ epithelial cells and blood vessels. C. Skin. Striking pattern of epidermal F4/80$^+$ Langerhans cells closely associated with groups of unlabelled keratinocytes, in horizontal thick section of ear. D. Submaxillary gland. Section shows F4/80$^+$ processes of macrophages penetrating between cuboidal duct epithelial cells, and occasional interstitial macrophages. E. Skin. Langerhans cells in transverse section (compare C). Lacunae that separate F4/80$^+$ cells and epidermal cells are artefacts of fixation. F. Bladder. F4/80$^+$ processes extend throughout transitional epithelium. Cells in lamina propria often lie adjacent to capillaries. For further details see Hume *et al.* (1983*a,b*; 1984*a*).

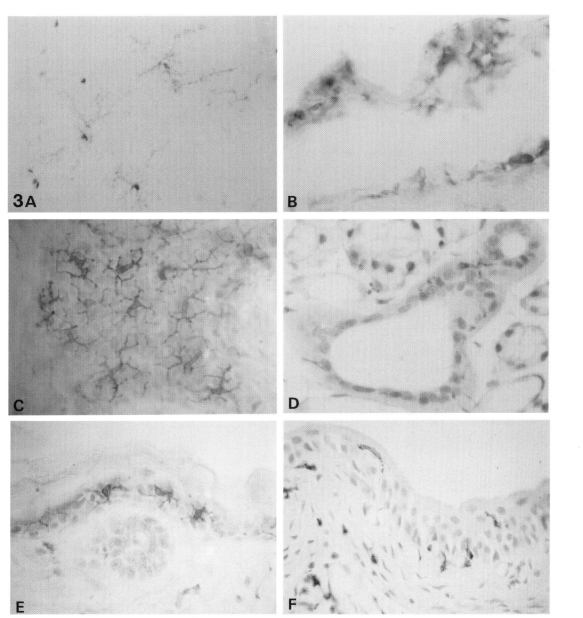

Table 1. *Macrophage plasma membrane receptors and glycoproteins structurally related to known superfamilies*

Superfamily	Molecule	$M_r \times 10^{-3}$ (reduced)	Reference
Immunoglobulin	FcR (various)	50–60	Mellman *et al.* (1988); Unkeless *et al.* (1988)
	MHC I	45	
	MHC II	27–33	see Williams (1987) for
	β_2-M	12	structural criteria
	CD4	55	
	CSF-1R	150	
	ICAM	92	Simmons *et al.* (1988)
Integrin	LFA-1	180 ⎫	Law (1988)
	CR3	170 ⎬ β95	Kishimoto *et al.* (1987)
	p150,95	150 ⎭ common	Corbi *et al.* (1987)
	IIb/IIIa	⎫	Burns *et al.* (1986)
	Fibronectin R	⎬ 150/130	Wright & Detmers (1988)
	Laminin R	⎪	
	VLA-4	⎭	Hemler *et al.* (1987). See Hynes (1987) for structural criteria
C3b/C4b interacting	CR1	160–250	Law (1988); Wong *et al.* (1986)
	DAF (decay accelerating factor)	70	
	MCP (membrane cofactor protein)	45–70	See Reid *et al.* (1986) for
	IL-2R	55	structural criteria

remarkable array of plasma membrane receptors. Their classification cannot yet be based on molecular structure, but a preliminary categorization is shown in the accompanying tables, based on known structures (Table 1) or reported ligands and functions (Table 2). Macrophages express surface receptors of several superfamilies (Ig, integrin and a family of structurally related proteins that interact with C3b or C4b). In addition there are various lectin-like receptors on macrophages (Table 3), one of which, the mannosyl–fucosyl receptor (MFR), is related to a circulating acute-phase mannose-binding plasma protein produced by the liver (Ezekowitz *et al.* 1988). The enumeration of receptors is complicated by the existence of different receptors for the same ligand (e.g. Ig subclasses) or multiple ligands for the same receptor molecule (e.g. CR3). The Fc, CR and mannosyl-specific receptors are discussed elsewhere in this volume and other chapters give details of the CSF-1 receptor and lipoprotein receptors. The various 'scavenger' receptor activities, which mediate endocytosis of modified proteins (e.g. acetyl low density lipoprotein (LDL), β very low density lipoprotein (βVLDL), formaldehyde-albumin, advanced glycosylation end product (AGE) protein) need to be better defined biochemically to establish how many different receptor molecules of this type exist. Many of the other receptor activities listed are still poorly characterized and cellular assignments

Table 2. *Ligands reported to bind to macrophage plasma membrane receptors*

	References
Opsonins/targeting	
Fc IgG (various), IgE, IgA	Mellman *et al.* (1988)
iC3b, adhesive	Law (1988)
C3b	Fearon (1980)
C3d	Inada *et al.* (1983)
C1q	Tenner & Cooper (1980); Loos (1982); Bobak *et al.* (1986); Ghebrehiwet (1986)
Coagulation	
Fibrinogen	Sherman & Lee (1977); Altieri *et al.* (1986)
Thrombospondin	Silverstein & Nachman (1987)
Thrombin	Bar-Shavit *et al.* (1983)
Factor VII, VIIA	Broze (1982)
Urokinase	Vassalli *et al.* (1985); Stoppelli *et al.* (1985)
Matrix	
Fibronectin	Hosein & Bianco (1985); Brown & Goodwin (1988)
Laminin	Bohnsack *et al.* (1985)
Sulphated polysaccharide	Chong & Parish (1986)
Hyaluronate	Green *et al.* (1988)
Cell adhesion and recognition	
Sheep erythrocytes (sialyl-gangliosides)	Crocker *et al.* (1988)
Erythroblasts	Morris *et al.* (1988)
ICAM	Makgobo *et al.* (1988); Simmons *et al.* (1988); Dougherty *et al.* (1988)
LFA-1	Dougherty & Hogg (1987)
Endothelium	Rosen & Gordon (1987)
Other endocytosis and transport	
Mannosyl, GlcNAc fucosyl glycoconjugates	Ezekowitz & Stahl (1988)
Galactosyl particles	Roos *et al.* (1985)
β glucan (yeast)	Czop & Austen (1985); Goldman (1988)
Fucosyl glycoconjugates	Lehrman & Hill (1986)
LDL Lipoprotein (various), native, modified (acetyl, malondialdehyde) βVLDL, apoE	Fogelman *et al.* (1988); Goldstein *et al.* (1979); Ellsworth *et al.* (1986); Floren & Chait (1981); Gianturco *et al.* (1986); Murakami *et al.* (1986)
Aldehyde-modified proteins	Horiuchi *et al.* (1986)
AGE (Advanced glycosylation end products)	Vlassara *et al.* (1985, 1986)
Transferrin	Wyllie (1977); Andreesen *et al.* (1984); Vogel *et al.* (1987)
Lactoferrin	Van Snick & Masson (1976); Birgens *et al.* (1983)
Caeruloplasmin	Kataoka & Tavassoli (1985)
α_2 macroglobulin	Kaplan & Neilsen (1979); Van Leuven *et al.* (1986)
Haemopexin	Taketani *et al.* (1987)
Mannose-6-phosphate glycoproteins	Hoflack & Kornfeld (1985); Shepherd *et al.* (1984)
Growth factors, cytokines, polypeptides	
CSF-1	Rettenmier *et al.* (1988); Guilbert & Stanley (1980)
GM-CSF	Walker & Burgess (1985, 1987); Metcalf (1987); Nicola (1987); Park *et al.* (1986)
Interleukin 1	Dower & Urdal (1987)
Interleukin 2	Holter *et al.* (1987)
Interleukin 3	Sorenson *et al.* (1986)

Table 2. *Continued*

	References
Interleukin 4	Crawford *et al.* (1987); McInnes & Rennick (1988)
TNF/cachectin	Watson (1987)
τ interferon	Langer *et al.* (1986); Aguet & Merlin (1987);
α, β interferon	Orchansky *et al.* (1986); Yoshida *et al.* (1988)
Insulin	Blecher & Goldstein (1977); Bautista *et al.* (1987)
Glucagon	Blecher & Goldstein (1977)
Somatomedin	Rosenfeld *et al.* (1979)
Vasopressin	
Parathormone	Perry *et al.* (1984)
Calcitonin	
TGF β	Nathan, unpublished
C5a	Chenoweth *et al.* (1984); Goodman *et al.* (1984)
Peptides and inflammatory mediators	
f-Met–Leu–Phe	Snyderman & Pike (1984); Becker (1987)
Angiotensin	Foris *et al.* (1983); Thomas & Hoffman (1984)
Bradykinin	Fauve & Hevin (1977)
Substance P	McGillis *et al.* (1987); Bar-Shavit & Goldman (1986)
VIP	O'Dorisio (1987)
Tuftsin	Bump *et al.* (1986)
Neurotensin	Bar-Shavit & Goldman (1986)
LTB4	Goetzl (1987)
Pharmacological	
β2 adrenergic	Rosati *et al.* (1986); Abrass *et al.* (1985); Henricks *et al.* (1987)
Nicotinic cholinergic	Whaley *et al.* (1981)
Histamine (H1)	Cameron *et al.* (1986); Diaz *et al.* (1979); Warlow & Bernard (1987)
Serotonin	Sternberg *et al.* (1986)
Benzodiazepine	Ruff *et al.* (1985)
Adenosine	Stiles (1987)
Phorbol myristate acetate/dibutyrate	Weinberg & Misukoni (1983)

(mononuclear cells, different macrophages) and plasma membrane localization also need further refinement.

Functions of macrophage plasma membrane receptors

Ligation of macrophage surface receptors induces responses as diverse as cell growth, chemotaxis, endocytosis and secretion. In the absence of structural information about all except a few macrophage membrane molecules, our present knowledge of receptor functions, signal transduction and alterations in macrophage gene expression remains superficial. We do not understand the role of receptor cross-linking and phosphorylation, or of association with clathrin (Aggeler & Werb, 1982) and other cytoskeletal proteins in membrane internalization, recycling and routing to

Table 3. *Lectin-like macrophage receptors*

Receptor	$M_r \times 10^{-3}$	Ligand	Expression	Function	Comment	References
MFR	175	Man α1,6 or GlcNAc β1,6 on high mannosyl core	Mature macrophage and hepatic endothelium	Endocytosis and secretion	Related to 30K serum Mannose-binding-protein	Ezekowitz & Stahl (1988); Maynard & Baenziger (1981); Wileman et al. (1986); Hubbard et al. (1979)
β-Glucan		β-1, 3-D-glucan on heat-killed yeast, glucan particles and zymosan	Peritoneal macrophages, human monocytes Inducible on macrophage-like cell lines 1,25(OH₂)D3 and retinoic acid	Endocytosis	? Relationship to lectin-like interaction of CR3 with zymosan	Czop & Austen (1985); Goldman (1988); Ross et al. (1985)
SER	185	Sialylated gangliosides, e.g. GD1a	Lymphohaematopoietic tissue macrophages	Intercellular adhesion	Plasma protein inducer	Crocker et al. (1988)
Gal R	30	Gal-particles	Rat Kupffer cells	Endocytosis	Membrane-associated (Ca²⁺). Distinct from hepatocyte R and tissue galaptins. Identical to SAP (serum amyloid P)	Schlepper-Schaffer et al. (1983); Roos et al. (1985); Kolb-Bachofen, personal communication
Fuc R	88, 77 sub-units	L-fucosyl-β-glyco-conjugates also gal-BSA	Rat Kupffer cells only	Endocytosis	Distinct from MFR	Lehrman & Hill (1986); Haltiwanger et al. (1986)
M.6.PR	215 (Cation-independent) 46 (cation-dependent)	Man-6-PO₄-terminal glycoproteins	Macrophages and other cells	Intra- and intercellular targeting lysosomal hydrolases	High molecular weight, cation-independent receptor cDNA identity with Insulin II-growth factor R	Shepherd et al. (1984); Sly & Fischer (1982); Hoflack & Kornfeld (1985); Morgan et al. (1987)
AGE R	90	Glucose-modified protein	Peritoneal macrophages, Kupffer cells, monocytes, endothelial cells, fibroblasts and lymphocytes	Endocytosis only by macrophages	Not strictly CHO ligand Distinct from other scavenger receptors	Vlassara et al. (1985, 1986) & personal communication

endosomes and lysosomes. In this section we consider general features of receptor function, for the most part derived from studies with macrophages in cell culture.

Growth, differentiation and modulation

Although production and modulation of macrophages can occur in different compartments of the body, it is useful to consider them as linked processes. Studies with primary bone-marrow-derived macrophages, monocytes, peritoneal cells and macrophage-like lines in cell culture have revealed complex regulation of the macrophage phenotype by colony-stimulating factors (CSF-1, GM-CSF, IL-3, IL-4), lymphokines (τ interferon) and other modulators (glucocorticoids (Flower, 1980), vitamin D metabolites, retinoids). Specific plasma membrane and other receptors play an important role in determining the effects of these agents on macrophages. Interactions of CSF-1 with murine macrophages, and activation of murine macrophages and human monocytes by τ interferon have been investigated in most detail. Cytokines such as IL-1, tumour necrosis factor (TNF), GM-CSF, which can be induced in macrophages, also influence the properties of macrophages themselves. Other examples of possible autocrine regulation include transforming growth factor (TGF) β and interferon $\alpha\beta$ which deactivate macrophage responses such as the respiratory burst (Yoshida *et al*. 1988) and altered MFR expression (Ezekowitz *et al*. 1986). Growth, differentiation and activation involve multiple regulators, which synergize or oppose one another, and an altered response of the macrophages to extrinsic regulators during its differentiation. Thus macrophages become progressively more refractory to growth stimulation as the cells mature and the monocytic stage may be more readily activatable, e.g. for cytotoxicity, than more terminally differentiated macrophages. Although cytokines and lymphokines induce pleiotypic, overlapping responses in macrophages, their effects are distinct, indicating that macrophage genes are co-ordinately, but selectively, regulated by each receptor–ligand interaction.

Interaction of CSF-1 with its normal receptor (CSF-1R) has been studied by Guilbert & Stanley (1980) who have shown that receptor molecules of mature macrophages are rapidly down-regulated after binding pure ligand. The role of abnormal CSF-1 receptors in leukaemogenesis is reviewed elsewhere in this volume by Rettenmier and colleagues. Recent studies indicate that the human CSF-1R gene is located in a region of the long arm of chromosome 5 that also codes for CSF-1 and several other haematopoietic growth factors and that deletions of this region are often associated with haematopoietic dysplasia (Bunn, 1986).

In contrast with CSF-1, interferon τ inhibits macrophage growth and is a potent modulator of macrophage differentiation. It induces a variety of surface and secretory products, but down-regulates other macrophage activities, thus reproducing many of the features of macrophages activated by T lymphocyte products *in vivo* (Nathan, 1986). The effects of interferons on target cell gene expression are under intense study (Revel & Chebath, 1986), but the interactions of τ interferon with its plasma membrane receptors are still poorly understood. Receptors are present in low numbers on many cell types, unlike the CSF-1R which is macrophage-restricted.

Differences have been reported between receptors for interferon on macrophages and other cells (Orchansky *et al.* 1986). The availability of pure ligand will facilitate further studies in this important area.

Cell–cell and cell–matrix interactions

It is only recently that we have begun to appreciate that macrophage adhesion to another cell does not inevitably result in phagocytosis or its extracellular destruction. Non-phagocytic adhesion is selective for different target cells and can be transient or relatively stable. As illustrated in two recently studied examples, macrophage receptors interact with endothelium during enhanced cell recruitment (Rosen & Gordon, 1987) and, within tissues, with haematopoietic cells in bone marrow and foetal liver (Crocker *et al.* (1988) this volume). The CR3 and other members of the leukocyte functional antigen (LFA) and integrin families play a role in endothelial and matrix adhesion of induced monocytes and neutrophils, whereas haemaggluti-nins expressed by resident stromal macrophages bind developing cells during haematopoiesis. Ligands for these adhesion receptors include iC3b and gangliosides, respectively, but other determinants induced on stimulated endothelial cells may contribute to leukocyte adhesion (Bevilacqua *et al.* 1987). Purified or genetically modified receptors expressed in non-macrophages (Qu *et al.* 1988) or in model membranes should help to define the mechanisms of adhesion and signalling of functional responses. Substratum and matrix molecules (fibronectin, laminin) profoundly influence macrophage adhesion, endocytosis and secretion. The recep-tors themselves and their interactions with other membrane molecules and the cytoskeleton presumably determine whether the macrophage ingests or destroys a bound target, rather than influence target cell activities by non-phagocytic trophic interactions. Further studies of receptor structure and functional modifications such as phosphorylation should clarify these differential cellular responses.

Endocytosis

Phagocytosis and receptor-mediated pinocytosis are hallmarks of the differentiated macrophage, which is able to bind and internalize a large range of particulate and soluble ligands efficiently and selectively. A great deal has been learnt concerning the role in this process of receptors for opsonins (Fc, CR1 and CR3) and of receptors that interact directly with other specific ligands such as sugar moieties. The mechanism of particle ingestion involves zipper-like interactions between ligands and receptors (Silverstein *et al.* 1977) and different receptors are able to synergize in phagocytosis (Wright & Silverstein, 1986). Continuous and induced endocytic activity in macrophages involves extensive membrane flow and recirculation (Stein-man *et al.* 1983). The role of the cytoskeleton and other determinants of ingestion has only been partially defined (Silverstein *et al.* 1977).

The technique of receptor modulation devised by Michl *et al.* (1979, 1983*a,b*) made it possible to cap receptors from the surface of adherent macrophages in culture and study their role in phagocytic recognition. If macrophages are cultivated on a defined ligand such as immune complexes, FcRs are selectively redistributed to the adherent surface and cleared by endocytosis, with resultant loss of receptor activity. The possibility that other molecules can be made to co-cap with the receptor under study has not been fully explored, nor have the effects of modulation been determined on receptor biosynthesis and turnover, or on polarized secretion by macrophages adherent to a surface-bound ligand.

An example that illustrates the value of this procedure is the identification of receptors that permit intracellular parasites such as *Leishmania* to penetrate macrophages (Blackwell *et al.* 1985; Mosser & Edelson, 1985). In the presence of fresh serum, a source of complement-derived ligands, promastigotes (the flagellated form) activate the alternative pathway and enter macrophages *via* CR3; in the absence of an exogenous opsonin, the entry mechanism is less efficient, but still involves the CR3 acting in concert with other sugar-recognizing receptors such as the MFR (Blackwell *et al.* 1985) or AGE-R (Mosser *et al.* 1987). Intriguingly, macrophages themselves are able to secrete all the components of the alternative pathway, but whether CR3 itself functions by 'local opsonization' (Ezekowitz & Gordon, 1984) or by a direct adhesive epitope is not clear. Parasite molecules that can be recognized directly through their sugar structures and as ligands for CR3 have recently been identified (Russell & Wright, 1988). Similar phagocytic recognition mechanisms extend to other invading organisms such as *Legionella pneumophila* (M. A. Horwitz, personal communication) and *Histoplasma capsulatum* (Bullock & Wright, 1987) and by virtue of macrophage-specific expression of receptors accounts for tissue tropism of several infectious agents.

Of the events that follow internalization, we have some knowledge of receptor retrieval and sorting, but little insight into the mechanisms. Intracellular fusion between endosomes and lysosomes involves saltatory movements of organelles (D'Arcy-Hart *et al.* 1983) and selective membrane fusion. The role of valency in targeting FcR molecules and ligands to lysosomes has been described by Mellman and his colleagues (Ukkonen *et al.* 1986). Together with studies of endosome acidification (Okhuma & Poole, 1981), this work has important implications for entry and neutralization of enveloped viruses in macrophages (Porterfield, 1986). Intracellular organisms such as *Toxoplasma* (Jones & Hirsch, 1972), *Legionella* (Horwitz, 1986), *Trypanosoma cruzi* (Nogueira *et al.* 1980) and *Leishmania* (Rabinovitch *et al.* 1986) are able to evade macrophage defence mechanisms during or after entry and provide fascinating insights into vacuolar function. They can avoid triggering a respiratory burst (Wilson *et al.* 1980), enter by an unusual coiling mechanism (Horwitz, 1986), inhibit acidification of phagosomes (Horwitz, 1987), prevent phagosome–lysosome fusion or disrupt phagosome membranes, remaining within or escaping from phagosomes or phagolysosomes into the cytosol.

Secretory responses and biosynthesis of effector molecules
It has now been recognized for some time that macrophages are not only 'professional' phagocytes, but also major secretory cells able to generate a large variety of products, which contribute to extracellular functions of macrophages in

inflammation and the steady state (Gordon, 1978). Recent compilations of macrophage products are given in the reviews by Nathan (1987) and Werb *et al.* (1986). Ligation of surface receptors plays an important role in triggering exocytosis and release of membrane-derived and other molecules, and modulates macrophage biosynthetic activities and effector functions. Release of reactive oxygen metabolites, arachidonates and neutral proteinases can be triggered *via* FcR (Johnston *et al.* 1976; Nathan, 1980) or MFR (Berton & Gordon, 1983), especially by endocytic stimuli (immune complexes, zymosan), although internalization of a particulate ligand is not required (Rouzer *et al.* 1980). The role of CR3 in triggering of secretion, acting alone or in combination with other receptors, is not clear (Wright & Silverstein, 1983; Yamamoto & Johnston, 1984; Aderem *et al.* 1985). Release of different products is independently regulated and also a function of macrophage heterogeneity. Signal transduction mechanisms have not been well studied in macrophages and some aspects are discussed by Aderem and by Yin & Hartwig in other chapters in this volume. Information on receptor structure and regulation of the genes involved in product formation may help us to understand the linkage between plasma membrane events and longer-term synthetic responses. It is curious that macrophages secrete several products that can themselves act as local opsonins (complement, fibronectin, α_2 macroglobulin), indicating a possible further link between secretion and endocytosis. Newly available probes for lysozyme (Chung *et al.* 1988), urokinase (Belin *et al.* 1985), α1-antitrypsin (Kurachi *et al.* 1987), complement proteins (Colten *et al.* 1986), GM-CSF (Gough *et al.* 1984), interleukin-1 (Lomedico *et al.* 1984) and TNF (Pennica *et al.* 1984; Fransen *et al.* 1985) should clarify the mechanisms that control their production and release in macrophage trophic and cytotoxic activities.

Heterogeneity of plasma membrane receptor expression

The recruitment of resident and induced macrophage populations to tissues and the varied nature of their resultant local interactions are reflected in considerable heterogeneity in receptor expression. We are still a long way from understanding the mechanisms that control expression of macrophage plasma membrane receptors *in vivo* or *in vitro*. Studies of FcR, CR3, MFR and CSF-1R have illustrated some of the factors that modulate their activity. Known modulating ligands include various colony stimulating factors and lymphokines, glucocorticosteroids and extracellular matrix proteins, which selectively alter the receptor phenotype of macrophages. For example, cell activation by BCG infection *in vivo* or τ interferon in cell culture enhances expression of murine FcR for Ig2a ligands (Ezekowitz *et al.* 1983), but down-regulates FcR for IgG1/2b ligands and also MFR activity (Ezekowitz & Gordon, 1984). This can be counteracted in part by dexamethasone, an inducer of MFR (Mokoena & Gordon, 1985). Future studies on receptor genes and their expression should clarify molecular mechanisms, but we also need to understand the synthesis, processing and transport of these molecules to and from the macrophage plasma membrane, as well as receptor modification and turnover (Mellman *et al.*

1983). Retention of differentiated trait function in cell culture makes the macrophage an attractive model to study cellular and molecular mechanisms involved in receptor expression.

There are other intriguing examples of heterogeneous macrophage receptor expression *in vivo*. We lack quantitative data on receptor numbers and on surface or intracellular distribution of macrophage receptors within the animal, but these can be determined by *in situ* methods and with freshly isolated cells. CR3 antigen is undetectable in murine Kupffer cells and other macrophages embedded in lympho-haematopoietic tissues, but receptor epitopes are present on monocytes, peritoneal macrophages and microglia. Another member of the LFA family, the p150,95 molecule is readily detectable on human tissue macrophages, which also lack CR3 antigen (Hogg *et al*. 1986). In mice, in contrast with resident Kupffer cells, macrophages recruited to liver by infection with *Plasmodium yoelii* or *Listeria monocytogenes* express high levels of CR3. These studies indicate that cell maturity and the local microenvironment influence macrophage CR3, although the mechanism of its regulation *in vivo* is not known. One possibility is that the CR3 plays a role in adhesion of circulating monocytes to liver sinusoids and is then selectively down-regulated by local interactions that do not occur elsewhere, e.g. in the CNS. Although less well documented, there is also developmental regulation of FcR expression and human tissue macrophages express FcR antigens which are not present on monocytes (Unkeless, 1986).

The importance of the CNS as a unique local microenvironment determining macrophage phenotype and receptor expression has been shown further in studies with CD4 antigens *versus* CR3 and FcR (Perry & Gordon, 1987). There is selective down-regulation of CD4 antigens on microglia within the blood–brain barrier, compared with elsewhere in the nervous system. These difference may be brought about by differential exposure to circulating plasma proteins or by local interactions with distinct populations of neuroglia. The receptors of macrophages within the brain are also modulated after monocyte entry and migration, during differentiation into mature microglia, reactivation of microglia, and enhanced monocyte recruitment after local injury or inflammation.

The human leukocyte adhesion deficiency syndrome in which CR3, LFA-1 and p150,95 molecules are all deficient has provided an informative inborn error to study macrophage receptor dysfunction *in vivo* (Springer & Anderson, 1986). A recent example of the use of transgenic mice to study macrophage growth factor overexpression (Lang *et al*. 1987) shows that experimental models can be developed to manipulate macrophage receptor expression *in vivo*. Macrophage FcR expression can also be influenced within an intact rodent or primate by injection of a specific anti-receptor mAb (Kurlander *et al*. 1984; Clarkson *et al*. 1986). This results in prolonged loss (lasting weeks) of receptor function in hepatic macrophages as judged by clearance studies. Administration of antibodies directed against a CR3 epitope (5C6) different from Mac-1 results in a more transient (lasting days), but marked loss of the ability of myelomonocytic cells to adhere to endothelium and enter an inflammatory site (Rosen & Gordon, 1987). Another way to deplete macrophages or modulate receptor activity is to target toxic lectins to macrophage populations by exploiting their known receptor activities, e.g. for sugar-specific (Simmons *et al.* 1986, 1987) or FcR-mediated uptake (Refnes & Munthe-Kaas, 1976). Restricted tissue expression and ready internalization make the endocytic receptors of macrophages attractive targets for such experiments.

Our inability to detect receptor activity in a particular macrophage population (e.g. CR3 on Kupffer cells) can be due to its absence or to blockade by bound ligand. cDNA probes make it possible to determine by *in situ* hybridization whether the mRNA is present. The combined used of nucleic acid and mAb probes should clarify some of the mechanisms by which different macrophages vary expression of receptors *in vivo*.

Conclusion

Plasma membrane receptors play a major role in every aspect of the complex life history of the macrophage. Genetic and immunochemical probes and advances in receptor biochemistry have now made it possible to characterize and define the functions of known macrophage receptors, and to discover new receptor molecules involved in macrophage biology. Differential regulation of plasma membrane receptors on macrophage subpopulations normally present in different sites within the body, or on cells recruited during an inflammatory or degenerative process, should permit selective modulation of macrophage functions. Future progress will depend on integrated investigations of receptor structure and function *in vitro* and within the host.

Supported by the Medical Research Council, U.K., the Arthritis and Rheumatism Council (HR) and the Wellcome Trust (VHP). We thank Elwena Gregory and Pam Woodward for typing, Stan Buckingham and Cathy Lee for photography, Dr David Hume and Peter Tree for unpublished photomicrographs and Dr Genevieve Milon for helpful comments on the manuscript.

References

ABRASS, C. K., O'CONNOR, S. W., SCARPACE, P. J. & ABRASS, I. B. (1985). Characterization of the β-adrenergic receptor of the rat peritoneal macrophage. *J. Immun.* **135**, 1338–1341.

ADEREM, A. A., WRIGHT, S. D., SILVERSTEIN, S. C. & COHN, Z. A. (1985). Ligated complement receptors do not activate the arachidonic acid cascade in resident peritoneal macrophages. *J. exp. Med.* **161**, 617–622.

AGGELER, J. & WERB, Z. (1982). Initial events during phagocytosis by macrophages viewed from the outside and the inside of the cell; membrane-particle interaction and clathrin. *J. Cell Biol.* **94**, 613–623.

AGUET, M. & MERLIN, G. (1987). Purification of human τ interferon receptors by sequential affinity chromatography on immobilized monoclonal antireceptor antibodies and human τ interferon. *J. exp. Med.* **165**, 988–999.

ALTIERI, D. C., MANNUCCIO, P. M. & CAPITANIO, A. M. (1986). Binding of fibrinogen to human monocytes. *J. clin. Invest.* **78**, 968–976.

ANDREESEN, R., OSTERLAZ, J., BODEMANN, H. H., BROSS, K. J., COSTABEL, U. & LÖHR, G. W. (1984). Expression of transferrin receptors and intracellular ferritin during terminal differentiation of human monocytes. *Blut* **49**, 195–202.

BAR-SHAVIT, Z. & GOLDMAN, R. (1986). Substance P and neurotensin. *Meth. Enzym.* **132**, 326–334.

BAR-SHAVIT, Z., KAHN, A., FENTON, J. W. & WILNER, G. D. (1983). Chemotactic response of monocytes to thrombin. *J. Cell Biol.* **96**, 282–285.

BAUTISTA, A. P., FLETCHER, D. J. & VOLKMAN, A. (1987). Down-regulation of insulin receptors in *Propionibacterium acnes*-activated macrophages in the mouse. *Molec. cell. Endocr.* **50**, 59–68.

BECKER, E. L. (1987). The formylpeptide receptor of the neutrophil: a search and conserve operation. *Am. J. Path.* **129**, 15–24.

BELIN, D., VASSALLI, J-D., COMBEPINE, C., GODEAU, F., NAGAMINE, Y., REICH, E., KOCHER, H. P. & DUVOISIN, R. M. (1985). Cloning, nucleotide sequencing and expression of cDNA's encoding mouse urokinase-type plasminogen activator. *Eur. J. Biochem.* **148**, 225–232.

BELLER, D. I., SPRINGER, T. A. & SCHREIBER, R. D. (1982). Anti-Mac-1 selectively inhibits the mouse and human type three complement receptor. *J. exp. Med.* **156**, 1000–1009.

BERKEN, A. & BENACERRAF, B. (1966). Properties of antibodies cytophilic for macrophages. *J. exp. Med.* **123**, 119–144.

BERTON, G. & GORDON, S. (1983). Modulation of macrophage mannose-specific receptors by cultivation on immobilised zymosan. Effects on phagocytosis and superoxide anion release. *Immunology* **49**, 705–715.

BEVILACQUA, M. P., POBER, J. S., MENDRICK, D. L., COTRAN, R. S. & GIMBRONE, M. A. JR (1987). Identification of an inducible endothelial-leukocyte adhesion molecule. *Proc. natn. Acad. Sci. U.S.A.* **84**, 9238–9242.

BIRGENS, H. S., HANSIEN, E., KARLE, H. & OSTERGAARD, K. L. (1983). Receptor binding of lactoferrin by human monocytes. *Br. J. Haemat.* **54**, 383–391.

BLACKWELL, J. M., EZEKOWITZ, R. A. B., ROBERTS, M. B., CHANNON, J. Y., SIM, R. B. & GORDON, S. (1985). Macrophage complement and lectin-like receptors bind *Leishmania* in the absence of serum. *J. exp. Med.* **162**, 324–331.

BLECHER, M. & GOLDSTEIN, S. (1977). Hormone receptors: VI. On the nature of binding of glucagon and insulin to human circulating mononuclear leukocytes. *Molec. cell. Endocr.* **8**, 301–315.

BOBAK, D. A., FRANK, M. M. & TENNER, A. J. (1986). Characterization of C1q Receptor expression on human phagocytic cells: effects of PDBu and fMLP. *J. Immun.* **136**, 4604–4610.

BOHNSACK, J. F., KLEINMAN, H., TAKAHASHI, T., O'SHEA, J. & BROWN, E. J. (1985). Connective tissue proteins and phagocytic cell formation: laminin enhances complement and Fc-mediated phagocytosis by cultured human macrophages. *J. exp. Med.* **161**, 912–923.

BROWN, E. J. & GOODWIN, J. L. (1988). Fibronectin receptors of phagocytes. Characterization of the Arg–Gly–Asp binding proteins of human monocytes and polymorphonuclear leukocytes. *J. exp. Med.* **167**, 777–793.

BROZE, G. J. (1982). Binding of human factor VII and VIIA to monocytes. *J. clin. Invest.* **70**, 526–535.

BULLOCK, W. E. & WRIGHT, S. D. (1987). Role of the adherence-promoting receptors CR3, LFA-1 and p150,95 in binding of *Histoplasma capsulatum* by human macrophages. *J. exp. Med.* **165**, 195–210.

BUMP, N. J., LEE, J., WLEKLIK, M., REICHLER, J. & NAJJAR, V. A. (1986). Isolation and subunit composition of tuftsin receptor. *Proc. natn. Acad. Sci. U.S.A.* **83**, 7187–7191.

BUNN, H. F. (1986). 5q⁻ and disordered haematopoiesis. *Clinics Haemat.* **15**, 1023–1035.

BURNS, G. F., COSGROVE, L., TRIGLA, T., BEALL, J. A., LOPEZ, A. F., WERKMEIST, T. A., BEGLEY, C. G., HODDARD, A. P., D'APICE, A. J. F., VADAS, M. A. & CAWLEY, J. C. (1986). IIb-IIIa glycoprotein complex that mediates platelet aggregation is directly implicated in leukocyte adhesion. *Cell* **45**, 269–280.

CAMERON, W., DOYLE, K. & ROCKLIN, R. E. (1986). Histamine type I (H₁) Receptor radioligand binding studies on normal T cell subsets, B cells and monocytes. *J. Immun.* **136**, 2116–2120.

CHENOWETH, D. E., GOODMAN, M. G. & WEIGLE, W. O. (1984). Demonstration of a specific receptor for human C5a anaphylotoxin on murine macrophages. *J. exp. Med.* **156**, 65–78.

CHERVINSKI, H. M., SCHUMACHER, J. H., BROWN, K. D. & MOSMANN, T. R. (1987). Two types of mouse helper T cell clone. III. Further differences in lymphokine synthesis between TH1 and TH2 clones revealed by RNA hybridization, functionally monospecific bioassays and monoclonal antibodies. *J. exp. Med.* **166**, 1229–1244.

CHONG, A. S. F. & PARISH, C. R. (1986). Cell surface receptors for sulphated polysaccharides – a potential marker for macrophage subsets. *Immunology* **58**, 277–284.

CHUNG, L. P., KESHAV, S. & GORDON, S. (1988). Cloning of the human lysozyme cDNA: Inverted Alu repeat in the mRNA and in situ hybridization for macrophages and Paneth cells. *Proc. natn. Acad. Sci. U.S.A.* (in press).

CLARKSON, S. B., KIMBERLEY, R. P., VALINSKY, J. E., WITMER, M. D., BUSSEL, J. B., NACHMAN, R. L. & UNKELESS, J. C. (1986). Blockade of clearance of immune complexes by an anti-Fc gamma receptor monoclonal antibody. *J. exp. Med.* **164**, 474–489.

COLTEN, H. R., STRUNK, R. C., PERLMUTTER, D. H. & COLE, F. S. (1986). Regulation of complement protein biosynthesis in mononuclear phagocytes. *Ciba Symp.* **118**, 141–151.

CORBI, A. L., MILLER, L. J., O'CONNOR, K., LARSON, R. S. & SPRINGER, T. (1987). cDNA cloning and complete primary structure of the subunit of a leukocyte adhesion glycoprotein p150 p95. *EMBO J.* **6**, 4023–4028.

CRAWFORD, R. M., FINBLOOM, D. S., OHARA, J., PAUL, W. E. & MELTZER, M. S. (1987). B cell stimulating factor-1 (interleukin 4) activates macrophages for increased tumoricidal activity and expression of Ia antigens. *J. Immun.* **139**, 135–141.

CROCKER, P. R. & GORDON, S. (1985). Isolation and characterization of resident stromal macrophages and hematopoietic cell clusters from mouse bone marrow. *J. exp. Med.* **162**, 993–1014.

CROCKER, P. R. & GORDON, S. (1986). Properties and distribution of a lectin-like haemagglutinin differentially expressed by stromal tissue macrophages. *J. exp. Med.* **164**, 1862–1875.

CROCKER, P. R., JEFFERIES, W. A., CLARK, S. J., CHUNG, L. P. & GORDON, S. (1987). Species heterogeneity in macrophage expression of the CD4 antigen. *J. exp. Med.* **166**, 613–618.

CROCKER, P. R., MORRIS, L. & GORDON, S. (1988). Novel cell surface adhesion receptors involved in interactions between stromal macrophages and haematopoietic cells *J. Cell Sci.* **Suppl. 9**, 185–206.

CZOP, J. K. & AUSTEN, K. F. (1985). A β-glucan inhibitable receptor on human monocytes and its identity with the phagocyte receptor for particulate activators of the alternative complement pathway. *J. Immun.* **134**, 2588–2593.

D'ARCY-HART, P., YOUNG, M. R., JORDON, M. M., PERKINS, W. J. & GEISOW, M. J. (1983). Chemical inhibitors of phagosome-lysosome fusion in cultured macrophages also inhibit saltatory lysosomal movements. *J. exp. Med.* **158**, 477–492.

DIAZ, P., JONES, D. G. & KAY, A. B. (1979). Histamine-coated particles generate superoxide and chemiluminescence in alveolar macrophages. *Nature, Lond.* **278**, 454–456.

DING, A. & NATHAN, C. (1988). Analysis of the non functional respiratory burst in murine Kupffer cells. *J. exp. Med.* **167**, 1154–1170.

DOUGHERTY, G. J. & HOGG, N. (1987). The role of monocyte lymphocyte function-associated antigen 1 (LFA-1) in accessory cell function. *Eur. J. Immun.* **17**, 943–947.

DOUGHERTY, G. J., MURDOCH, S. & HOGG, N. (1988). The function of human intracellular adhesion molecule 1 (ICAM-1) in the generation of an immune response. *Eur. J. Immun.* **18**, 35–39.

DOWER, S. K. & URDAL, D. L. (1987). The interleukin-1 receptor. *Immun. Today* **8**, 46–51.

EHLENBERGER, A. G. & NUSSENZWEIG, V. (1977). The role of membrane receptors C3b and C3d in phagocytosis. *J. exp. Med.* **145**, 357–371.

ELLSWORTH, J. L., COOPER, A. D. & KRAEMER, F. B. (1986). Evidence that chylomicron remnants and β-VLDL are transported by the same receptor pathway in J774 murine macrophage-derived cells. *J. Lipid Res.* **27**, 1062–1072.

EZEKOWITZ, R. A. B., AUSTYN, J. M., STAHL, P. D. & GORDON, S. (1981). Surface properties of BCG-activated mouse macrophages. Reduced expression of mannose-specific endocytosis, Fc receptors and antigen F4/80 accompanies induction of Ia. *J. exp. Med.* **154**, 60–76.

EZEKOWITZ, R. A. B., BAMPTON, M. & GORDON, S. (1983). Macrophage activation selectively enhances expression of Fc receptors for IgG2a. *J. exp. Med.* **157**, 807–812.

EZEKOWITZ, R. A. B., DAY, L. E. & HERMAN, G. A. (1988). A human mannose-binding protein is an acute-phase reactant that shares sequence homology with other vertebrate lectins. *J. exp. Med.* **167**, 1034–1046.

EZEKOWITZ, R. A. B. & GORDON, S. (1984). Alterations of surface properties by macrophage activation. Expression of receptors for Fc and mannose-terminal glycoproteins and differentiation antigens. In *Contemporary Topics in Immunobiology*, vol. 18 (ed. D. O. Adams & M. G. Hanna Jr), pp. 33–56. New York: Plenum Press.

EZEKOWITZ, R. A. B., HILL, M. & GORDON, S. (1986). Selective antagonism by interferon α/β of interferon-τ-induced marker of macrophage activation. *Biochem. biophys. Res. Commun.* **136**, 737–744.

EZEKOWITZ, R. A. B., SIM, R., HILL, M. & GORDON, S. (1984). Local opsonisation by secreted macrophage complement components. Role of receptors for complement in uptake of zymosan. *J. exp. Med.* **159**, 244–260.

EZEKOWITZ, R. A. B. & STAHL, P. D. (1988). The structure and function of vertebrate mannose lectin-like proteins. *J. Cell Sci.* **Suppl. 9**, 121–133.

FAUVE, R. M. & HEVIN, M. B. (1977). Inflammation et resistance antitumorale. II. Effets antagonistes de la bradykinine et d'une fraction isolée d'un surnageant de culture de cellules malignes sur l'étalement des macrophages. *Annls Immun. (Inst. Pasteur)* **128**C, 1079–1083.

FEARON, D. T. (1980). Identification of the membrane glycoprotein that is the C3b receptor of the human erythrocyte polymorphonuclear leukocyte B lymphocyte and monocytes. *J. exp. Med.* **152**, 20–30.

FLOREN, C.-D. & CHAIT, A. (1981). Uptake of chylomicron remnants by the native LDL Receptor in human monocyte-derived macrophages. *Biochim. biophys. Acta* **665**, 608–611.

FLOWER, R. J. (1986). The mediators of steroid action. *Nature, Lond.* **320**, 20.

FOGELMAN, A. M., VAN LENTEN, B. J., WARDEN, C., HABERLAND, M. E. & EDWARDS, P. A. (1988). Macrophage lipoprotein receptors. *J. Cell Sci.* **Suppl. 9**, 135–149.

FORIS, G., DEZSO, B., MEDGYESI, G. A. & FÜST, G. (1983). Effect of angiotensin II on macrophage functions. *Immunology* **48**, 529–535.

FRANSEN, L., MULLER, R., MEARMENOUT, A., TEVERNIER, J., VAN DER HEYDEN, J., KAWASHIMA, E., CHOLLET, A., TIZARD, R., VAN HEUVERSWYN, H., VAN VLIET, A., RIYSSCHAERT, M.-R. & FIERS, W. (1985). Molecular cloning of mouse tumour necrosis factor cDNA and its eukaryotic expression. *Nucl. Acids Res.* **13**, 4417–4429.

GHEBREHIWET, B. (1986). Production and characterization of a murine monoclonal IgM antibody to human Clq receptor (ClqR). *J. Immun.* **137**, 618–624.

GIANTURCO, S. H., BROWN, S. A., VIA, D. P. & BRADLEY, W. A. (1986). The β-VLDL receptor pathway of murine P388D$_1$ macrophages. *J. Lipid Res.* **27**, 412–420.

GOETZL, E. J. (1987). Leukocyte receptors for lipid and peptide mediators. *Fedn Proc. Fedn Am. Socs exp. Biol.* **46**, 190–191.

GOLDMAN, R. (1988). Characteristics of the β-Glucan receptor of murine macrophages. *Expl Cell Res.* **174**, 481–490.

GOLDSTEIN, J. L., HO, K. Y., BASU, S. K. & BROWN, M. S. (1979). A binding site on macrophages that mediates the uptake and degradation of acetylated low density lipoproteins, producing massive cholesterol deposition. *Proc. natn. Acad. Sci. U.S.A.* **76**, 333–337.

GOODMAN, M. G., CHENOWETH, D. E. & WEIGLE, W. O. (1984). Induction of Il-1 secretion and enhancement of humoral immunity by binding of human C5a to macrophage surface C5a Receptors. *J. exp. Med.* **156**, 912–917.

GORDON, S. (1978). Regulation of enzyme secretion by mononuclear phagocytes: Studies with macrophage plasminogen activator and lysozyme. *Fedn Proc. Fedn Am. Socs exp. Biol.* **37**, 2754–2758.

GORDON, S. (1986). Biology of the macrophage. *J. Cell Sci.* **Suppl. 4**, 267–286.

GORDON, S., CROCKER, P. R., LEE, S-H., MORRIS, L. & RABINOWITZ, S. (1986a). Trophic and defense functions of murine macrophages. In *Host-Resistance Mechanisms to Infectious Agents, Tumors and Allografts* (ed. R. S. Steinman & R. J. North), pp. 121–137. New York: Rockefeller University Press.

GORDON, S. & EZEKOWITZ, R. A. B. (1985). Macrophage neutral proteinases. Nature, regulation and role. In *The Reticuloendothelial System. A Comprehensive Treatise*, vol. 78 (ed. S. M. Reichard & J. P. Filkins), pp. 95–141. New York: Plenum Press.

GORDON, S., STARKEY, P., HUME, D., EZEKOWITZ, R. A. B., HIRSCH, S. & AUSTYN, J. (1986b). Plasma membrane markers to study differentiation, activation and localisation of murine macrophages. Ag F4.80 and the mannosyl fucosyl receptor. In *Handbook of Experimental Immunology*, 4th edn (ed. D. M. Weir, L. A. Herzenberg & L. A. Herzenberg), pp. 43.1–43.14. Oxford: Blackwell Scientific.

GOUGH, N. M., GOUGH, J., METCALF, D., KELSO, A., GRAIL, D., NICOLA, N. A., BURGESS, A. W. & DUNN, A. R. (1984). Molecular cloning of cDNA encoding a murine haematopoietic growth regulator, granulocyte-macrophaging colony stimulating factor. *Nature, Lond.* **309**, 763–767.

GREEN, S. J., TARONE, G. & UNDERHILL, C. B. (1988). Distribution of hyaluronate and hyaluronate receptors in the adult lung. *J. Cell Sci.* **90**, 145–156.

GUILBERT, L. J. & STANLEY, E. R. (1980). Specific interaction of murine colony-stimulating factor with mononuclear phagocytic cells. *J. Cell Biol.* **85**, 153–159.

HALTIWANGER, R. S., LEHRMAN, M. A., ECKHARDT, A. E. & HILL, R. C. (1986). The distribution and localization of the fucose-binding lectin in rat tissues and the identification of a high affinity form of the mannose/N-acetylglucosamine-binding lectin in rat liver. *J. biol. Chem.* **261**, 7433–7439.

HEMLER, M. E., HUANG, C. & SCHWARTZ, L. (1987). The VLA protein family. *J. biol. Chem.* **262**, 3300–3309.

HENRICKS, P. A. J., VAN ESCH, B. & NIJKAMP, F. P. (1987). β-agonists can depress oxidative metabolism of alveolar macrophages. *Agent Actions* **19**, 353–355.

HIBBS, M. L., WALKER, I. D., KIRZBAUM, L., PIETERSZ, G. A., DEACON, N. J., CHAMBERS, G. W., MCKENZIE, I. F. & HOGARTH, P. M. (1986). The murine Fc receptor for immunoglobulin, purification, partial amino acid sequence, and isolation of cDNA clones. *Proc. natn. Acad. Sci. U.S.A.* **83**, 6980–6984.

HOFLACK, B. & KORNFELD, S. (1985). Lysosomal enzyme binding to mouse P388D$_1$ macrophage membranes lacking the 215-kDa mannose 6-phosphate receptor: Evidence for the existence of a second mannose 6-phosphate receptor. *Proc. natn. Acad. Sci. U.S.A.* **82**, 4428–4432.

HOGG, N., SELVENDRAM, Y., DOUGHERTY, G. & ALLEN, C. (1986). Macrophage antigens and the effect of a macrophage activating factor, interferon τ. In *Biochemistry of Macrophages Ciba Symp.* **118**, 68–76.

HOLTER, W., GOLDMAN, C. K., CASABO, L., NELSON, D. L., GREENE, W. C. & WALDMANN, T. A. (1987). Expression of functional IL-2 receptors by lipopolysaccharide and interferon-τ stimulated human monocytes. *J. Immun.* **138**, 2917–2922.

HORIUCHI, S., MURAKAMI, M., TAKATA, K. & MORINO, Y. (1986). Scavenger receptor for aldehyde-modified proteins. *J. biol. Chem.* **261**, 4962–4966.

HORWITZ, M. A. (1986). The *Legionella pnuemophilia* model. In *Mechanisms of Host Resistance to Infectious Agents, Tumors, and Allografts* (ed. R. J. Steinman & R. J. North), pp. 154–164. New York: Rockefeller University Press.

HORWITZ, M. A. (1987). Characterization of avirulent mutant *Legionella pneumophila* that survive but do not multiply within human monocytes. *J. exp. Med.* **166**, 1310–1328.

HOSEIN, B. & BIANCO, C. (1985). Monocyte receptors for fibronectin characterized by a monoclonal antibody that interferes with receptor activity. *J. exp. Med.* **162**, 157–170.

HUBBARD, A. L., WILSON, G., ASHWELL, G. & STUKENBROK, H. (1979). An electron microscope and autoradiographic study of the carbohydrate recognition system in rat liver. *J. Cell Biol.* **83**, 47–64.

HUME, D. A. & GORDON, S. (1983). The mononuclear phagocyte system of the mouse defined by immunohistochemical localisation of antigen F4/80. Identification of resident macrophages in renal medullary and cortical interstitium and the juxtaglomerular complex. *J. exp. Med.* **157**, 1704–1709.

HUME, D. A., HALPIN, D., CHARLTON, H. & GORDON, S. (1984*a*). The mononuclear phagocyte system of the mouse defined by immunohistochemical localisation of antigen F4/80. Macrophages of endocrine organs. *Proc. natn. Acad. Sci. U.S.A.* **81**, 4174–4177.

HUME, D. A., PERRY, V. H. & GORDON, S. (1983*a*). The immunohistochemical localisation of a macrophage-specific antigen in developing mouse retina. Phagocytosis of dying neurons and differentiation of microglial cells to form a regular array in the plexiform layers. *J. Cell Biol.* **97**, 253–257.

HUME, D. A., PERRY, V. H. & GORDON, S. (1984*b*). The mononuclear phagocyte system of the mouse defined by immunohistochemical localisation of antigen F4/80. Macrophages associated with epithelia. *Anat. Rec.* **210**, 503–572.

HUME, D. A., ROBINSON, A. P., MACPHERSON, G. G. & GORDON, S. (1983*b*). The immunohistochemical localisation of antigen F4/80. The relationship between macrophages, Langerhans cell, reticular cells and dendritic cells in lymphoid and hemopoietic organs. *J. exp. Med.* **158**, 1522–1536.

HUMPHREY, J. H. & GRENNAN, D. (1981). Different macrophage populations distinguished by means of fluorescent polysaccharides. Recognition and properties of marginal zone macrophages. *Eur. J. Immun.* **11**, 221–229.

HYNES, R. O. (1987). Integrins: a family of cell surface receptors. *Cell* **48**, 549–554.

INADA, S., BROWN, E. J., GAITHER, T. A., HAMMER, G. H., TAKAHASHI, T. & FRANK, M. M. (1983). C3d receptors are expressed on human monocytes after *in vitro* cultivation. *Proc. natn. Acad. Sci. U.S.A.* **80**, 2351–2355.

JOHNSTON, R. B. JR, LEHMEYER, J. E. & GUTHRIE, L. A. (1976). Generation of superoxide anion and chemiluminescence by human monocytes during phagocytosis and on contact with surface-bound immunoglobulin G. *J. exp. Med.* **143**, 1551–1556.

JONES, T. C. & HIRSCH, J. G. (1972). The interaction between *Toxoplasma gondii* and mammalian cells. II. The absence of lysosomal fusion with phagocytic vacuoles containing living parasites. *J. exp. Med.* **136**, 1173–1194.

KAPLAN, J. & NEILSEN, M. L. (1979). Analysis of macrophage surface receptors. (I) Binding of α-macroglobulin-protease complexes to rabbit alveolar macrophages. *J. biol. Chem.* **254**, 7323–7328.

KATAOKA, M. & TAVASSOLI, M. (1985). Identification of caeruloplasmin receptors on the surface of human blood monocytes, granulocytes and lymphocytes. *Expl Hemat.* **13**, 806–810.

KELSO, A. & GOUGH, N. (1987). Expression of hemopoietic growth factor genes in murine T lymphocytes. *Lymphokines* **13**, 209–238.

KISHIMOTO, T. K., O'CONNOR, K., LEE, A., ROBERTS, T. M. & SPRINGER, T. A. (1987). Cloning of the β subunit of the leukocyte adhesion proteins: Homology to an extracellular matrix receptor defines a novel supergene family. *Cell* **48**, 681–690.

KRAAL, G., BREEL, M., JANSE, M. & BRUIN, G. (1986). Langerhans cells, veiled cells and interdigitating cells in the mouse recognized by a monoclonal antibody. *J. exp. Med.* **163**, 981–987.

KURACHI, K., CHANDRA, T., DEGEN, S. J. F., WHITE, T. T., MARCHIORO, T. L., WOO, S. L. C. & DAVIE, E. W. (1987). Cloning and sequence of cDNA for alpha-1-antitrypsin. *Proc. natn. Acad. Sci. U.S.A.* **84**, 6826–6830.

KURLANDER, R. J., ELLISON, D. M. & HALL, J. (1984). The blockade of Fc receptor-mediated clearance of immune complexes in vivo by monoclonal antibody (2.4G2) directed against Fc receptors on murine leukocytes. *J. Immun.* **133**, 855–862.

LANG, R. A., METCALF, D., CUTHBERTSON, R. A., LYONS, J., STANLEY, E., KELSO, A., KANOURAKIS, G., WILLIAMSON, D. J., KLINTWORTH, G. K., GANDA, T. J. & DUNN, A. R. (1987). Transgenic mice expressing a hemopoietic growth factor gene (GM-CSF) develop accumulations of macrophages, blindness and fatal syndrome of tissue damage. *Cell* **51**, 675–686.

LANGER, J. A., RASHIDBAIGI, A. & PESTKA, S. (1986). Preparation of ^{32}P-labeled murine immune interferon and its binding to the mouse immune interferon receptor. *J. biol. Chem.* **261**, 9801–9804.

LAW, S. K. A. (1988). C3 receptors on macrophages. *J. Cell Sci.* **Suppl. 9**, 67–97.

LAY, W. H. & NUSSENZWEIG, V. (1968). Receptors for complement on leukocytes. *J. exp. Med.* **128**, 991–1009.

LEE, S.-H., CROCKER, P. & GORDON, S. (1986). Macrophage plasma membrane and secretory properties in murine malaria. Effects of *Plasmodium yoelii* infection on macrophages in the liver, spleen and blood. *J. exp. Med.* **163**, 54–74.

LEHRMAN, M. A. & HILL, R. C. (1986). The binding of fucose-containing glycoproteins by hepatic lectins. Purification of a fucose-binding lectin from rat liver. *J. biol. Chem.* **261**, 7419–7425.

LEPAY, D. A., STEINMAN, R. M., NATHAN, C. F., MURRAY, H. W. & COHN, Z. A. (1985). Liver macrophages in murine Listeriosis: cell-mediated immunity is correlated with an influx of macrophages capable of generating reactive oxygen intermediates. *J. exp. Med.* **161**, 1503–1512.

LEWIS, V. A., KOCH, T., PLUTNER, H. & MELLMAN, I. (1986). A complementary DNA clone for a macrophage-lymphocyte Fc receptor. *Nature, Lond.* **324**, 372–375.

LOMEDICO, P. T., GUBLER, U., HELLMAN, C. P., DUKOVICH, M., GIRI, J. G., PAN, Y-C. E., COLLIER, K., SEMIONOW, R., CHUA, A. O. & MIZEL, S. B. (1984). Cloning and expression of murine interleukin-1 cDNA in *Escherichia coli*. *Nature, Lond.* **312**, 458–461.

Loos, M. (1982). The functions of endogenous C1q, a subcomponent of the first component of complement, as a receptor on the membrane of macrophages. *Molec. Immun.* **19**, 1229–1238.

Makgoba, M. W., Sanders, M. E., Luce, G. E. G., Dustin, M. L., Springer, T. A., Clark, E. D., Mannoni, P. & Shaw, S. (1988). ICAM-1 a ligand for LFA-1 dependent adhesion of B, T and myeloid cells. *Nature, Lond.* **331**, 86–88.

Maynard, Y. & Baenziger, J. U. (1981). Oligosaccharide specific endocytosis by isolated rat hepatic reticuloendothelial cells. *J. biol. Chem.* **256**, 8063–8068.

McGillis, J. P., Organist, M. L. & Payan, D. G. (1987). Substance P and immunoregulation. *Fedn Proc. Fedn Am. Socs exp. Biol.* **46**, 196–199.

McInnes, A. & Rennick, D. M. (1988). Interleukin 4 induces cultured monocytes/macrophages to form giant multinucleated cells. *J. exp. Med.* **167**, 598–611.

Mellman, I. S., Plutner, H., Steinman, R. M., Unkeless, J. C. & Cohn, Z. A. (1983). Internalization and degradation of macrophage Fc receptors during receptor mediated phagocytosis. *J. Cell Biol.* **96**, 887–895.

Mellman, I. S., Koch, T., Healey, G., Hunziker, W., Lewis, V., Plutner, H., Miettinen, H., Vaux, D., Moore, K. & Stuart, S. (1988). Structure and function of Fc receptors on macrophages and lymphocytes. *J. Cell Sci.* **Suppl. 9**, 45–65.

Metcalf, D. (1987). Membrane receptors for the colony-stimulating factors on haemopoietic cells. In *Leucocyte Typing III White Cell Differentiation Antigens* (ed. A. J. McMichael), pp. 908–913. Oxford, New York, Tokyo: Oxford University Press.

Michl, J., Pieczonka, M. M., Unkeless, J. C., Bell, G. I. & Silverstein, S. C. (1983a). Fc receptor modulation in mononuclear phagocytes maintained on immobilized immune complexes occurs by diffusion of the receptor molecule. *J. exp. Med.* **157**, 2121–2139.

Michl, J., Pieczonka, M. M., Unkeless, J. C. & Silverstein, S. C. (1979). Effects of immobilized immune complexes on Fc- and complement receptor function in resident and thioglycollate-elicited mouse peritoneal macrophages. *J. exp. Med.* **150**, 607–621.

Michl, J., Unkeless, J. C., Pieczonka, M. M. & Silverstein, S. C. (1983b). Modulation of Fc receptors of mononuclear phagocytes by immobilized antigen-antibody complexes. Quantitative analysis of the relationship between ligand concentration and Fc receptor response. *J. exp. Med.* **157**, 1746–1757.

Mokoena, T. & Gordon, S. (1985). Activation of human macrophages. Modulation of mannosyl, fucosyl receptors for endocytosis by lymphokine, gamma and alpha interferons and dexamethasone. *J. clin. Invest.* **75**, 624–631.

Morgan, D. O., Edman, J. C., Standring, D. N., Fried, V. A., Smith, M. C., Roth, R. A. & Rutter, W. J. (1987). Insulin-like growth factor II receptor as a multifunctional binding protein. *Nature, Lond.* **329**, 301–307.

Morris, L., Crocker, P. R. & Gordon, S. (1988). Murine foetal liver macrophages bind developing erythroblasts by a divalent cation-dependent haemagglutinin. *J. Cell Biol.* **106**, 649–656.

Mosser, D. M. & Edelson, P. J. (1985). The mouse macrophage receptor for C3bi(CR3) is a major mechanism in the phagocytosis of *Leishmania* promastigotes. *J. Immun.* **135**, 2785–2789.

Mosser, D. M., Vlassara, H., Edelson, P. J. & Cerami, A. (1987). *Leishmania* promastigotes are recognised by the macrophage receptor for advanced glycosylation end products. *J. exp. Med.* **165**, 140–145.

Murakami, M., Horiuchi, S., Takata, K. & Morino, Y. (1986). Scavenger receptor for malondialdehyde-modified high-density lipoprotein on rat sinusoidal liver cells. *Biochem. biophys. Res. Commun.* **137**, 29–35.

Nathan, C. F. (1980). The release of hydrogen peroxide from mononuclear phagocytes and its role in extracellular cytosis. In *Mononuclear Phagocytes: Functional Aspects* (ed. R. van Furth), pp. 1165–1183. The Hague: Martinus Nijhoff.

Nathan, C. (1986). Interferon-gamma and macrophage activation in cell-mediated immunity. In *Mechanisms of Host Resistance to Infectious Agents, Tumors and Allografts* (ed. R. J. Steinman & R. J. North), pp. 165–184. New York: Rockefeller University Press.

Nathan, C. F. (1987). Secretory products of macrophages. *J. clin. Invest.* **79**, 319–326.

Nicola, N. A. (1987). Hemopoietic growth factors and their interactions with specific receptors. *J. cell Physiol.* **Suppl. 5**, 9–14.

NOGUEIRA, N., KAPLAN, G. & COHN, Z. A. (1980). Induction of macrophage microbicidal activity. In *Mononuclear Phagocytes: Functional Aspects* (ed. R. van Furth), pp. 1587–1606. The Hague: Martinus Nijhoff.

O'DORISIO, M. S. (1987). Biochemical characteristics of receptors for vasoactive intestinal polypeptide in nervous, endocrine and immune systems. *Fedn Proc. Fedn Am. Socs exp. Biol.* **46**, 192–195.

OHKUMA, S. & POOLE, B. (1981). Cytoplasmic vacuolation of mouse peritoneal macrophages and the uptake into lysosomes of weakly basic substances. *J. Cell Biol.* **90**, 656–664.

ORCHANSKY, P., RUBINSTEIN, M. & FISHER, D. G. (1986). The interferon τ receptor in human monocytes is different from one in nonhaemopoietic cells. *J. Immun.* **136**, 169–173.

PARK, L. S., FRIEND, D., GILLIS, S. & URDAL, D. L. (1986). Characterization of the cell surface receptor for human granulocyte/macrophage colony-stimulating factor. *J. exp. Med.* **164**, 251–262.

PENNICA, D., NEDWIN, G. E., HAYFLICK, J. S., SEEBURG, P. H., DERYNCK, R., PALLADINO, M. A., KOHR, W. J., AGGARWAL, B. B. & GOEDDEL, D. V. (1984). Human tumour necrosis factor: precursor structure, expression and homology to lymphotoxin. *Nature, Lond.* **312**, 724–729.

PERRY, H. M., CHAPPEL, J. C., BELLORIN-FONT, E., TAMAO, J., MARTIN, K. J. & TEITELBAUM, S. L. (1984). Parathyroid hormone receptors in circulating human mononuclear leukocytes. *J. biol. Chem.* **259**, 5531–5535.

PERRY, V. H. & GORDON, S. (1987). Modulation of CD4 antigen on macrophages and microglia in rat brain. *J. exp. Med.* **166**, 1138–1143.

PERRY, V. H. & GORDON, S. (1988). Macrophages and microglia in the nervous system. *Trends Neurosci.* **11**, 273–277.

PERRY, V. H., HUME, D. A. & GORDON, S. (1985). Immunohistochemical localization of macrophages and microglia in the adult and developing mouse brain. *Neuroscience* **15**, 313–326.

PORTERFIELD, J. S. (1986). Antibody-dependent enhancement of viral infectivity. *Adv. virus Res.* **31**, 335–355.

QU, Z., ODIN, J., GLASS, J. D. & UNKELESS, J. C. (1988). Expression and characterization of a truncated murine Fc α receptor. *J. exp. Med.* **167**, 1195–1210.

RABINOVITCH, M., ZILBERFARB, V. & RAMAZEILLES, C. (1986). Destruction of *Leishmania mexicana amazonensis* amastigotes within macrophages by lysosomotropic amino acid esters. *J. exp. Med.* **163**, 520–535.

RAVETCH, J. V., LUSTER, A. D., WEINSHANK, R., KOCHAN, J., PAVLOVEC, A., PORTNOY, D. A., HULMES, J., PAN, Y-C. & UNKELESS, J. C. (1986). Structural heterogeneity and functional domains of murine immunoglobulin G Fc receptors. *Science* **234**, 718–725.

REFNES, K. & MUNTHE-KAAS, A. C. (1976). Introduction of B-chain inactivated ricin into mouse macrophages and rat Kupffer cells via their Fc receptors. *J. exp. Med.* **143**, 1464–1474.

REID, K. B. M., BENTLEY, D. R., CAMPBELL, R. D., CHUNG, L. P., SIM, R. B., KRISTENSEN, T. & TACK, B. F. (1986). Complement system proteins which interact with C3b or C4b. *Immun. Today* **7**, 230–234.

RETTENMIER, C. W., ROUSSEL, M. F. & SHERR, C. J. (1988). The CSF-1 receptor (c-*fms* proto-oncogene product) and its ligand. *J. Cell Sci.* **Suppl. 9**, 27–44.

REVEL, M. & CHEBATH, J. (1986). Interferon-activated genes. *Trends Biochem. Sci.* **11**, 166–170.

ROOS, P. H., HARTMAN, H-J., SCHLEPPER-SCHÄFER, J., KOLB, H. & KOLB-BACHOFEN, V. (1985). Galactose-specific receptors on liver cells II. Characterization of the purified receptor from macrophages reveals no structural relationship to the hepatocyte receptor. *Biochim. biophys. Acta* **847**, 115–121.

ROSATI, C., HANNAERT, P., DAUSSE, J-P., BRAQUET, P. & GARAY, R. (1986). Stimulation of beta-adrenoreceptors inhibits calcium-dependent potassium-channels in mouse macrophages. *J. cell. Physiol.* **129**, 310–314.

ROSEN, H. & GORDON, S. (1987). Monoclonal antibody to the murine type 3 complement receptor inhibits adhesion of myelomonocytic cells in vitro and inflammatory cell recruitment in vivo. *J. exp. Med.* **166**, 1685–1701.

ROSENFELD, R., THORSSON, A. V. & HINTZ, R. L. (1979). Increased somatomedin receptor sites in newborn circulating mononuclear cells. *J. clin. Endocr. Metab.* **48**, 456–461.

Ross, G. M., Cain, J. A. & Lachmann, P. J. (1985). Membrane complement receptor type three (CR3) has lectin-like properties analogous to bovine conglutinin and functions as a receptor for zymosan and rabbit erythrocytes as well as a receptor for iC3b. *J. Immun.* **134**, 3307–3315.

Rouzer, C. A., Scott, W. A., Kempe, J. & Cohn, Z. A. (1980). Prostaglandin synthesis by macrophages requires a specific receptor-ligand interaction. *Proc. natn. Acad. Sci. U.S.A.* **77**, 4279–4282.

Ruff, M. R., Pert, C. B., Weber, R. J., Wahl, L. M., Wahl, S. M. & Paul, S. M. (1985). Benzodiazepine receptor-mediated chemotaxis of human monocytes. *Science* **229**, 1281–1283.

Ruoslahti, E. & Pierschbacher, M. D. (1987). New perspectives in cell adhesion: RGD and integrins. *Science* **238**, 491–497.

Russell, D. G. & Wright, S. D. (1988). Complement receptor type 3 (CR3) binds to an Arg–Gly–Asp-containing region of the major surface glycoprotein, gp63, of *Leishmania* promastigotes. *J. exp. Med.* (in press).

Sacca, R., Stanley, E. R., Sherr, C. J. & Rettenmier, C. W. (1986). Specific binding of the mononuclear phagocyte colony-stimulating factor CSF-1 to the product of the v-*fms* oncogene. *Proc. natn. Acad. Sci. U.S.A.* **83**, 3331–3335.

Schlepper-Schaffer, J., Kolb-Bachofen, V. & Kolb, H. (1983). Identification of a receptor for senescent erythrocytes on liver macrophages. *Biochem. biophys. Res. Commun.* **115**, 551–559.

Schuler, G. & Steinman, R. M. (1985). Murine epidermal Langerhans cells mature into potent immunostimulatory dendritic cells *in vitro*. *J. exp. Med.* **161**, 526–546.

Shepherd, V. L., Freeze, H. H., Miller, A. L. & Stahl, P. D. (1984). Identification of Mannose 6-Phosphate receptors in rabbit alveolar macrophages. *J. biol. Chem.* **259**, 2257–2261.

Sherman, L. A. & Lee, J. (1977). Specific binding of soluble fibrin to macrophages. *J. exp. Med.* **145**, 76–85.

Sherr, C. J., Rettenmier, C. W., Sacca, R., Roussel, M. F., Look, A. T. & Stanley, E. R. (1985). The c-*fms* proto-oncogene product is related to the receptor for the mononuclear phagocyte growth factor, CSF-1. *Cell* **41**, 665–676.

Silverstein, R. L. & Nachman, R. L. (1987). Thrombospondin binds to monocytes, macrophages and mediates platelet monocyte adhesion. *J. clin. Invest.* **79**, 867–874.

Silverstein, S. C., Steinman, R. M. & Cohn, Z. A. (1977). Endocytosis. *A. Rev. Biochem.* **46**, 669–722.

Simmons, B. M., Stahl, P. D. & Russell, J. H. (1986). Mannose receptor-mediated uptake of ricin toxin and ricin A chain by macrophages. *J. biol. Chem.* **261**, 7912–7920.

Simmons, B. M., Stahl, P. D. & Russell, J. H. (1987). *In vivo* depletion of mannose receptor bearing cells from rat liver by ricin A chain: effects on clearance of β-glucuronidase. *Biochem. biophys. Res. Commun.* **146**, 849–854.

Simmons, D., Makgoba, M. W. & Seed, B. (1988). ICAM, an adhesion ligand of LFA-1 is homologous to the neural cell adhesion molecule NCAM. *Nature, Lond.* **331**, 624–627.

Sly, W. S. & Fischer, A. D. (1982). The phospho-mannosyl recognitions system for intracellular and intercellular transport of lysosomal enzymes. *J. cell. Biochem.* **18**, 67–85.

Snyderman, R. & Pike, M. C. (1984). Chemoattractant receptors on phagocytic cells. *A. Rev. Immun.* **2**, 257–281.

Sorensen, P., Farber, N. M. & Krystal, G. (1986). Identification of the interleukin-3 receptor using an iodinatable, cleavable, photoreactive cross-linking agent. *J. biol. Chem.* **261**, 9094–9097.

Springer, T., Galfre, G., Secher, G. S. & Milstein, C. (1979). Mac I: A macrophage differentiation antigen identified by monoclonal antibody. *Eur. J. Immun.* **9**, 301–306.

Springer, T. A. & Anderson, D. C. (1986). The importance of the Mac-1, LFA-1 glycoprotein family in monocyte and granulocyte adherence, chemotaxis and migration. *Ciba Symp.* **118**, 102–126.

Springer, T. A., Thompson, W. S., Miller, L. J., Schmalstieg, F. C. & Anderson, D. C. (1984). Inherited deficiency of the Mac-1, LFA-1, p150,95 glycoprotein family and its molecular basis. *J. exp. Med.* **160**, 1901–1918.

Stahl, P., Schlesinger, H., Rodman, J. S. & Doebber, T. (1976). Recognition of lysosomal glycosidases *in vivo* inhibited by modified glycoproteins. *Nature, Lond.* **264**, 86–88.

STAHL, P. D., RODMAN, J. S., MILLER, M. J. & SCHLESINGER, P. H. (1978). Evidence for receptor-mediated binding of glycoproteins, glycoconjugates, and lysomal glycosidases by alveolar macrophages. *Proc. natn. Acad. Sci. U.S.A.* **75**, 1399–1403.

STEINMAN, R. M., INABA, K., SCHULER, G. & WITMER, M. (1986). Stimulation of the immune response: Contributions of dendritic cells. In *Mechanisms of Host Resistance to Infectious Agents, Tumors and Allografts* (ed. R. M. Steinman & R. J. North), pp. 71–97. New York: Rockefeller University Press.

STEINMAN, R. M., MELLMAN, I. S., MULLER, W. A. & COHN, Z. A. (1983). Endocytosis and the recycling of plasma membrane. *J. Cell Biol.* **96**, 1–26.

STERNBERG, E. M., TRIAL, J. & PARKER, C. W. (1986). Effect of serotonin on murine macrophages: suppression of Ia expression by serotonin and its reversal by 5-HT$_2$ serotonergic receptor antagonists. *J. Immun.* **137**, 276–282.

STILES, G. L. (1987). Adenosine receptors: structure, function and regulation. *Trends Pharmac. Sci.* **7**, 486–489.

STOPPELLI, M. P., CONTI, A., SOFFIENTINI, A., CASSANI, G., BLASI, F. & ASSOIAN, R. K. (1985). Differentiation-enhanced binding of the amino-terminal fragment of human urokinase plasminogen activator to a specific receptor on U937 monocytes. *Proc. natn. Acad. Sci. U.S.A.* **82**, 4939–4944.

TAKETANI, S., KAHNO, H. & TAKUNAGA, R. (1987). Cell surface receptor of hemopexin in human leukemia HL60 cells. Specific binding, affinity labelling and fate of heme. *J. biol. Chem.* **262**, 4639–4643.

TENNER, A. J. & COOPER, N. R. (1980). Analysis of receptor-mediated C1q binding to human peripheral blood mononuclear cells. *J. Immun.* **125**, 1658–1664.

THOMAS, D. W. & HOFFMAN, M. D. (1984). Identification of macrophage receptors for angiotensin: a potential role in antigen uptake for T lymphocyte responses. *J. Immun.* **132**, 2807–2812.

UKKONEN, P., LEWIS, V., MARSH, M., HELENIUS, A. & MELLMAN, I. (1986). Transport of macrophage Fc receptors and Fc receptor-bound ligands to lysosomes. *J. exp. Med.* **163**, 952–971.

UNKELESS, J. C. (1979). Characterization of a monoclonal antibody directed against mouse macrophage and lymphocyte Fc receptors. *J. exp. Med.* **150**, 580–596.

UNKELESS, J. C. (1986). Heterogeneity of human and murine Fc τ receptors. *Ciba Symp.* **118**, 89–96.

UNKELESS, J. C., FLEIT, H. & MELLMAN, I. S. (1981). Structural aspects and heterogeneity of immunoglobulin Fc receptors. *Adv. Immun.* **31**, 247–270.

UNKELESS, J. C., SCIGLIANO, E. & FREEDMAN, V. (1988). Structure and function of human and murine receptors for IgG. *A. Rev. Immun.* **6**, 251–281.

VAN FURTH, R. (ed.) (1980). *Mononuclear Phagocytes: Functional Aspects.* The Hague: Martinus Nijhoff.

VAN FURTH, R. (ed.) (1985). *Mononuclear Phagocytes: Characteristics, Physiology and Function.* The Hague: Martinus Nijhoff.

VAN LEUVEN, F., MARYNEN, P., SOTTRUP-JENSEN, L., CASEIMAN, J. J. & VAN DEN BERGHE, H. (1986). The receptor-binding domain of human α2m macroglobulin. *J. biol. Chem.* **261**, 11 369–11 373.

VAN SNICK, J. L. & MASSON, P. L. (1976). The binding of human lactoferrin to mouse peritoneal cells. *J. exp. Med.* **144**, 1568–1580.

VASSALLI, J-D., BACCINO, D. & BELIN, D. (1985). A cellular binding site for the M_r 55,000 form of the human plasminogen activator urokinase. *J. Cell Biol.* **100**, 86–92.

VLASSARA, H., BROWNLEE, M. & CERAMI, A. (1985). High affinity receptor-mediated uptake and degradation of glucose-modified proteins: A potential mechanism for the removal of senescent macromolecules. *Proc. natn. Acad. Sci. U.S.A.* **82**, 5588–5593.

VLASSARA, H., BROWNLEE, M. & CERAMI, A. (1986). Novel macrophage receptor for glucose-modified proteins is distinct from previously described scavenger receptors. *J. exp. Med.* **164**, 1301–1309.

VOGEL, W., BOMFORD, A., YOUNG, S. & WILLIAMS, R. (1987). Heterogeneous distribution of transferrin receptors on parenchymal and nonparenchymal liver cells. Biochemical and Morphological evidence. *Blood* **69**, 264–270.

WALKER, F. & BURGESS, A. W. (1985). Specific binding of radioiodinated granulocyte-macrophage colony-stimulating factor to hemopoietic cells. *EMBO J.* **4**, 933–939.

WALKER, F. & BURGESS, A. W. (1987). Internalisation and recycling of the granulocyte-macrophage colony-stimulating factor (GM-CSF) receptor on a murine myelomonocytic leukemia. *J. cell. Physiol.* **130**, 255–261.

WARLOW, R. S. & BERNARD, C. C. A. (1987). Solubilization and characterization of moderate and high affinity histamine binding sites on human blood mononuclear cells. *Molec. Immun.* **24**, 27–38.

WATSON, J. D. (1987). Cytokines and their receptors. *Immun. Today* **7**, 320–321.

WEINBERG, B. J. & MISUKONI, M. A. (1983). Phorbol Diester – H_2O_2 production by peritoneal macrophages. Different H_2O_2 production by macrophages from normal and BCG-infected mice despite comparable phorbol diester receptors. *Cell. Immun.* **80**, 405–415.

WERB, Z., BANDA, M. J., TAKEMURA, R. & GORDON, S. (1986). Secreted proteins of resting and activated macrophages. In *Handbook of Experimental Immunology*, 4th edn (ed. D. M. Weir, L. A. Herzenberg, & L. A. Herzenberg), pp. 47.1–147.29. Oxford: Blackwell Scientific Publications.

WHALEY, K., LAPPIN, D. & BARKAS, T. (1981). C_2 synthesis by human monocytes is modulated by a nicotinic cholinergic receptor. *Nature, Lond.* **293**, 580–583.

WILEMAN, T. E., LENNARTZ, M. R. & STAHL, P. D. (1986). Identification of the macrophage mannose receptor as a 175-kDa membrane protein. *Proc. natn. Acad. Sci. U.S.A.* **83**, 2501–2505.

WILLIAMS, A. F. (1987). A year in the life of the immunoglobulin superfamily. *Immun. Today* **8**, 298–303.

WILSON, C. B., TSAI, V. & REMINGTON, J. S. (1980). Failure to trigger the oxidative metabolic burst by normal macrophages: Possible mechanism for survival of intracellular parasites. *J. exp. Med.* **151**, 328–346.

WONG, W. W., KENNEDY, C. A., BONACCIO, E. T., WILSON, J. G., KLICKSTEIN, L. B., WEIS, J. H. & FEARON, D. T. (1986). Analysis of multiple restriction fragment length polymorphisms of the gene for the human complement receptor Type I. Duplication of genomic sequences occurs in association with a high molecular mass receptor allotype. *J. exp. Med.* **164**, 1531–1546.

WRIGHT, S. D. & DETMERS, P. A. (1988). Adhesion-promoting receptors on phagocytes. *J. Cell Sci.* **Suppl. 9**, 99–120.

WRIGHT, S. & SILVERSTEIN, S. C. (1986). Overview: the function of receptors in phagocytosis. In *Handbook of Experimental Immunology, Cellular Immunol.* (ed. D. M. Weir), pp. 41.1–41.14. Oxford: Blackwell Scientific Publications.

WRIGHT, S. D. & SILVERSTEIN, S. C. (1983). Receptors for C3b and C3bi promote phagocytosis but not the release of toxic oxygen from human phagocytes. *J. exp. Med.* **158**, 2016–2023.

WYLLIE, J. C. (1977). Transferrin uptake by rabbit alveolar macrophages *in vitro*. *Br. J. Haemat.* **37**, 17–24.

YAMAMOTO, K. & JOHNSTON, R. B. JR (1984). Dissociation of phagocytosis from stimulation of the oxidative metabolic burst in macrophages. *J. exp. Med.* **159**, 405–416.

YOKOTA, T., ARAI, N., DE VRIES, J., SPITS, H., BANCHEREAU, J., ZLOTNIK, A., RENNICK, D., HOWARD, M., TAKEBE, Y., MIYATAKE, S., LEE, F. & ARAI, K. I. (1988). Molecular biology of IL4 and IL5 genes and biology of their products that stimulate B cells, T cells and hemopoietic cells. *Immun. Rev.* **102**, 137–187.

YOSHIDA, R., MURRAY, H. W. & NATHAN, C. F. (1988). Agonist and antagonist effects of interferon α and β on activation of human macrophages. Two classes of interferon α receptors and blockade of the high-affinity sites by interferon α and β. *J. exp. Med.* **167**, 1171–1185.

J. Cell Sci. Suppl. 9, 27–44 (1988)
Printed in Great Britain © The Company of Biologists Limited 1988

The colony-stimulating factor 1 (CSF-1) receptor (c-*fms* proto-oncogene product) and its ligand

CARL W. RETTENMIER, MARTINE F. ROUSSEL AND CHARLES J. SHERR

Department of Tumor Cell Biology, St. Jude Children's Research Hospital, 332 N. Lauderdale, Memphis, Tennessee 38105, USA

Summary

Alterations in genes that function in normal growth and development have been linked to malignant cell transformation. The mononuclear phagocyte colony-stimulating factor (CSF-1 or M-CSF) is a polypeptide growth factor synthesized by mesenchymal cells, which stimulates the survival, proliferation, and differentiation of haematopoietic cells of the monocyte-macrophage series. Multiple forms of soluble CSF-1 are produced by proteolytic cleavage of membrane-bound precursors, some of which are stably expressed at the cell surface. The c-*fms* proto-oncogene encodes the CSF-1 receptor, which is composed of an extracellular ligand-binding domain linked by a single membrane-spanning segment to a cytoplasmic tyrosine-specific protein kinase domain. Whereas the tyrosine kinase activity of the normal receptor is stimulated by CSF-1, mutations in the c-*fms* gene can constitutively activate the kinase to provide growth-stimulatory signals in the absence of the ligand. Oncogenic activation of the c-*fms* gene product appears to involve removal of a negative regulatory tyrosine residue near the carboxyl terminus of the receptor and one or more additional mutations that may simulate a conformational change induced by CSF-1 binding. Expression of the human c-*fms* gene in mouse NIH-3T3 cells confers a CSF-1 stimulated growth phenotype, indicating that receptor transduction is sufficient for fibroblasts to respond to a haematopoietic growth factor. In contrast, the v-*fms* oncogene induces factor-independent growth and tumorigenicity in factor-dependent myeloid cell lines, and contributes to the development of proliferative disorders of multiple haematopoietic lineages when introduced into murine bone marrow progenitors. Aberrant expression of an endogenous c-*fms* gene secondary to proviral insertion and transcriptional activation has also been implicated in virus-induced myeloblastic leukaemia in mice. The c-*fms* and CSF-1 genes have been mapped on the long arm of human chromosome 5, a region that frequently undergoes interstitial deletions in certain haematopoietic disorders including acute myelogenous leukaemia. The study of CSF-1 and its receptor should provide information concerning the role of tyrosine kinases in regulating the normal growth and differentiation of haematopoietic cells and in contributing to their malignant transformation.

Introduction

The macrophage colony-stimulating factor (CSF-1 or M-CSF) is a lineage-specific haematopoietic growth factor required for the proliferation, differentiation, and viability of mononuclear phagocytes (Stanley *et al.* 1983). CSF-1 also stimulates a variety of specialized macrophage functions including tumoricidal activity (Ralph & Nakoinz, 1987) and the production of other cytokines (Metcalf & Nicola, 1985; Warren & Ralph, 1986). The growth factor is a glycosylated polypeptide homodimer (Stanley & Heard, 1977) whose pleiotropic actions on mononuclear phagocytes are mediated by binding to a single class of high-affinity receptors at the cell surface (Guilbert & Stanley, 1980, 1986). Expression of the receptor for CSF-1 is an early marker of commitment to the monocyte-macrophage series. Low numbers of CSF-1 receptors are present on immature bone marrow progenitors, and a 10-fold increase in receptor number takes place as the cells differentiate (Bartelmez *et al.* 1985). Circulating monocytes and tissue macrophages maintain high numbers of cell surface CSF-1 receptors (ca. 50 000 per cell).

The receptor for CSF-1 is encoded by the c-*fms* proto-oncogene (Sherr *et al.* 1985) and is one of a family of oncogene products and growth factor receptors, which exhibit a tyrosine-specific protein kinase activity (Hunter & Cooper, 1985). The enzymatic activity appears to be required for the generation of mitogenic signals by this class of proteins. In this paper, we will briefly review the evidence that the CSF-1 receptor is the c-*fms* gene product and focus on recent investigations of the interaction between this receptor and its ligand in normal and malignant cells.

The CSF-1 receptor is the product of the c-*fms* gene

In recent years, experimental evidence has been obtained establishing a relationship between malignant transformation and alterations of genes that are involved in normal growth and differentiation. These observations have generally followed from the study of retroviral oncogenes (v-*onc* genes) that were generated by recombination between replicating viruses and proto-oncogene (c-*onc*) sequences present in normal cellular DNA. The v-*onc* genes are responsible for the ability of these viruses to cause tumours in animals and to transform cells in culture. Our interest in the CSF-1 receptor and its ligand evolved from the study of v-*fms*, a viral oncogene transduced from the feline c-*fms* proto-oncogene.

The Susan McDonough strain of feline sarcoma virus (SM-FeSV) was isolated from a spontaneously occurring multicentric fibrosarcoma of a domestic cat (McDonough *et al.* 1971). SM-FeSV transforms established fibroblast cell lines from several species in culture and induces fibrosarcomas when re-inoculated into kittens (Sarma *et al.* 1972). Acquired cellular sequences are localized as a contiguous segment in the middle of the SM-FeSV genome, which was designated v-*fms* (Donner *et al.* 1982). Nucleotide sequence analysis of the v-*fms* gene predicted that its product was a transmembrane protein and revealed that the carboxyl-terminal domain exhibited amino acid sequence similarity with the family of tyrosine-specific protein kinases (Hampe *et al.* 1984).

The product of the v-*fms* oncogene is an integral transmembrane glycoprotein with an associated tyrosine kinase activity. The glycoprotein contains asparagine(N)-linked oligosaccharides, which are processed during transport to the plasma membrane (Anderson *et al.* 1982, 1984). A single membrane-spanning segment of 26 hydrophobic amino acids near the middle of the protein divides it into two domains (Hampe *et al.* 1984). The v-*fms* gene product is oriented in the plasma membrane with its glycosylated amino-terminal domain exposed at the cell surface and its carboxyl-terminal tyrosine kinase domain in the cytoplasm (Rettenmier *et al.* 1985a). Cell surface expression is required to elicit the transformed phenotype (Roussel *et al.* 1984; Nichols *et al.* 1985; Hadwiger *et al.* 1986). The v-*fms*-coded glycoproteins on the plasma membrane become associated with clathrin-coated pits and are internalized in endocytic vesicles (Manger *et al.* 1984). These findings provided a basis for the hypothesis that the viral oncogene was derived from a cellular gene encoding a growth factor receptor. Indeed, precedents for a link between oncogenes and growth factors, or their receptors, were first established by the findings that the v-*sis* oncogene encodes a chain of the platelet-derived growth factor (PDGF) (Doolittle *et al.* 1983; Waterfield *et al.* 1983) whereas the v-*erb*B oncogene product represents a truncated version of the epidermal growth factor (EGF) receptor (Downward *et al.* 1984).

Although transcripts of the c-*fms* gene were first detected in mouse and human placental tissue (Müller *et al.* 1983*a,b*) and in human choriocarcinoma (Müller *et al.* 1983*b*) and murine myeloid leukaemia (Gonda & Metcalf, 1984) cell lines, we were initially unable to precipitate a presumptive c-*fms* protein from these sources using the then available antibodies to the v-*fms* gene product. Since the v-*fms* gene of SM-FeSV was derived from a feline cellular gene, the viral oncogene product was more likely to exhibit antigenic cross-reactivity with the c-*fms* product of the cat. Normal adult cat tissues were therefore surveyed for the presence of c-*fms* transcripts, and the highest levels of the 4·0-kb c-*fms* mRNA were present in the spleen.

When the v-*fms* gene products are precipitated with antisera and the immune complexes incubated with $[\gamma\text{-}^{32}P]ATP$ in the presence of manganese ions, the glycoproteins are phosphorylated on tyrosine residues (Barbacid & Lauver, 1981). Using monoclonal antibodies raised against the viral oncogene product, the feline c-*fms*-coded glycoprotein was similarly identified in detergent homogenates of cat spleen by an immune complex protein kinase assay (Rettenmier *et al.* 1985*b*). High levels of the c-*fms* gene product were also detected in cat peritoneal inflammatory exudates. We reasoned that determination of the phenotype of cells expressing the c-*fms*-coded glycoprotein might provide an important clue to the identity of its putative ligand. Fluorescence-activated flow cytometry and cell sorting with a monoclonal antibody to a v-*fms*-coded epitope revealed that the c-*fms* product was preferentially expressed on mature feline macrophages (Sherr *et al.* 1985). The restricted distribution of the c-*fms* gene product suggested that its ligand might be the mononuclear phagocyte colony-stimulating factor CSF-1. A series of collaborative experiments was therefore initiated with Dr E. Richard Stanley who had previously purified and characterized both murine and human CSF-1.

Because antibodies to the feline v-*fms* protein did not cross-react with the mouse or human c-*fms* gene product, additional antisera were prepared by immunizing rabbits with a recombinant v-*fms*-coded polypeptide expressed in bacteria (Furman *et al.* 1986). The latter antibodies primarily recognize conserved epitopes in the cytoplasmic carboxyl-terminal domain, and specifically precipitated presumptive c-*fms* products from other species (Sherr *et al.* 1985; Rettenmier *et al.* 1986). The mouse c-*fms* gene product was identified as a glycoprotein of 165K ($K = 10^3 M_r$), in close agreement with the molecular weight of the cell surface CSF-1 receptor estimated from chemical cross-linking studies with radiolabelled ligand (Morgan & Stanley, 1984). The murine c-*fms* gene product also exhibited functional properties of the

CSF-1 receptor (Sherr *et al.* 1985). In membrane preparations, the tyrosine kinase activity of the c-*fms*-coded glycoprotein was stimulated by CSF-1. Moreover, ^{125}I-ligand–receptor complexes formed at the surface of viable macrophages were quantitatively precipitated by the antisera after detergent lysis. These results established that the c-*fms* gene product was closely related, and possibly identical, to the CSF-1 receptor.

This conclusion has been confirmed by subsequent investigations. As a consequence of the recombination event that generated SM-FeSV, the v-*fms* oncogene product retains the complete extracellular domain of its c-*fms* progenitor (Coussens *et al.* 1986; Wheeler *et al.* 1986a). Cells infected by SM-FeSV therefore acquire binding sites for CSF-1, and chemical cross-linking studies demonstrated that specific binding was mediated by the cell surface form of the v-*fms*-coded glycoprotein (Sacca *et al.* 1986). Direct genetic evidence that the c-*fms* gene encodes a functional CSF-1 receptor came from studies using the molecularly cloned c-*fms* and CSF-1 cDNAs (Roussel *et al.* 1987). Expression of a human c-*fms* cDNA in mouse NIH-3T3 cells enables them to form colonies in semi-solid medium when grown in the presence of recombinant human CSF-1. Moreover, co-transfection of NIH-3T3 cells with the human c-*fms* and CSF-1 genes transforms these cells by an autocrine mechanism. Although the parental cells constitutively produce low amounts of mouse CSF-1 (Sacca *et al.* 1986), the murine growth factor is not biologically active for human mononuclear phagocytes. Therefore, the requirement for human CSF-1 to stimulate the human c-*fms* gene product in this system is consistent with the known species specificity of the growth factor. These results also demonstrate that transduction of a CSF-1 receptor, which is normally expressed in mononuclear phagocytes, is sufficient to render fibroblasts responsive to the ligand. The intracellular targets for growth-promoting signals generated by the CSF-1 receptor thus appear to be shared by macrophages and fibroblasts.

Structure and function of the *fms* oncogene product

A schematic diagram depicting the structure of the v-*fms* and human c-*fms* gene products is shown in Fig. 1. The primary translation product of the human c-*fms* gene is 972 amino acids in length (Coussens *et al.* 1986). Removal of a 19-residue amino-terminal signal peptide yields a polypeptide of 953 amino acids compared to 922 in the corresponding form of the viral oncogene product (Hampe *et al.* 1984). The mature cell surface form of the v-*fms*-coded glycoprotein has an apparent molecular weight of about 140K (Anderson *et al.* 1984; Manger *et al.* 1984), although slight variations of size in different cell types are related to differences in the patterns and extent of glycosylation. The mature form of the human c-*fms* gene product is a glycoprotein of apparent molecular weight 150K (Woolford *et al.* 1985; Rettenmier *et al.* 1986). Canonical sequences for *N*-linked glycosylation (Asn-X-Ser/Thr) are clustered in the extracellular amino-terminal domain, and the carboxyl-terminal domain exhibits sequence similarity with other members of the protein-tyrosine kinase gene family. The gp140$^{v\text{-}fms}$ and human gp150$^{c\text{-}fms}$ share extensive

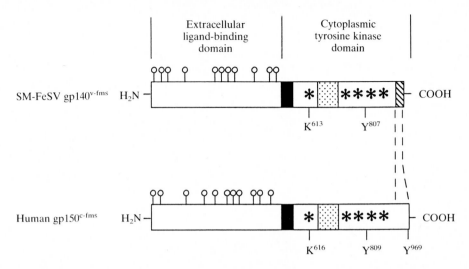

Fig. 1. Structure of the v-*fms* and c-*fms* gene products. Schematic diagrams of the mature cell surface forms of SM-FeSV gp140$^{v\text{-}fms}$ and the human gp150$^{c\text{-}fms}$ are shown. A transmembrane segment of hydrophobic amino acids (black bar) divides the proteins into an extracellular domain for ligand binding and a cytoplasmic tyrosine kinase domain. Potential sites for the addition of asparagine-linked oligosaccharides in the amino-terminal domain are marked by open circles. The portion of the carboxyl-terminal domain that exhibits sequence homology with other protein tyrosine kinases is indicated by asterisks. Within this region of each protein, the position of a critical lysine residue (K) at the ATP-binding site is noted. The segment of 70 *fms*-specific amino acids that interrupts the core kinase consensus sequence is stippled. The region of carboxyl-terminal sequence divergence between the v-*fms* and c-*fms* gene products is indicated by the cross-hatched area in gp140$^{v\text{-}fms}$. The location of a negative-regulatory tyrosine residue (Y^{969}) near the carboxyl-terminus of gp150$^{c\text{-}fms}$ is noted.

amino acid sequence identity in the extracellular (75%) and cytoplasmic (95%) domains but differ at their extreme carboxyl termini. As discussed below, this carboxyl-terminal region of divergence includes a single tyrosine residue (Tyr^{969}), which may play a role in modulating the response of the normal receptor to CSF-1.

The differences in amino acid sequence of the extracellular domains of the v-*fms* and human c-*fms* gene products are largely due to interspecies divergence between cats and man. The amino-terminal domain of the *fms*-coded glycoprotein lacks the cysteine-rich repeats found in the receptors for EGF and insulin (Coussens *et al.* 1986). However, the common spacing of individual cysteine residues and short segments of amino acid sequence homology in their ligand-binding domains suggest that the *fms* product and the receptor for PDGF were derived from a common ancestor (Yarden *et al.* 1986). Both CSF-1 and PDGF are dimeric growth factors, and the similarity of structure in the extracellular domains of their receptors may be related to conformational requirements for binding dimeric ligands.

The cytoplasmic domain of the *fms* gene product has sequence similarity with other protein tyrosine kinases. By analogy (Kamps *et al.* 1984), a lysine residue, located at position 613 of the viral protein and 616 of the normal human receptor, is presumed to be the critical ATP-binding site required for enzymatic activity. A tyrosine residue at positions 807 and 809 of the respective proteins is homologous to the major site of autophosphorylation in many other tyrosine kinases (Hunter & Cooper, 1985). The v-*fms* gene product is constitutively phosphorylated on tyrosine in transformed cells (Tamura *et al.* 1986), whereas significant tyrosine phosphorylation of the CSF-1 receptor has not been detected in the absence of ligand. The *fms* gene products have a segment of about 70 amino acids interposed between the ATP-binding region and the rest of the core kinase consensus sequence. The PDGF receptor (Yarden *et al.* 1986) and the *kit* oncogene product (Besmer *et al.* 1986a) have a similar organization of their respective tyrosine kinase domains. Although there is very little homology among the inserted segments in the kinase domains of these three proteins, the extensive amino acid sequence similarity within their core kinase regions again suggests that they represent a family of closely related receptors. The inserted sequences may affect the activity of these kinases or their interaction with cellular substrates in the signal transduction pathway.

The v-*fms* and c-*fms* gene products differ conspicuously at their carboxyl-terminal ends where the 40 carboxyl-terminal amino acids of the normal receptor have been replaced by 11 unrelated residues in the SM-FeSV oncogene product (Hampe *et al.* 1984; Coussens *et al.* 1986). The alteration deletes a single tyrosine residue at position 969 (Tyr^{969}) which, by analogy to studies on the products of the v-*src* and c-*src* genes (Courtneidge, 1985; Iba *et al.* 1985; Cooper *et al.* 1986), may represent a negative regulatory site of tyrosine phosphorylation. Another independent isolate of feline sarcoma virus contains a v-*fms* gene encoding a different carboxyl-terminal alteration, which also lacks this terminal tyrosine residue (Besmer *et al.* 1986b). A chimeric v-*fms*/c-*fms* construct in which sequences for the normal human c-*fms* coded carboxyl terminus were substituted in the v-*fms* gene was more than 10-fold reduced in its transforming efficiency for NIH-3T3 cells (Browning *et al.* 1986; Roussel *et al.* 1987). A point mutation replacing Tyr^{969} with a phenylalanine residue restored the transforming activity of the chimeric construct to the level of v-*fms* itself (Roussel *et al.* 1987). NIH-3T3 cells expressing the human c-*fms* gene with either the wild-type Tyr^{969} or with the Phe^{969} mutation were not transformed. However, when plated in semi-solid medium in the presence of recombinant human CSF-1, NIH-3T3 cells expressing the receptor with the Phe^{969} mutation yielded consistently larger colonies than cells expressing the wild-type c-*fms*(Tyr^{969}) (Roussel *et al.* 1987). Moreover, in cells transformed by co-transfection of c-*fms* alleles with human CSF-1 cDNA, the efficiency of transformation induced by the wild-type c-*fms*(Tyr^{969}) was about 10-fold less than that of c-*fms*(Phe^{969}); co-transfection of the latter construct with the CSF-1 gene yielded a transforming efficiency equivalent to that of v-*fms*.

Taken together, these results suggest that Tyr^{969} plays a negative regulatory role in the activity of the CSF-1 receptor. Removal of this residue, while not an activating transforming mutation by itself, may up-regulate the receptor kinase activity, thereby enhancing the autocrine transforming efficiency of the receptor in a co-transfection assay with the CSF-1 gene. The fact that v-*fms* is a transforming gene in the absence of its ligand, whereas c-*fms*(Phe^{969}) is not, suggests that there are one or more additional mutations in v-*fms* that contribute to its transforming activity. These latter mutations may mimic a ligand-induced conformational change in the receptor, thus rendering the kinase independent of CSF-1. It should be possible to pinpoint these mutations by comparing the sequence of v-*fms* with a cDNA of the feline c-*fms* gene and testing appropriate c-*fms* mutants for transforming activity.

The CSF-1 receptor exhibits typical properties of a growth factor receptor. Binding of CSF-1 results in autophosphorylation (Sherr *et al.* 1985; Yeung *et al.* 1987), rapid internalization, and degradation of both the ligand and the receptor (Guilbert & Stanley, 1986; Wheeler *et al.* 1986*b*; Downing *et al.* 1988). The ability to confer a CSF-1-responsive phenotype by expression of the receptor in heterologous NIH-3T3 cells will allow dissection of the components of receptor function through site-directed mutagenesis. For example, appropriate mutants can be constructed to assess the possible role of Tyr^{809} in activation of the receptor kinase and signal transduction. Reduction of a CSF-1-mediated response by substitution of a phenylalanine residue at this position would suggest that autophosphorylation of Tyr^{809} in response to ligand binding is a component of receptor activation. By analogy to results in other receptor systems, replacement of $lysine^{616}$ would be expected to abolish both the kinase activity and signal transduction without affecting ligand binding. Down-modulation of CSF-1 receptors by either CSF-1 or other compounds such as phorbol esters (Wheeler *et al.* 1986*b*) could then be assessed directly in the absence of receptor activation.

The intracellular events leading to a CSF-1 response after binding of the ligand are poorly understood. Autophosphorylation at one or more tyrosine residues is probably associated with activation of the receptor. Ligand–receptor complexes are returned to the interior of the cell *via* the endocytic pathway and rapidly degraded. The signals for receptor down-modulation and the identity of cellular substrates for the receptor kinase are not known. The production of intracellular second messengers in response to receptor activation may be involved. Cells transformed by the v-*fms* oncogene exhibit an elevated rate of phosphatidylinositol (PI) turnover (Jackowski *et al.* 1986) with cleavage of phosphatidylinositol 4,5-diphosphate (PIP_2) generating inositol-1,4,5-triphosphate to mobilize intracellular calcium and diacylglycerol, which activates protein kinase C. This is associated with increased activities of a membrane-associated PIP_2 phospholipase C (Jackowski *et al.* 1986) and a PI kinase (Kaplan *et al.* 1987). However, it has been reported that CSF-1 stimulation is not associated with PI turnover in macrophages (Whetton *et al.* 1986). Thus, a role for PIP_2-derived second messengers in signal transduction by the normal receptor has not been established.

The sequence of events leading to changes in nuclear function after CSF-1 stimulation are also unknown. As for a variety of stimuli in many other cell systems, CSF-1 rapidly induces transient high levels of expression of the c-*fos* proto-oncogene within 15 min in macrophages (Bravo *et al.* 1987), followed by a sustained increase in c-*fos* expression at lower levels 4–12 h after stimulation (Müller *et al.* 1985). The addition of CSF-1 also leads to a decrease in the rate of protein turnover within 2 h (Tushinski & Stanley, 1983) and stimulation of DNA synthesis within 8–12 h

(Tushinski & Stanley, 1985). Clearly, considerable effort will be necessary to elucidate the signal transduction mechanism initiated by binding of CSF-1 to its receptor. Working from both ends of the pathway by defining the physiologically relevant substrates for the CSF-1 receptor kinase and identifying CSF-1-inducible genes is a reasonable approach to this difficult and important problem.

Synthesis and expression of CSF-1

CSF-1 is a glycosylated polypeptide homodimer of identical subunits assembled through disulphide bonds (Stanley & Heard, 1977). The biological activity of the growth factor is dependent on its dimeric structure and is abolished by disulphide reduction. The carbohydrate component includes *N*-linked oligosaccharides, which do not appear to be required for CSF-1 function (Das & Stanley, 1982). The human growth factor has been purified from urine, and oligonucleotide probes deduced from the amino-terminal amino acid sequence were used to clone genomic sequences coding for CSF-1. Human CSF-1 is encoded by a single gene, which maps to the long arm of chromosome 5 (Pettenati *et al.* 1987). Transcripts of this gene undergo differential splicing to generate multiple mRNAs (Ladner *et al.* 1987), which specify at least two biologically active forms of the growth factor (Kawasaki *et al.* 1985; Wong *et al.* 1987). A cDNA encoding murine CSF-1 has also been isolated from the mouse L929 fibroblast cell line (DeLamarter *et al.* 1987).

A schematic diagram of two primary translation products deduced from the nucleotide sequences of various human and murine CSF-1 cDNAs is shown in Fig. 2. Analysis of the sequences suggested that soluble CSF-1 is generated by proteolytic cleavage of a membrane-bound precursor. All of the precursors contain a 32-residue amino-terminal signal peptide for membrane insertion followed by sequences of the secreted growth factor, a presumptive transmembrane segment of hydrophobic amino acids, and a short carboxyl-terminal tail. The cysteine residues and potential sites for *N*-linked glycosylation are present on the amino-terminal side of the putative membrane-spanning sequence. These features suggested that the CSF-1 precursor is synthesized as an integral transmembrane glycoprotein cotranslationally oriented in the membrane of the endoplasmic reticulum (ER) with its glycosylated amino-terminal domain in the ER cisterna and its carboxyl-terminal tail in the cytoplasm.

A 1·6-kb CSF-1 cDNA cloned from a human pancreatic carcinoma cell line encodes a 256 amino acid CSF-1 precursor (Kawasaki *et al.* 1985). The 554-residue polypeptide specified by a 4-kb human cDNA from this and other sources includes the complete coding sequence of the smaller clone, with a block of 298 additional amino acids inserted after residue 149 on the amino-terminal side of the transmembrane segment (Wong *et al.* 1987; Ladner *et al.* 1987). The two human cDNAs are generated by alternative splicing of the primary transcript (Ladner *et al.* 1987). The additional coding sequences of the 4-kb cDNA include some tryptic peptides detected in a purified form of human urinary CSF-1 (Wong *et al.* 1987). Thus, the soluble growth factors specified by these two cDNAs have different carboxyl termini.

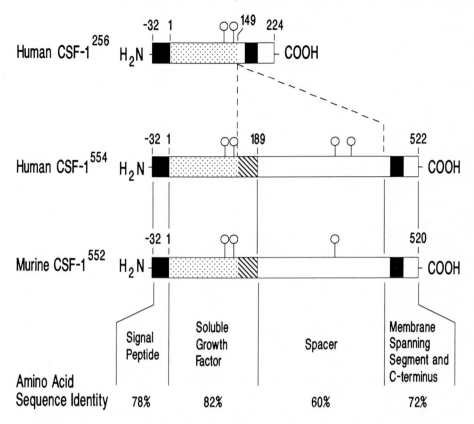

Fig. 2. Primary translation products encoded by biologically active human and mouse CSF-1 cDNAs. Each CSF-1 precursor consists of an amino-terminal signal peptide (black bar) and sequence for the secreted growth factor (stippled), a transmembrane segment (black bar), and a carboxyl-terminal tail. Canonical sequences for N-linked glycosylation are indicated by open circles. Human CSF-1[256] and CSF-1[554] are encoded by mRNAs derived by alternative splicing of the primary transcript. A contiguous segment of 298 amino acids present in human CSF-1[554] and absent in CSF-1[256] is delimited by the dashed lines. Polypeptide sequences from this insert, which are present in the soluble growth factor derived from CSF-1[554], are cross-hatched. Murine CSF-1[552] is similar in structure to the large human CSF-1 precursor. The extent of amino acid sequence identity between the corresponding regions of the mouse and human CSF-1 precursors is indicated.

The 552 amino acid murine CSF-1 precursor encoded by a cDNA cloned from mouse L929 cells (DeLamarter *et al.* 1987) is similar in structure to the product of the 4-kb human cDNA. The sequences of the soluble human and murine growth factors (residues 1–ca. 189) exhibit more than 80 % amino acid identity. The remainder of the inserted segment in the larger CSF-1 precursor shows less amino acid sequence conservation than the secreted growth factor.

Expression of CSF-1 cDNAs in viral vectors has allowed biochemical analysis of the products. The 1·6-kb human CSF-1 cDNA directs the synthesis of a membrane-bound 34K glycoprotein, which is rapidly assembled into disulphide-linked dimers and externalized on the plasma membrane (Rettenmier *et al.* 1987). Proteolysis of this 68K homodimer at the cell surface yields soluble 44K CSF-1 dimers composed of 22K subunits. In cell culture systems, less than 10% of the precursors on the plasma membrane are recovered in the form of extracellular growth factor. The role of the membrane-spanning sequence has been directly tested by insertion of an upstream termination codon after amino acid 158 in the coding sequence of the 1·6-kb cDNA (Heard *et al.* 1987*a*). The truncated clone produces a biologically active, soluble growth factor, which is not membrane-associated and is efficiently secreted from cells. The similarity in size between the product of the truncated clone and the soluble growth factor released by cleavage of the membrane-bound precursor indicates that the termination codon was placed in the coding sequence of the 1·6-kb cDNA near the site of proteolysis.

Soluble CSF-1 encoded by the 4-kb human cDNA includes additional carboxyl-terminal amino acid residues not present in the secreted product of the smaller clone (Wong *et al.* 1987). Thus, the sites for proteolytic cleavage are different for the two CSF-1 precursors, and it appears that they are processed by different mechanisms. In contrast to the product of the 1·6-kb cDNA, which is detected at the cell surface, the CSF-1 precursor encoded by the 4-kb clone is cleaved within the cell and rapidly secreted. Differences in the mechanism of CSF-1 biosynthesis may reflect diverse physiological roles for various forms of the growth factor. Although the 4-kb mRNA is the major CSF-1 transcript detected in a variety of human cell lines, in at least one inducible system, production of biologically active human CSF-1 is correlated with the appearance of the smaller species (Ralph *et al.* 1986). In addition, two mRNAs of the corresponding sizes are differently expressed in various mouse tissues (Raja-vashisth *et al.* 1987). The function of the different CSF-1 precursors *in vivo* is as yet unclear. One possibility is that product of the 4-kb cDNA is the major source of CSF-1 released into the circulation, whereas the membrane-bound form of CSF-1 encoded by the 1·6-kb clone primarily stimulates receptor-bearing cells in circumstances involving direct cell–cell contact.

CSF-1 is produced by mesenchymal cells and interacts with its receptor on mononuclear phagocytes (Tushinski *et al.* 1982). The growth factor appears in the circulation, and its concentration is determined by monocytes and macrophages, which bind and degrade the hormone after receptor-mediated endocytosis (Bartocci *et al.* 1987). The pleiotropic effects of CSF-1 include maintaining the viability of mature monocytes and macrophages and stimulating the proliferation and differentiation of committed bone marrow progenitors (Stanley *et al.* 1983). More immature haematopoietic precursors are also rendered responsive to CSF-1 in the presence of interleukin-3 (Multi-CSF) or haemopoietin-1 (Bartelmez & Stanley, 1985; Stanley *et al.* 1986). The latter molecule is now known to be the macrophage product, interleukin-1α (Mochizuki *et al.* 1987), indicating that differentiated macrophages can release mediators that stimulate the production of immature bone marrow progenitors. Positive and negative feed-back mechanisms therefore regulate the production of mononuclear phagocytes. In addition, it has recently been reported that monocytes and macrophages themselves produce CSF-1 in response to phorbol esters and the physiological inducers, γ-interferon and granulocyte-macrophage CSF (Horiguchi *et al.* 1986, 1987; Rambaldi *et al.* 1987). This suggests that autocrine or paracrine mechanisms might also be involved in modulating the activity of these cells during inflammatory reactions.

An intriguing area for future investigations is a possible function for CSF-1 and its receptor beyond their role in the haematopoietic compartment. Transcripts of the c-*fms* gene are found in mouse and human placental tissue (Müller *et al.* 1983*a,b*), and the c-*fms*-coded glycoprotein has been identified in two independently derived human choriocarcinoma cell lines (Woolford *et al.* 1985; Rettenmier *et al.* 1986). The c-*fms* product in these malignant trophoblasts is indistinguishable from that detected on normal peripheral blood monocytes, and both cell types display high-affinity binding sites for CSF-1 (Rettenmier *et al.* 1986). Pregnancy results in a 1000-fold increase in the concentration of CSF-1 in the mouse uterus with the highest levels being detected at term (Bartocci *et al.* 1986). During the latter half of gestation, placental concentrations of the growth factor are higher than those detected in foetal tissues or in a variety of maternal organs. The simplest interpretation is that CSF-1 produced by stromal cells of the uterus stimulates receptors expressed on normal placental trophoblasts during embryogenesis. Thus, although CSF-1 was initially identified as a lineage-specific colony-stimulating factor in haematopoiesis, it is likely that this growth factor has additional physiological roles in other circumstances.

The role of CSF-1 and its receptor in oncogenesis

Due to its identification as the product of the c-*fms* gene, the ability of the CSF-1 receptor to induce malignant cell transformation has already been tested in a number of contexts. The v-*fms* gene was isolated from a feline fibrosarcoma, and it transforms a variety of fibroblast cell lines in culture. Because these mesenchymal cells also produce CSF-1, it was possible that transformation was mediated by an autocrine mechanism involving transduction of a competent CSF-1 receptor into cells that synthesized the corresponding growth factor. To test this hypothesis, the v-*fms* gene was expressed in murine haematopoietic cell lines that require colony-stimulating factors for their proliferation and survival in culture and do not produce CSF-1. Introduction of the v-*fms* gene induced growth factor independence and tumorigenicity in the CSF-1-dependent macrophage cell line BAC1.2F5 (Wheeler *et al.* 1986*b*) and the interleukin-3-dependent myeloid cell line FDC-P1 (Wheeler *et al.* 1987). The factor-independent cells did not synthesize CSF-1, nor did expression of the v-*fms*-coded glycoprotein alter the number or affinity of the receptors for the corresponding growth factors required by the parental cells. Thus, transformation of these cells did not involve an autocrine mechanism, and there was no evidence for transmodulation of the murine CSF-1 or IL-3 receptors by the v-*fms* gene product.

The c-*fms* gene product is expressed at high levels by mature mononuclear phagocytes, and introduction of the c-*fms* gene into NIH-3T3 cells did not induce transformation (Roussel *et al.* 1987). These findings indicate that the v-*fms* gene product is constitutively activated to provide growth-stimulatory signals in the absence of ligand as a result of critical structural alterations. As discussed above, one of the activating mutations involves removal of a carboxyl-terminal tyrosine residue that may modulate the response of the normal receptor to ligand binding. Because the latter mutation alone is insufficient to activate the transforming potential of the c-*fms* gene, the v-*fms*-coded glycoprotein must contain one or more additional alterations that contribute to its oncogenic properties.

Expression of the human c-*fms* gene enables mouse NIH-3T3 fibroblasts to respond mitogenically to exogenously added human CSF-1 (Roussel *et al.* 1987). Constitutive co-expression of human c-*fms* and CSF-1 cDNAs transforms these cells by an autocrine mechanism. Rearrangement and expression of the endogenous murine CSF-1 gene has been implicated as a second transforming event leading to tumorigenicity in a CSF-1-dependent macrophage cell line immortalized by a retrovirus containing the c-*myc* oncogene (Baumbach *et al.* 1987). These results support the notion that unregulated expression of a growth factor and its receptor in the same cell may contribute to neoplastic progression. However, this circumstance by itself does not appear to be sufficient fully to transform all established cell lines. In the SV40-immortalized BAC1.2F5 mouse macrophage cell line (Morgan *et al.* 1987), expression of an introduced human CSF-1 gene abrogated the requirement of exogenously added CSF-1 for growth *in vitro*, but the factor-independent cells were not tumorigenic in nude mice (Roussel *et al.* 1988). Human CSF-1 is biologically active for stimulation of murine mononuclear phagocytes, and the factor-independent cells produced sufficient amounts of the growth factor to constitutively down-modulate their CSF-1 receptors. The fact that the v-*fms* gene did render these same cells factor-independent and tumorigenic (Wheeler *et al.* 1986*b*) underscores the critical differences between the viral transforming protein and the normal receptor.

The results of these studies in cell culture systems are currently being extended to expression of these genes *in vivo*. Although SM-FeSV encodes an analogue of the CSF-1 receptor, it was isolated from a mesenchymal tumour and has not been reported to induce haematopoietic neoplasms in its natural host. However, when mouse bone marrow cells containing an introduced v-*fms* gene were used to repopulate lethally irradiated recipients, diseases of multiple haematological lineages were observed (Heard *et al.* 1987*b*). After a latency period, several primary recipients developed myeloproliferative disorders, which lacked evidence of clonality and were not efficiently transplanted to secondary hosts. In contrast, other primary recipients developed in their spleens provirus-positive clones, which were transplantable to secondary, lethally-irradiated recipients and gave rise to clonal erythroleukaemias and B-cell lymphomas. Although cells expressing v-*fms* did not appear to have an obligate proliferative advantage during serial transfers, the correlation between expression of the v-*fms* gene and disease indicated that the oncogene product contributed to the development of these disorders. Clearly, similar types of experiments using molecular clones of the c-*fms* and CSF-1 genes will be of interest.

Evidence has recently been obtained for involvement of the CSF-1 receptor in the development of a naturally occurring leukaemia. The replication-competent Friend murine leukaemia virus induces myeloblastic leukaemia in mice with a latency of 6–12 months. In approximately 20 % of these cases the provirus is integrated in a region upstream of the first coding exon of the c-*fms* gene in host cell DNA (Gisselbrecht *et al.* 1987). This proviral insertion results in high level expression of c-*fms* transcripts that encode the full-sized CSF-1 receptor. These myeloblasts might be unusually responsive to CSF-1 due to the high levels of receptor synthesis. Leukaemia might ultimately develop in the clonally expanded population as a result of secondary genetic changes involving either the c-*fms* gene itself or other cellular genes. The loss of the germ line c-*fms* allele in some of these tumours is consistent with the possibility that activating mutations may also have occurred in the affected c-*fms* locus to unmask the latent transforming potential of its product and provide a further proliferative advantage. Whatever the mechanism, the fact that the c-*fms* gene is a target for proviral insertion resulting in transcriptional activation indicates that this is an initiating event for the development of leukaemia in these animals.

The genes for several CSFs and cell surface receptors have been localized to the long arm of human chromosome 5, including c-*fms* at 5q33.2–33.3 (Le Beau *et al.* 1986*a*) and CSF-1 at 5q33.1 (Pettenati *et al.* 1987). Acquired interstitial deletions of 5q are a frequent cytogenetic abnormality in patients who develop acute myelogenous leukaemia after exposure to toxic chemicals (Rowley *et al.* 1981; Pedersen-Bjergaard *et al.* 1984; Le Beau *et al.* 1986*b*). Deletions of this region are also characteristic of the '5q⁻ syndrome' (Van den Berghe *et al.* 1974), a refractory anaemia with thrombocytosis and hypolobulated megakaryocytes (Sokal *et al.* 1975; Wieniewski & Hirschhorn, 1983). Bone marrow cells from some patients with the 5q⁻ syndrome have been shown to be hemizygous for the c-*fms* gene (Nienhuis *et al.* 1985). These results raise the possibility that alterations in the structure or expression of CSF-1 or its receptor may contribute to these haematological disorders in man. A careful dissection of the genes encoding growth factors and their receptors that are clustered in this region of chromosome 5 will be required to resolve these possibilities.

Work in the authors' laboratory is supported by grants CA38187 and CA20180 from the National Cancer Institute, National Institutes of Health and by the American Lebanese Syrian Associated Charities (ALSAC) of St. Jude Children's Research Hospital.

References

ANDERSON, S. J., FURTH, M., WOLFF, L., RUSCETTI, S. K. & SHERR, C. J. (1982). Monoclonal antibodies to the transformation-specific glycoprotein encoded by the feline retroviral oncogene v-*fms*. *J. Virol.* **44**, 696–702.

ANDERSON, S. J., GONDA, M. A., RETTENMIER, C. W. & SHERR, C. J. (1984). Subcellular localization of glycoproteins encoded by the viral oncogene v-*fms*. *J. Virol.* **51**, 730–741.

BARBACID, M. & LAUVER, A. V. (1981). Gene products of McDonough feline sarcoma virus have an *in vitro*-associated protein kinase that phosphorylates tyrosine residues: Lack of detection of this enzymatic activity *in vivo*. *J. Virol.* **40**, 812–821.

BARTELMEZ, S. H., SACCA, R. & STANLEY, E. R. (1985). Lineage specific receptors used to identify a growth factor for developmentally early hemopoietic cells: Assay of hemopoietin-2. *J. cell. Physiol.* **122**, 362–369.

BARTELMEZ, S. H. & STANLEY, E. R. (1985). Synergism between hemopoietic growth factors (HGFs) detected by their effects on cells bearing receptors for a lineage specific HGF: Assay of hemopoietin-1 *J. cell. Physiol.* **122**, 370–378.

BARTOCCI, A., MASTROGIANNIS, D. S., MIGLIORATI, G., STOCKERT, R. J., WOLKOFF, A. W. & STANLEY, E. R. (1987). Macrophages specifically regulate the concentration of their own growth factor in the circulation. *Proc. natn. Acad. Sci. U.S.A.* **84**, 6179–6183.

BARTOCCI, A., POLLARD, J. W. & STANLEY, E. R. (1986). Regulation of colony-stimulating factor 1 during pregnancy. *J. exp. Med.* **164**, 956–961.

BAUMBACH, W. R., STANLEY, E. R. & COLE, M. D. (1987). Induction of clonal monocyte-macrophage tumours *in vivo* by a mouse c-*myc* retrovirus: Rearrangement of the CSF-1 gene as a secondary transforming event. *Molec. Cell. Biol.* **7**, 664–671.

BESMER, P., LADER, E., GEORGE, P. C., BERGOLD, P. J., QIU, F-H., ZUCKERMAN, E. E. & HARDY, W. D. (1986*b*). A new acute transforming feline retrovirus with *fms* homology specifies a C-terminally truncated version of the c-*fms* protein that is different from SM-feline sarcoma virus v-*fms* protein. *J. Virol.* **60**, 194–203.

BESMER, P., MURPHY, J. E., GEORGE, P. C., QIU, F., BERGOLD, P. J., LEDERMAN, L., SNYDER, H. W. JR, BRODEUR, D., ZUCKERMAN, E. E. & HARDY, W. D. (1986*a*). A new acute transforming feline retrovirus and relationship of its oncogene v-*kit* with the protein kinase gene family. *Nature, Lond.* **320**, 415–421.

BRAVO, R., NEUBERG, M., BURCKHARDT, J., ALMENDRAL, J., WALLICH, R. & MÜLLER, R. (1987). Involvement of common and cell type-specific pathways in c-*fos* gene control: Stable induction by cAMP in macrophages. *Cell* **48**, 251–260.

BROWNING, P. J., BUNN, H. F., CLINE, A., SHUMAN, M. & NIENHUIS, A. W. (1986). "Replacement" of COOH-terminal truncation of v-*fms* with c-*fms* sequences markedly reduces transformation potential. *Proc. natn. Acad. Sci. U.S.A.* **83**, 7800–7804.

COOPER, J. A., GOULD, K. L., CARTWRIGHT, C. A. & HUNTER, T. (1986). Tyr^{527} is phosphorylated in pp60^{c-src}: Implications for regulation. *Science* **231**, 1431–1434.

COURTNEIDGE, S. A. (1985). Activation of the pp60^{c-src} kinase by middle T antigen binding or by dephosphorylation. *EMBO J.* **4**, 1471–1477.

COUSSENS, L., VAN BEVEREN, C., SMITH, D., CHEN, E., MITCHELL, R. L., ISACKE, C. M., VERMA, I. M. & ULLRICH, A. (1986). Structural alteration of viral homologue of receptor proto-oncogene *fms* at carboxyl terminus. *Nature, Lond.* **320**, 277–280.

DAS, S. K. & STANLEY, E. R. (1982). Structure-function studies of a colony stimulating factor (CSF-1). *J. biol. Chem.* **257**, 13 679–13 684.

DELAMARTER, J. F., HESSION, C., SEMON, D., GOUGH, N. M., ROTHENBUHLER, R. & MERMOD, J.-J. (1987). Nucleotide sequence of a cDNA encoding murine CSF-1 (macrophage-CSF). *Nucl. Acids Res.* **15**, 2389–2390.

DONNER, L., FEDELE, L. A., GARON, C. F., ANDERSON, S. J. & SHERR, C. J. (1982). McDonough feline sarcoma virus: characterization of the molecularly cloned provirus and its feline oncogene (v-*fms*). *J. Virol.* **41**, 489–500.

DOOLITTLE, R. F., HUNKAPILLER, M. W., HOOD, L. E., DEVARE, S. G., ROBBINS, K. C., AARONSON, S. A. & ANTONIADES, H. N. (1983). Simian sarcoma virus *onc* gene, v-*sis*, is derived from the gene (or genes) encoding a platelet-derived growth factor. *Science* **221**, 275–277.

DOWNING, J. R., RETTENMIER, C. W. & SHERR, C. J. (1988). Ligand-induced tyrosine kinase activity of the colony-stimulating factor 1 receptor in a murine macrophage cell line. *Molec. cell. Biol.* **8**, 1797–1799.

DOWNWARD, J., YARDEN, Y., MAYES, E., SCRACE, G., TOTTY, N., STOCKWELL, P., ULLRICH, A., SCHLESSINGER, J. & WATERFIELD, M. D. (1984). Close similarity of epidermal growth factor receptor and v-*erb*B oncogene protein sequences. *Nature, Lond.* **307**, 521–527.

FURMAN, W. L., RETTENMIER, C. W., CHEN, J. H., ROUSSEL, M. F., QUINN, C. O. & SHERR, C. J. (1986). Antibodies to distal carboxyl terminal epitopes in the v-*fms*-coded glycoprotein do not cross-react with the c-*fms* gene product. *Virology* **152**, 432–445.

GISSELBRECHT, S., FICHELSON, S., SOLA, B., BORDEREAUX, D., HAMPE, A., ANDRE, C., GALIBERT, F. & TAMBOURIN, P. (1987). Frequent c-*fms* activation by proviral insertion in mouse myeloblastic leukaemias. *Nature, Lond.* **329**, 259–261.

GONDA, T. J. & METCALF, D. (1984). Expression of *myb*, *myc* and *fos* proto-oncogenes during the differentiation of a murine myeloid leukaemia. *Nature, Lond.* **310**, 249–251.

GUILBERT, L. J. & STANLEY, E. R. (1980). Specific interaction of murine colony-stimulating factor with mononuclear phagocytic cells. *J. Cell Biol.* **85**, 153–159.

GUILBERT, L. J. & STANLEY, E. R. (1986). The interaction of ^{125}I-colony-stimulating factor-1 with bone marrow-derived macrophages. *J. biol. Chem.* **261**, 4024–4032.

HADWIGER, A., NIEMANN, H., KÄBISCH, A., BAUER, H. & TAMURA, T. (1986). Appropriate glycosylation of the *fms* gene product is a prerequisite for its transforming potency. *EMBO J.* **5**, 689–694.

HAMPE, A., GOBET, M., SHERR, C. J. & GALIBERT, F. (1984). Nucleotide sequence of the feline retroviral oncogene v-*fms* shows unexpected homology with oncogenes encoding tyrosine-specific protein kinases. *Proc. natn. Acad. Sci. U.S.A.* **81**, 85–89.

HEARD, J. M., ROUSSEL, M. F., RETTENMIER, C. W. & SHERR, C. J. (1987*a*). Synthesis, post-translational processing, and autocrine transforming activity of a carboxylterminal truncated form of colony stimulating factor-1. *Oncogene Res.* **1**, 423–440.

HEARD, J. M., ROUSSEL, M. F., RETTENMIER, C. W. & SHERR, C. J. (1987*b*). Multilineage hematopoietic disorders induced by transplantation of bone marrow cells expressing the v-*fms* oncogene. *Cell* **51**, 663–673.

HORIGUCHI, J., WARREN, M. K. & KUFE, D. (1987). Expression of the macrophage-specific colony-stimulating factor in human monocytes treated with granulocyte-macrophage colony-stimulating factor. *Blood* **69**, 1259–1261.

HORIGUCHI, J., WARREN, M. K., RALPH, P. & KUFE, D. (1986). Expression of the macrophage specific colony-stimulating factor (CSF-1) during human monocytic differentiation. *Biochem. biophys. Res. Commun.* **141**, 924–930.

HUNTER, T. & COOPER, J. A. (1985). Protein-tyrosine kinases. *A. Rev. Biochem.* **54**, 897–930.

IBA, H., CROSS, F. R., GARBER, E. A. & HANAFUSA, H. (1985). Low level of cellular protein phosphorylation by nontransforming overproduced p60^{c-src}. *Molec. Cell Biol.* **5**, 1058–1066.

JACKOWSKI, S., RETTENMIER, C. W., SHERR, C. J. & ROCK, C. O. (1986). A guanine nucleotide-dependent phosphatidylinositol-4,5-disphosphate phospholipase C in cells transformed by the v-*fms* and v-*fes* oncogenes. *J. biol. Chem.* **261**, 4978–4985.

KAMPS, M. P., TAYLOR, S. S. & SEFTON, B. M. (1984). Direct evidence that oncogenic tyrosine kinases and cyclic AMP-dependent protein kinase have homologous ATP-binding sites. *Nature, Lond.* **310**, 589–592.

KAPLAN, D. R., WHITMAN, M., SCHAFFHAUSEN, B., PALLAS, D. C., WHITE, M., CANTLEY, L. & ROBERTS, T. M. (1987). Common elements in growth factor stimulation and oncogenic transformation: 85 kd phosphoprotein and phosphatidylinositol kinase activity. *Cell* **50**, 1021–1029.

KAWASAKI, E. S., LADNER, M. B., WANG, A. M., VAN ARSDELL, J., WARREN, M. K., COYNE, M. Y., SCHWEICKART, V. L., LEE, M. T., WILSON, K. J., BOOSMAN, A., STANLEY, E. R., RALPH, P. & MARK, D. F. (1985). Molecular cloning of a complementary DNA encoding human macrophage-specific colony stimulating factor (CSF-1). *Science* **230**, 291–296.

LADNER, M. B., MARTIN, G. A., NOBLE, J. A., NIKOLOFF, D. M., TAL, R., KAWASAKI, E. S. & WHITE, T. J. (1987). Human CSF-1: Gene structure and alternative splicing of mRNA precursors. *EMBO J.* **6**, 2693–2698.

LE BEAU, M. M., ALBAIN, K. S., LARSON, R. A., VARDIMAN, J. W., DAVIS, E. M., BLOUGH, R. R., GOLOMB, H. M. & ROWLEY, J. D. (1986*b*). Clinical and cytogenetic correlations in 63 patients with therapy-related myelodysplastic syndromes and acute nonlymphocytic leukemia: Further evidence for characteristic abnormalities of chromosomes No. 5 and 7. *J. clin. Oncol.* **4**, 325–345.

LE BEAU, M. M., WESTBROOK, C. A., DIAZ, M. O., LARSON, R. A., ROWLEY, J. D., GASSON, J. C., GOLDE, D. W. & SHERR, C. J. (1986*a*). Evidence for the involvement of *GM-CSF* and *fms* in the deletion (5q) in myeloid disorders. *Science* **231**, 984–987.

MANGER, R., NAJITA, L., NICHOLS, E. J., HAKOMORI, S.-I. & ROHRSCHNEIDER, L. (1984). Cell surface expression of the McDonough strain of feline sarcoma virus *fms* gene product (gp140^{fms}). *Cell* **39**, 327–337.

McDONOUGH, S. K., LARSEN, S., BRODEY, R. S., STOCK, N. D. & HARDY, W. D. JR (1971). A transmissible feline fibrosarcoma of viral origin. *Cancer Res.* **31**, 953–956.

METCALF, D. & NICOLA, A. (1985). Synthesis by mouse peritoneal cells of G-CSF, the differentiation inducer for myeloid leukemia cells: Stimulation by endotoxin, M-CSF, and multi-CSF. *Leukaemia Res.* **9**, 35–50.

MOCHIZUKI, D. Y., EISENMAN, J. R., CONLON, P. J., LARSEN, A. D. & TUSHINSKI, R. J. (1987). Interleukin 1 regulates hematopoietic activity, a role previously ascribed to hemopoietin 1. *Proc. natn. Acad. Sci. U.S.A.* **84**, 5267–5271.

MORGAN, C., POLLARD, J. W. & STANLEY, E. R. (1987). Isolation and characterization of a cloned growth factor dependent macrophage cell line, BAC1.2F5. *J. cell Physiol.* **130**, 420–427.

MORGAN, C. J. & STANLEY, E. R. (1984). Chemical crosslinking of the mononuclear phagocyte specific growth factor CSF-1 to its receptor at the cell surface. *Biochem. biophys. Res. Comm.* **119**, 35–41.

MÜLLER, R., CURRAN, T., MÜLLER, D. & GUILBERT, L. (1985). Induction of c-*fos* during myelomonocytic differentiation and macrophage proliferation. *Nature, Lond.* **314**, 546–548.

MÜLLER, R., SLAMON, D. J., ADAMSON, E. D., TREMBLAY, J. M., MÜLLER, D., CLINE, M. J. & VERMA, I. M. (1983*a*). Transcription of c-*onc* genes c-*ras*^{ki} and c-*fms* during mouse development. *Molec. Cell. Biol.* **3**, 1062–1069.

MÜLLER, R., TREMBLAY, J. M., ADAMSON, E. D. & VERMA, I. M. (1983*b*). Tissue and cell type specific expression of two human c-*onc* genes. *Nature, Lond.* **304**, 454–456.

NICHOLS, E. J., MANGER, R., HAKOMORI, S., HERSCOVICS, A. & ROHRSCHNEIDER, L. R. (1985). Transformation by the v-*fms* oncogene product: Role of glycosylational processing and cell surface expression. *Molec. Cell Biol.* **5**, 3467–3475.

NIENHUIS, A. W., BUNN, H. F., TURNER, P. H., GOPAL, T. V., NASH, W. G., O'BRIEN, S. J. & SHERR, C. J. (1985). Expression of the human c-*fms* proto-oncogene in hematopoietic cells and its deletion in the 5q$^-$ syndrome. *Cell* **42**, 421–428.

PEDERSEN-BJERGAARD, J., PHILIP, P., PEDERSEN, N. T., HOU-JENSEN, K., SVEJGAARD, A., JENSEN, G. & NISSEN, N. I. (1984). Acute nonlymphocytic leukemia, preleukemia, and acute myeloproliferative syndrome secondary to treatment of other malignant diseases. II. Bone marrow cytology, cytogenetics, results of HLA typing, response to antileukemic chemotherapy, and survival in a total series of 55 patients. *Cancer* **54**, 452–462.

PETTENATI, M. J., LE BEAU, M. M., LEMONS, R. S., SHIMA, E. A., KAWASAKI, E. S., LARSON, R. A., SHERR, C. J., DIAZ, M. O. & ROWLEY, J. D. (1987). Assignment of *CSF-1* to 5q33.1: Evidence for clustering of genes regulating hematopoiesis and for their involvement in the deletion of the long arm of chromosome 5 in myeloid disorders. *Proc. natn. Acad. Sci. U.S.A.* **84**, 2970–2974.

RAJAVASHISTH, T. B., ENG, R., SHADDUCK, R. K., WAHEED, A., BEN-AVRAM, C. M., SHIVELY, J. E. & LUSIS, A. J. (1987). Cloning and tissue-specific expression of mouse macrophage colony-stimulating factor mRNA. *Proc. natn. Acad. Sci. U.S.A.* **84**, 1157–1161.

RALPH, P. & NAKOINZ, I. (1987). Stimulation of macrophage tumoricidal activity by the growth and differentiation factor CSF-1. *Cell. Immunol.* **105**, 270–279.

RALPH, P., WARREN, M. K., LEE, M. T., CSEJTEY, J., WEAVER, J. F., BROXMEYER, H. E., WILLIAMS, D. E., STANLEY, E. R. & KAWASAKI, E. S. (1986). Inducible production of human macrophage growth factor, CSF-1. *Blood* **68**, 633–639.

RAMBALDI, A., YOUNG, D. C. & GRIFFIN, J. D. (1987). Expression of the M-CSF (CSF-1) gene by human monocytes. *Blood* **69**, 1409–1413.

RETTENMIER, C. W., CHEN, J. H., ROUSSEL, M. F. & SHERR, C. J. (1985*b*). The product of the c-*fms* proto-oncogene: a glycoprotein with associated tyrosine kinase activity. *Science* **228**, 320–322.

RETTENMIER, C. W., ROUSSEL, M. F., ASHMUN, R. A., RALPH, P., PRICE, K. & SHERR, C. J. (1987). Synthesis of membrane-bound colony-stimulating factor-1 (CSF-1) and downmodulation of CSF-1 receptors in NIH 3T3 cells transformed by cotransfection of the human CSF-1 and c-*fms* (CSF-1 receptor) genes. *Molec. Cell. Biol.* **7**, 2378–2387.

RETTENMIER, C. W., ROUSSEL, M. F., QUINN, C. O., KITCHINGMAN, G. R., LOOK, A. T. & SHERR, C. J. (1985a). Transmembrane orientation of glycoproteins encoded by the v-*fms* oncogene. *Cell* **40**, 971–981.

RETTENMIER, C. W., SACCA, R., FURMAN, W. L., ROUSSEL, M. F., HOLT, J. T., NIENHUIS, A. W., STANLEY, E. R. & SHERR, C. J. (1986). Expression of the human c-*fms* proto-oncogene product (colony-stimulating factor-1 receptor) on peripheral blood mononuclear cells and choriocarcinoma cell lines. *J. clin. Invest.* **77**, 1740–1746.

ROUSSEL, M. F., DULL, T. J., RETTENMIER, C. W., RALPH, P., ULLRICH, A. & SHERR, C. J. (1987). Transforming potential of the c-*fms* proto-oncogene (CSF-1 receptor). *Nature, Lond.* **325**, 549–552.

ROUSSEL, M. F., RETTENMIER, C. W., LOOK, A. T. & SHERR, C. J. (1984). Cell surface expression of v-*fms*-coded glycoproteins is required for transformation. *Molec. Cell Biol.* **4**, 1999–2009.

ROUSSEL, M. F., RETTENMIER, C. W. & SHERR, C. J. (1988). Introduction of a human colony stimulating factor-1 gene into a mouse macrophage cell line induces CSF-1 independence but not tumorigenicity. *Blood* **71**, 1218–1225.

ROWLEY, J. D., GOLOMB, H. M. & VARDIMAN, J. W. (1981). Nonrandom chromosome abnormalities in acute leukemia and dysmyelopoietic syndromes in patients with previously treated malignant disease. *Blood* **58**, 759–767.

SACCA, R., STANLEY, E. R., SHERR, C. J. & RETTENMIER, C. W. (1986). Specific binding of the mononuclear phagocyte colony-stimulating factor CSF-1 to the product of the v-*fms* oncogene. *Proc. natn. Acad. Sci. U.S.A.* **83**, 3331–3335.

SARMA, P. S., SHARAR, A. L. & McDONOUGH, S. (1972). The SM strain of feline sarcoma virus. Biologic and antigenic characterization of virus. *Proc. Soc. exp. Biol. Med.* **140**, 1365–1368.

SHERR, C. J., RETTENMIER, C. W., SACCA, R., ROUSSEL, M. F., LOOK, A. T. & STANLEY, E. R. (1985). The c-*fms* proto-oncogene product is related to the receptor for the mononuclear phagocyte growth factor, CSF-1. *Cell* **41**, 665–676.

SOKAL, G., MICHAUX, J. L., VAN DEN BERGHE, H., CORDIER, A., RODHAIN, J., FERRANT, A., MORIAU, M., DEBRUYERE, M. & SONNET, J. (1975). A new hematologic syndrome with a distinct karyotype: The 5q⁻ chromosome. *Blood* **46**, 519–533.

STANLEY, E. R., BARTOCCI, A., PATINKIN, D., ROSENDAAL, M. & BRADLEY, T. R. (1986). Regulation of very primitive, multipotent, hematopoietic cells by hemopoietin-1. *Cell* **45**, 667–674.

STANLEY, E. R., GUILBERT, L. J., TUSHINSKI, R. J. & BARTELMEZ, S. H. (1983). CSF-1 – A mononuclear phagocyte lineage-specific hemopoietic growth factor. *J. cell. Biochem.* **21**, 151–159.

STANLEY, E. R. & HEARD, P. M. (1977). Factors regulating macrophage production and growth. Purification and some properties of the colony stimulating factor from medium conditioned by mouse L cells. *J. biol. Chem.* **252**, 4305–4312.

TAMURA, T., SIMON, E., NIEMANN, H., SNOEK, G. T. & BAUER, H. (1986). gp140ᵛ⁻*fms* molecules expressed at the surface of cells transformed by the McDonough strain of feline sarcoma virus are phosphorylated in tyrosine and serine. *Molec. Cell. Biol.* **6**, 4745–4748.

TUSHINSKI, R. J., OLIVER, I. T., GUILBERT, L. J., TYNAN, P. W., WARNER, J. R. & STANLEY, E. R. (1982). Survival of mononuclear phagocytes depends on a lineage-specific growth factor that the differentiated cells selectively destroy. *Cell* **28**, 71–81.

TUSHINSKI, R. J. & STANLEY, E. R. (1983). The regulation of macrophage protein turnover by a colony stimulating factor (CSF-1). *J. cell Physiol.* **116**, 67–75.

TUSHINSKI, R. J. & STANLEY, E. R. (1985). The regulation of mononuclear phagocyte entry into S phase by the colony stimulating factor CSF-1. *J. cell Physiol.* **122**, 221–228.

VAN DEN BERGHE, H., CASSIMAN, J.-J., DAVID, G., FRYNS, J.-P., MICHAUX, J.-L. & SOKAL, G. (1974). Distinct haematological disorder with deletion of long arm of No. 5 chromosome. *Nature, Lond.* **251**, 437–438.

WARREN, M. K. & RALPH, P. (1986). Macrophage growth factor CSF-1 stimulates human monocyte production of interferon, tumor necrosis factor, and colony stimulating activity. *J. Immun.* **137**, 2281–2285.

WATERFIELD, M. D., SCRACE, G. T., WHITTLE, N., STROOBANT, P., JOHNSSON, A., WASTESON, A., WESTERMARK, B., HELDIN, C.-H., HUANG, J. S. & DEUEL, T. F. (1983). Platelet-derived growth factor is structurally related to the putative transforming protein p28^{sis} of simian sarcoma virus. *Nature, Lond.* **304**, 35–39.

WHEELER, E. F., ASKEW, D., MAY, S., ILHE, J. N. & SHERR, C. J. (1987). The v-*fms* oncogene induces factor-independent growth and transformation of the interleukin-3-dependent myeloid cell line FDC-P1. *Molec. Cell. Biol.* **7**, 1673–1680.

WHEELER, E. F., RETTENMIER, C. W., LOOK, A. T. & SHERR, C. J. (1986b). The v-*fms* oncogene induces factor independence and tumorigenicity in CSF-1 dependent macrophage cell line. *Nature, Lond.* **324**, 377–380.

WHEELER, E. F., ROUSSEL, M. F., HAMPE, A., WALKER, M. H., FRIED, V. A., LOOK, A. T., RETTENMIER, C. W. & SHERR, C. J. (1986a). The amino-terminal domain of the v-*fms* oncogene product includes a functional signal peptide that directs synthesis of a transforming glycoprotein in the absence of feline leukemia virus *gag* sequences. *J. Virol.* **59**, 224–233.

WHETTON, A. D., MONK, P. N., CONSALVEY, S. D. & DOWNES, C. P. (1986). The haemopoietic growth factors interleukin 3 and colony stimulating factor-1 stimulate proliferation but do not induce inositol lipid breakdown in murine bone-marrow-derived macrophages. *EMBO J.* **5**, 3281–3286.

WISNIEWSKI, L. P. & HIRSCHHORN, K. (1983). Acquired partial deletions of the long arm of chromosome 5 in hematologic disorders. *Am. J. Hematol.* **15**, 295–310.

WONG, G. G., TEMPLE, P. A., LEARY, A. C., WITEK-GIANNOTTI, J. S., YANG, Y.-C., CIARLETTA, A. B., CHUNG, M., MURTHA, P., KRIZ, R., KAUFMAN, R. J., FERENZ, C. R., SIBLEY, B. S., TURNER, K. J., HEWICK, R. M., CLARK, S. C., YANAI, N., YOKOTA, H., YAMADA, M., SAITO, M., MOTOYOSHI, K. & TAKAKU, F. (1987). Human CSF-1: Molecular cloning and expression of 4 kb cDNA encoding the human urinary protein. *Science* **235**, 1504–1508.

WOOLFORD, J., ROTHWELL, V. & ROHRSCHNEIDER, L. (1985). Characterization of the human c-*fms* gene product and its expression in cells of the monocyte-macrophage lineage. *Molec. Cell Biol.* **5**, 3458–3466.

YARDEN, Y., ESCOBEDO, J. A., KUANG, W. J., YANG-FENG, T. L., DANIEL, T. O., TREMBLE, P. M., CHEN, E. Y., ANDO, M. E., HARKINS, R. N., FRANCKE, U., FRIED, V. A., ULLRICH, A. & WILLIAMS, L. T. (1986). Structure of the receptor for platelet-derived growth factor helps define a family of closely related growth factor receptors. *Nature, Lond.* **323**, 226–232.

YEUNG, Y. G., JUBINSKY, P. T., SENGUPTA, A., YEUNG, D. C. Y. & STANLEY, E. R. (1987). Purification of the colony-stimulating factor 1 receptor and demonstration of its tyrosine kinase activity. *Proc. natn. Acad. Sci. U.S.A.* **84**, 1268–1271.

J. Cell Sci. Suppl. 9, 45–65 (1988)
Printed in Great Britain © The Company of Biologists Limited 1988

Structure and function of Fc receptors on macrophages and lymphocytes

IRA MELLMAN[1], TERRY KOCH[1], GLENN HEALEY[1],
WALTER HUNZIKER[1], VICTORIA LEWIS[1], HELEN PLUTNER[1],
HEINI MIETTINEN[1], DAVID VAUX[1], KEVIN MOORE[2]
AND SUSAN STUART[3]

[1]*Department of Cell Biology, Yale University School of Medicine, PO Box 3333, New Haven, Connecticut 06510, USA,* [2]*DNAX Research Institute, Palo Alto, California* and [3]*Triton Biosciences Inc., Alameda, California, USA*

Summary

Cell surface receptors for the Fc portion of immunoglobulin confer on most cells of the immune system the ability to communicate with the humoral antibody response. These Fc receptors are known to be particularly important for the function of various effector cells, such as macrophages, since they are involved in mediating a variety of activities including endocytosis, antibody-dependent cellular cytotoxicity, and triggering the release of potent inflammatory agents. Over the past few years, a considerable amount has been learned about the structure and functions of the Fc receptors expressed by murine and human cells, due to the availability of specific anti-receptor antibodies and the isolation of Fc receptor cDNA clones. In general, these receptors are transmembrane proteins whose extracellular domains contain two immunoglobulin-like regions and are thus members of the immunoglobulin gene family. Their domain structure consists of a glycosylated extracellular domain, a single membrane-spanning segment, and a relatively long cytoplasmic domain. The cytoplasmic tails exhibit a surprising degree of variation in length and amino acid sequence. This review summarizes some recent information concerning the structure and expression of the Fc receptors found on murine and human macrophages and lymphocytes. Particular attention is paid to the functional activities of these receptors, and the possible relationship between receptor function and receptor structure.

Introduction

Macrophages, granulocytes, many lymphocytes, and certain epithelial cells express receptors for the Fc domains of immunoglobulin. While these Fc receptors (FcRs) can be associated with a range of cellular activities and exhibit binding specificities for a variety of immunoglobulin classes or subclasses, in general, one can view FcRs as forming a critical bridge between the humoral and cellular responses of the vertebrate immune system. By providing the means to bind the invariant Fc portion of antibody molecules, FcRs enable immune effector cells to interpret and respond to the highly variable and specific events involved in antibody–antigen recognition. Thus cells such as the macrophage, which are otherwise incapable of detecting antigens directly, are incorporated as important elements of the humoral response. In addition, B cell FcRs may even be involved in directly regulating the events leading to antibody secretion.

The fact that distinct FcRs have been described, which bind virtually all classes of immunoglobulin (Unkeless *et al.* 1981) itself suggests that considerable heterogenity must exist amongst this class of receptors. Only within the past 1–2 years, however, have we begun to appreciate the true extent of this heterogeneity. Macrophage-lymphocyte-epithelial cell FcRs are now known to belong to one of two large families, the first (and quantitatively more important) being a derivative of an ancestral immunoglobulin-like gene and the second being closely related to cellular lectins (lymphocyte IgE receptors). The structural heterogeneity also appears to extend to within individual classes of FcR specific for single immunoglobulin isotypes. Such heterogeneity must reflect significant functional and/or developmental differences, which were previously unexpected, for this family of invariant or 'monotypic' membrane receptors. In this brief review, we will summarize recent results, emphasizing those from our laboratory, that shed some light on the structure, functions, and cell biology of the IgG FcR found on murine and human mononuclear cells.

Distribution of Fc receptors

FcRs are widely distributed in nature on cells both in and out of the immune system, as well as on cells in and out of the animal kingdom. A survey of the receptors described to date is compiled in Table 1. A large number of receptors, distinguished biochemically by their different specificities for various forms of immunoglobulin (Ig), have been identified as being membrane-associated or secreted by a large number of mammalian cell types. These include receptors for IgA, IgM, IgD, IgE, and various subclasses of IgG found on cells of the immune system (mononuclear cells, granulocytes, B cells, some T cells, NK cells) and various transporting epithelia (mammary cells, hepatocytes, intestinal epithelia in newborn rodents). Certain FcR-negative cells, such as fibroblasts, can be induced to express FcR following infection with certain DNA viruses (Epstein-Barr virus, cytomegalovirus, herpes simplex virus (HSV) types 1 and 2, varicella-zoster virus). In the case of at least HSV, this receptor is encoded by a viral gene (glycoprotein E or gE) (Para *et al.* 1980). Finally, various strains of *Staphylococci* and *Streptococci* express well-characterized FcR activities (protein A, protein G).

Fc receptors for IgG on murine macrophages and lymphocytes

The IgG1/IgG2 Fc receptor

Mouse macrophages and lymphocytes express at least three biochemically distinct receptors for different IgG subclasses (Unkeless *et al.* 1981) (Table 1). At least on macrophages, the three receptor types can be expressed simultaneously. By far the best characterized is the receptor specific for immune complexes or aggregates of murine IgG1 or IgG2b, designated FcRII. While the ligand-binding activity of this receptor is relatively resistant to inactivation by trypsin, it binds monomeric IgG poorly. Most importantly, this receptor is recognized specifically by the rat monoclonal antibody 2.4G2, a reagent that has allowed its identification and characterization as a 60K ($K = 10^3 M_r$) membrane glycoprotein (Unkeless, 1979; Mellman & Unkeless, 1980) as well as facilitating a variety of other structural and

Table 1. *The family of Fc receptors*

(A) *Immune cells*

	Cell type	$M_r \times 10^{-3}$	Function(s)	References
IgG Murine				Dickler (1976) Fridman *et al.* (1984) Unkeless *et al.* (1981)
IgG1/2b multimers (*mFcRII*)	Macrophages Monocytes Lymphocytes Neutrophils	47–60† 45‡	Endocytosis, immune clearance, ADCC inflammatory, cytotoxic response	Lewis *et al.* (1986) Ravetch *et al.* (1986) Unkeless (1977)
IgG2a monomers (*mFcRI*)	Macrophages	60, 70†	Endocytosis, immune clearance, ADCC inflammatory, cytotoxic response	Unkeless (1977)
IgG3 multimers	Macrophages	ND	ND	Diamond & Yelton (1981)
IgG human Multimers only IgG1,IgG3 > IgG2,IgG4 (*hFcRII*)	Neutrophil Eosinophils Monocytes B lymphocytes Platelets	40†‡	ND	Anderson & Looney (1986) Looney *et al.* (1986) Boyle (1984)
Multimers > monomers IgG1,IgG3 > IgG4 (*hFcRI*)	Monocytes (HL60, U937 cells) Granulocytes	65–72†	ADCC, phagocytosis	Looney *et al.* (1986) Cohen *et al.* (1983)
Multimers only, low affinity (*hFcR-N*)	NK and K cells Neutrophils Eosinophils Macrophages Some T lymphocytes	50–70* or 60/70 doublet	Anti-tumour and parasite toxicity	Perussia *et al.* (1983) Peter *et al.* (1975)
IgE				
Low affinity, dimers > monomers	Platelets Eosinophils Macrophages Monocytes Lymphocytes	86, 49*, 23	ADCC, inflammatory, cytotoxic and anti-parasitic response	Healicon & Foreman (1984) Ishizaka (1984) Kikutani *et al.* (1986) Conrad & Peterson (1984)
High affinity, monomers	Basophils (RBL cells) Mast cells	40–70†, 33	Reactivity to allergins, degranulation, anti-parasitic response	Metzger (1984) Kinet *et al.* (1987)

Table 1. Continued

	Cell type	$M_r \times 10^{-3}$	Function(s)	References
Monomers	IgM[+]/IgD[+] B lymphocytes	46‡	Control of B cell differentiation	Lydyard & Farger (1982) Moretta et al. (1975)
IgM Pentamer > monomer	T and B lymphocytes +/− activated macrophages	ND	Stimulate antibody production	Roubin & Zolla-Puzner (1979)
IgD	T and B lymphocytes +/− null cells	ND	?Regulate immune response	Kinet et al. (1987) Roubin & Zolla-Puzner (1979)
IgA1/2	T and B lymphocytes	ND	?Regulate immune response	Kinet et al. (1987) Cioco et al. (1985) Hoover et al. (1981)

(B) Non-immune cells

	Cell type	$M_r \times 10^{-3}$	Function(s)	References
Polymeric Ig (pIgR) Dimeric IgA/pentameric IgM (human, mouse, rabbit)	Epithelia	95–120‡	Transcytosis: serosal to secretions	Bradtzaeg (1981) Kuhn & Kraehenbuhl (1982) Mostov et al. (1984)
IgG Neonatal rat, human, bovine	Duodenum/jejunum epithelial brush border	100–110†, 41–57, 15–18,	Transcytosis of maternal Ig	Rodewald et al. (1988) Simister & Rees (1985)
IgG1/3/4 Human, mouse, rat, guinea pig	Placental trophoblast and endothelium	3 reports* (i) 47 (ii) 74, 104 (iii) 37–60	Transcytosis of maternal Ig	Balfour & Jones (1978) Matre et al. (1984)
Rabbit	Yolk sac endoderm	ND	Transcytosis of maternal Ig	Niezgodka et al. (1981)

IgG1/2/4 Human virus induced (HSV1,2, CMV, VZV, EBV)	Infected fibroblasts of all species tested and on virion	HSV:* 65, 80 CMV: 43	ND	Liteplo et al. (1982) Costa et al. (1978) Ogata & Sigeta (1979) Sakuma et al. (1977) Wiger & Michaelson (1985) Yee et al. (1982)
Bacterial Reactivity with all species except bird and rat	*Staphylococcus* and *Streptococcus* stains	37–130*†‡	ND	Langone (1982) Boyle (1984)

(C) Soluble Ig binding factors (IBFs)

IgE				
Rat, human	Basophils RBL cells	31‡	(?)Stimulation/ suppression Ig response	Ishizaka (1984) Liu et al. (1985)
Rat, human, murine	T lymphocytes	60‡ 13–15	Stimulation/suppression Ig response	Martens et al. (1985) Neauport-Sautes et al. (1979)
Human	B lymphocytes	25‡	ND	Conrad & Peterson (1984)
IgG				
Rat, human	T lymphocytes 'activated'	60† 40 +/− 20	Suppresses Ig response	Fridman et al. (1984) Neauport-Sautes et al. (1979) Fridman & Golstein (1974)
IgG1/2b murine	B lymphocyte cell lines Spleen cultures	48†	ND	Fridman & Golstein (1974) Loube & Dorrington (1980) Pituch-Noworolska et al. (1985) Pure et al. (1984)
IgG2a > IgG1 > IgG2b	L1210 leukemia cells	65, 45*, 28	ND	Cooper & Sambray (1977)

Compilation of Fc-binding molecules described to date. The molecular weights indicated have been derived from SDS–polyacrylamide gel electrophoresis analysis of proteins isolated by affinity chromatography on Ig-columns (*) or immunoprecipitated with specific anti-receptor monoclonal antibodies (†), or determined from the amino acid sequence deduced from cDNA clones (‡). While most of the FcR indicated will bind immunoglobulins from various species, the high-affinity receptor for IgE binds only homologous IgE. Similarly, the placental IgG FcR will only recognize IgG from those species that use transplacental transfer of maternal immunoglobulin to convey passive immunity *in utero* (human, mouse, rat, guinea pig). ND, not determined; ADCC, antibody-dependent cellular cytotoxicity.

functional studies (see below). The IgG1/IgG2b FcR is widely distributed on cells of the immune system, being found on macrophages, lymphocytes and granulocytes. However, immunoprecipitation using 2.4G2 of the mature cell-surface form of the receptor from these diverse cell types has indicated the existence of considerable molecular weight heterogeneity on SDS–polyacrylamide gels (Mellman & Unkeless, 1980). On macrophages and many lymphocytes, the receptor is generally the most abundant, being expressed in amounts of up to $2-6 \times 10^5$ per cell (Mellman & Unkeless, 1980; Mellman *et al.* 1983; Mellman & Plutner, 1984). Functionally, macrophage FcRII is capable of mediating the endocytosis of soluble immune complexes and phagocytosis of large IgG-coated particles, and of triggering a variety of other important effector cell functions (see below).

Other murine IgG Fc receptors

Relatively little is known about the two remaining murine FcRs. The IgG2a receptor, also referred to as FcRI, is specific for monomeric IgG2a but can also bind aggregated immunoglobulin (Unkeless, 1977; Mellman & Unkeless, 1980). Its activity is sensitive to trypsin and has a much more restricted pattern of expression: FcRI has thus far only been detected on macrophages. Like the IgG1/IgG2b FcR, however, the IgG2a receptor is capable of mediating the phagocytosis of opsonized particles. A monoclonal antibody to murine FcRI has yet to be produced and the polypeptide(s) responsible for receptor activity has not been definitively identified. The structure of macrophage IgG3 receptor (FcRIII) also remains unidentified, and is characterized only as a trypsin-resistant molecule capable of mediating the phagocytosis of IgG3-sensitized particles (Diamond & Yelton, 1981).

Functions of the murine IgG1/IgG2b Fc receptor (mFcRII)

Given its relative abundance, wide distribution, and the availability of specific anti-receptor antibodies, most of what we know concerning the functional activities of FcR derives from studies of the murine IgG1/IgG2b receptor (mFcRII). As mentioned above, the receptor is associated with an impressive array of activities, all of which are critical to effector-cell function and all of which illustrate many important principles of membrane biology. These activities range from the clearance of antibody–antigen complexes via receptor-mediated endocytosis to the ligand-triggered transmission of signals across the plasma membrane, which result in alterations in secretion, exocytosis and cellular metabolism.

Fc receptor-mediated endocytosis

Unlike most other well studied receptors, the macrophage IgG1/IgG2b FcR is physiologically associated with two important forms of endocytosis: receptor-mediated pinocytosis of soluble antibody–antigen complexes and the phagocytosis of large IgG-coated particles. The internalization of soluble immune complexes proceeds via the standard pathway of receptor-mediated endocytosis described for a variety of cell surface receptors (Steinman *et al.* 1983; Helenius *et al.* 1983; Mellman *et al.* 1986, 1987). These events include binding to cell surface receptors, accumulation of the receptor–ligand complexes at clathrin-coated pits, internalization in coated vesicles and subsequent delivery of the ligand to acidic endosomes and finally to lysosomes for degradation (Mellman & Plutner, 1984; Ukkonen *et al.* 1986; Mellman *et al.* 1986).

Aside from the importance of this process to normal macrophage function, FcR-mediated endocytosis is of interest since the pattern of intracellular receptor transport after internalization appears to be regulated by the type of ligand bound. If the receptor is allowed to bind a monovalent ligand, namely Fab fragments derived from the anti-receptor antibody 2.4G2, the receptor–ligand complex is internalized, delivered to endosomes, and then rapidly returned ('recycled') back to the plasma membrane without requiring transit through lysosomes (Mellman *et al.* 1984).

On the other hand, if the ligand is multivalent, e.g. aggregated 2.4G2 Fab or polyvalent antibody–antigen complexes, the receptor is again internalized and delivered to endosomes, but its participation in the recycling portion of the pathway is rendered less efficient. The receptor–ligand complex remains intact (ligand binding to FcR is not disrupted by the slightly acidic pH of endosomes) and is transferred from endosomes to lysosomes where both ligand and receptor are degraded (Mellman & Plutner, 1984; Ukkonen *et al.* 1986). While the macrophage FcR in control cells turns over with a $t_{1/2}$ of approximately 15–20 h, in cells exposed continuously to immune complexes the $t_{1/2}$ is reduced to <5 h. This results in a net decrease in the number of cell surface FcR and, presumably, in the 'down-regulation' of a macrophage's responsiveness to subsequent exposure to ligand. Recovery of normal amounts of cell surface FcR requires new receptor synthesis. Given the role of FcR in triggering the release of inflammatory and cytotoxic agents by macrophages, this type of regulation may be important in attenuating macrophage function at sites of chronic inflammation. FcR-mediated phagocytosis also leads to the removal of receptors from the plasma membrane and intralysosomal receptor degradation (Mellman *et al.* 1983).

The importance of these events goes beyond the general implications for the regulation of macrophage function, i.e. the probable attenuation of FcR-triggered macrophage effector functions following immune complex endocytosis. As illustrated in Fig. 1, the finding that the pathway of intracellular transport of FcR, recycling or transport to lysosomes, can be regulated by the valency of the bound ligand suggests a possible mechanism governing membrane protein traffic in general. Indeed, many other receptors, such as the low density lipoprotein and transferrin receptors, which normally recycle rapidly during endocytosis can also be diverted to lysosomes if allowed to interact with artificial non-dissociating multivalent ligands (e.g. polyclonal anti-receptor antibody) (Mellman *et al.* 1987). It is thus conceivable that relatively simple alterations in the aggregation state or the degree of oligomerization of membrane receptors may influence their patterns of intracellular transport. However, it is not at all clear whether the signal generated by such ligand-induced changes in quaternary structure is manifested at the level of a receptor's cytoplasmic, membrane-spanning, or extracellular domain.

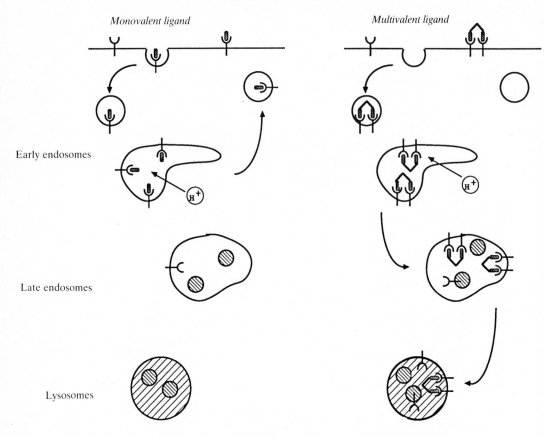

Fig. 1. Pathways of Fc receptor-mediated endocytosis in mouse macrophages. The left-hand panel illustrates the intracellular pathway taken by the receptor when bound to monovalent ligands (e.g. Fab fragment of 2.4G2). The receptor and ligand are internalized, delivered to endosomes and recycled intact back to the plasma membrane. The right-hand panel illustrates the pathway taken when the bound ligand is multivalent. Receptor and ligand are now targeted from endosomes to lysosomes and degraded. The diversion of FcR along the lysosomal pathway is probably not all or none, but reflects an alteration in the equilibrium distribution due to ligand valency (Mellman *et al.* 1984; Mellman & Plutner, 1984; Ukkonen *et al.* 1986).

Transmembrane signalling

In addition to endocytosis, binding of ligand to FcR generates a transmembrane signal, which triggers a variety of other events important for macrophage function. Typically, these include a localized reorganization of actin-containing microfilaments directly beneath the plasma membrane at the site of particle attachment (facilitating phagocytosis), the synthesis and release of bioactive lipids (i.e. prostaglandins and leukotrienes), the secretion of neutral proteases (e.g. plasminogen activator), and the release of hydrogen peroxide and other active oxygen intermediates that mediate antibody-dependent cellular cytotoxicity (ADCC) (Unkeless *et al.* 1981). These events occur rapidly and apparently do not require ligand internalization (Rouzer *et al.* 1980).

The mechanism of FcR-mediated transmembrane signalling remains unclear. As discussed further below, the receptor does not appear to be phosphorylated, either in the presence or absence of bound ligand, suggesting that kinase-like phosphorylation events are not involved. However, ligand binding to FcR can result in a depolarization response and a transient increase in cytosolic free Ca^{2+} (Young *et al.* 1984). Conceivably, a ligand-dependent alteration in transmembrane ion fluxes, as occurs in the case of receptors such as the acetylcholine receptor, could mediate the signal. That such changes in ion permeability may even be due to an intrinsic ligand-activated channel activity associated with the FcR itself has been suggested by experiments using isolated receptor protein reconstituted into artificial bilayers (Young *et al.* 1983). More recent data have shown, however, that at least some FcR-triggered functions, such as phagocytosis, can proceed without alterations in cytosolic free Ca^{2+} (DiVirgilio *et al.* 1988) and other functions (oxidative burst) are perhaps independent of changes in membrane potential (Pfefferkorn, 1984). In addition, the known structure of the receptor, which is a membrane protein with a single highly hydrophobic membrane-spanning segment (see below), places some constraints on the applicability of the ion channel concept.

Whatever the nature of the actual signal, it is clear that ligand binding does rapidly transmit information to cytosolic elements. One interesting manifestation of these events is an alteration in the pattern of protein myristylation which appears to correlate with macrophage secretory events (Aderem *et al.* 1986). The possible involvement of myristoylation in macrophage function is described elsewhere in this volume.

The function of the IgG1/IgG2b Fc receptor on lymphocytes

In contrast to macrophages, the function of the IgG1/IgG2b FcR on lymphocytes is poorly understood (Lydyard & Fanger, 1982; Fridman *et al.* 1984) although recent evidence suggests that it may be important in the regulation of T- and B-cell activation and proliferation, and in antibody secretion by B cells. Bijsterbosch & Klaus (1985) have shown that triggering of FcR-positive B cells to mature and proliferate could be stimulated by specific antigen or by the binding of surface IgM with the $F(ab')_2$ fragment of an anti-IgM monoclonal antibody. However, when intact anti-IgM was used instead of the $F(ab')_2$, an additional signal was provided preventing the proliferative response necessary for terminal differentiation and antibody synthesis. The effect was believed to be mediated by the cross-linking of surface Ig with FcR (Phillips & Parker, 1984) and subsequent inhibition of the phosphatidyl inositol cascade (Bijsterbosch & Klaus, 1985).

Although lymphocyte membrane-bound FcRs are primarily associated with negative regulation (Lydyard & Fanger, 1982; Spiegelberg, 1981), these cells also appear to secrete one or more soluble FcRs or immunoglobulin-binding factors (IBFs) capable of positively or negatively influencing the immune response. Distinct IBFs have now been reported for all Ig isotypes and subclasses (see Table 1). The best studied are those synthesized and released from human or rodent FcR^+ T lymphocytes (Fridman & Golstein, 1974; Fridman *et al.* 1984; Ishizaka, 1984). The synthesis and secretion of IgM and IgG antibodies are regulated, in part, by the secretion of soluble IBFs from FcR^+ T cells (Fridman *et al.* 1984), while other IgE-binding T-cell factors selectively regulate the IgE response (Ishizaka, 1984; Spiegelberg, 1981). IgE-potentiating factors or IgE-suppressive factors are formed and released depending on the isotypic restriction of the membrane FcR, and on the exposure to additional T-cell factors affecting their ability to glycosylate (Ishizaka, 1984). In addition, a soluble FcR is secreted from stimulated B cells, which reacts with 2.4G2 and is thus antigenically similar to the cell-associated form of IgG1/IgG2b FcR; however, the function of this FcR is not known (Pure *et al.* 1984). B cell activation by lipopolysaccharide also results in the expression of a unique FcR epitope, recognized by monoclonal antibody 6B7c, which may correlate with the release of the soluble form of the receptor (Pure *et al.* 1987).

Structure of the murine IgG1/IgG2b Fc receptor (mFcRII)

Given its involvement in a variety of activities such as endocytosis, transmembrane signalling, and secretion, all of which are critically important for macrophage function as well as being of general cell biological interest, understanding the structural features of the IgG1/IgG2b FcR has proved particularly important. We have approached this problem using both biochemical and molecular biological methods.

The IgG1/IgG2b FcR has been purified by immunoaffinity chromatography using 2.4G2–Sepharose, and used as immunogen to produce a variety of domain-specific anti-receptor monoclonal and polyclonal antibodies (Mellman *et al.* 1983; Green *et al.* 1985; Pure *et al.* 1987). These antibodies have permitted a preliminary characterization of receptor structure by immunoprecipitation of antigen from metabolically labelled cells. Using the J774 macrophage cell line, we found that the major receptor species was synthesized in the rough endoplasmic reticulum (RER) as a 53K precursor containing four asparagine-linked oligosaccharides, which were terminally glycosylated in the Golgi complex (Green *et al.* 1985). The *N*-linked chains were tri- or tetra-antennary and contained internal lactosamine (GlcNAc- -Gal) repeats; no *O*-linked sugar was detected (Howe *et al.* 1988). Microsome digestion experiments demonstrated that the receptor was a transmembrane protein, with a relatively large cytoplasmic tail, 10–15K in length, recognized by a particular anti-receptor monoclonal antibody designated C14 (Green *et al.* 1985). Thus far, the receptor does not appear to be phosphorylated either in the presence or absence of bound ligand (unpublished results).

Characterization of murine Fc receptor cDNA clones

Using amino acid sequence data derived from the purified J774 cell receptor and a monospecific anti-mFcRII antiserum, several cDNA clones encoding the murine IgG1/IgG2b FcR have been isolated and sequenced. One of these, designated pFcR13, was found to contain the complete coding region as well as >90% of the 5′

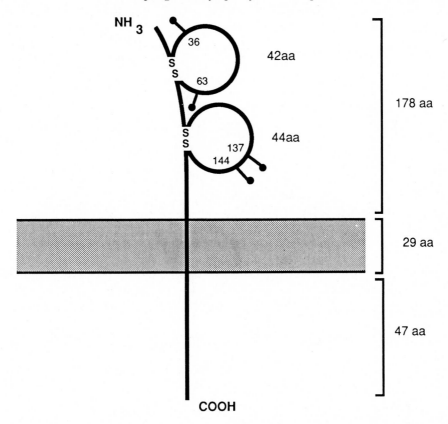

NH₃

36

S
S

63

42aa

S
S

137

144

44aa

178 aa

29 aa

47 aa

COOH

Fig. 2. Structure of the mouse macrophage-lymphocyte IgG1/IgG2b Fc receptor (mFcRII). The amino acid sequence was deduced from the cDNA clone pFcR13, and the insertion in the membrane derived from biochemical determinations of receptor structure.

and 3′ untranslated regions (Lewis *et al.* 1986). As deduced from the nucleotide sequence, the structure of the FcR was in general agreement with the biochemical data (Fig. 2). The receptor was a transmembrane protein containing a single hydrophobic membrane-spanning segment. The extracellular domain contained four predicted sites for *N*-linked glycosylation. Interestingly, the cytoplasmic domain of the receptor obtained from a P388D$_1$ cDNA library, 47 amino acid residues, corresponding to approximately 6K in molecular weight, was somewhat shorter than predicted by the biochemical experiments using J774 cells (10–15K; Green *et al.* 1985). The cytoplasmic tail did not exhibit sequence homology with any other known protein; more specifically, there was no obvious kinase-like domain, which might be implicated in some of the receptor's transmembrane signalling functions. This was consistent with our inability thus far to identify a phosphorylated form of mFcRII by immunoprecipitation.

Expression of pFcR13 has been obtained in COS cells using a late SV40 replacement vector and found to yield a glycoprotein, which reacts with all available anti-receptor antibodies. Permanently expressing CHO cell lines have also been produced using a selectable vector containing a methotrexate-resistant dihydrofolate reductase cDNA (H. Miettinen *et al.*, unpublished results). Most importantly, mFcRII is also functionally active even when expressed in fibroblast lines (see below).

The Fc receptor is a member of the immunoglobulin gene family

The receptor's extracellular domain was found to contain four regularly spaced cysteine residues which define two internal sequence repeats. Examination of the sequences directly surrounding these cysteines revealed significant homology to sequences associated with the V and/or C domains of immunoglobulin molecules, as well as other members of the immunoglobulin gene superfamily (Lewis *et al.* 1986; Barclay *et al.* 1987). Interestingly, however, the number of amino acids between the two domains was only 42–44, considerably shorter than that typically found in the constant and variable domains of immunoglobulin molecules (usually 70–80 residues). These truncated domains were quite similar to those found in at least one other immunoglobulin-like molecule, the neural cell adhesion molecule N-CAM (Hemperly *et al.* 1986). While the shortened domains presumably result from the deletion of β strands from within the immunoglobulin fold, the functional significance of this arrangement is unknown.

Unique features of the Fc receptor signal sequence

The sequence of pFcR13 indicated that mFcRII has an amino-terminal signal sequence which must be cleaved to generate the mature amino terminus determined by *N*-terminal protein sequencing (Lewis *et al.* 1986). The signal sequence is atypical, however, since there are potential start sites for translation at positions -13, -29, and -39. Each of these initiator methionines begins a possibly functional signal and none is associated with any consensus nucleotide sequence thought to represent preferred start sites (Lewis *et al.* 1986). Cell-free translation of *in vitro* transcribed pFcR13 mRNA (using pGEM vectors) has demonstrated that translation can, in principle, be initiated at any of the methionines (G. Healey, W. Hunziker *et al.*, unpublished results). In reticulocyte lysates, initiation consistent with a start at Met_{-13} or (to a lesser extent) Met_{-29} occurs; in wheat germ lysates, initiation at Met_{-39} appears to be favoured. Irrespective of which initiator methionine is used, however, translated FcR is efficiently inserted into dog pancreas microsomes, glycosylated, and its signal cleaved to yield the same polypeptides. Thus, the FcR mRNA appears to encode three functional signal sequences, which nevertheless generate identical glycoproteins after translocation across the RER. While the biological significance of this observation is not known, it should not contribute to the observed size heterogeneity of mFcRII found in different cell types. In the case of the Ia invariant chain, which unlike the FcR is oriented with its amino terminus towards the cytosol, a similar existence of multiple start sites for translation does indeed result in the production of polypeptides of different lengths (O'Sullivan *et al.* 1987).

The molecular basis of mFcRII size heterogeneity

FcR immunoprecipitated with 2.4G2 or other anti-mFcRII reagents from a variety of cell types has demonstrated the existence of considerable size heterogeneity among the receptors expressed in cells of diverse origins. For example, labelled receptor from thioglycollate-elicited peritoneal macrophages behaves like a 47K protein on SDS–polyacrylamide gels, whereas receptor isolated from the S49.1 T cell line is closer to 60K (Mellman & Unkeless, 1980). Much of this heterogeneity can be explained by cell type-specific differences in glycosylation; digestion of terminally glycosylated mFcRII from different sources with endoglycosidase F (which removes all *N*-linked oligosaccharides) almost always yields deglycosylated polypeptides of identical sizes (Lewis *et al.* 1986).

Three Fc receptor cDNAs

However, it is likely that some of the observed heterogeneity is due to the existence of other closely related FcR isoforms. Two additional murine FcR cDNAs have also been isolated using cDNA libraries constructed from J774 macrophages and S49.1 T cells (Ravetch *et al.* 1986). One of these, designated β-1, is identical to the sequence encoded by pFcR13 (hereafter referred to as β-2) except for a 47 amino acid in-frame insertion in the cytoplasmic domain (Fig. 3). This predicts a cytoplasmic tail for β-1 of some 94 amino acids, much closer in size to the 10–15K predicted from microsome digestion experiments using J774 cells (Green *et al.* 1985). Presumably, this insertion was the result of alternative splicing at the 3′ end of a single mFcRII gene.

The second cDNA, designated α, was isolated from the J774 library and appears to encode the product of a distinct gene (Ravetch *et al.* 1986). The extracellular domain of this sequence is 95 % homologous to the β sequence, with isolated single amino acid changes (Fig. 3). The two immunoglobulin-like domains and four *N*-glycosylation sites remain intact. However, the putative membrane-spanning and cytoplasmic domains are totally non-homologous to either β sequence, nor do they bear striking similarity to any other known protein.

Northern blot analysis of mRNA from various cell lines using cDNA probes that would selectively detect either α or β sequences, has suggested that β-specific mRNA is transcribed in virtually all mFcRII-positive cells (macrophages, B cells and T cells) while α-specific message can be detected in variable amounts only in macrophage cell lines (Ravetch *et al.* 1986; Lewis *et al.* 1986; T. Koch *et al.*, unpublished results). Thus, while it is tempting to suggest that the α cDNA encodes the monomeric IgG2a receptor (mFcRI), whose expression also appears to be limited to mouse macrophages (Table 1), this is far from clear. Expression of protein from transfected α cDNA has proved unsuccessful (Ravetch *et al.* 1986; H. Miettinen *et al.*, unpublished results) and, in addition, no mFcRI-specific monoclonal antibodies are yet available. We have also been unable unequivocally to detect the

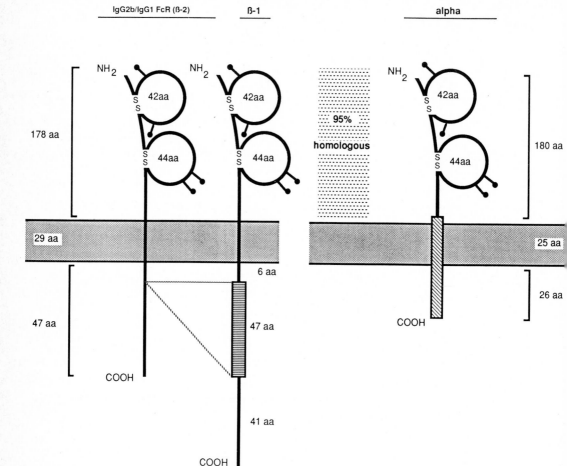

Fig. 3. The structure of three distinct murine Fc receptors deduced from cDNAs. The structures shown correspond to cDNAs encoding the β-2 (identical to pFcR13), the β-1 and the α isoforms of the receptor.

presence of protein corresponding to α even in cells possessing α-specific mRNA (see below).

Differential expression of murine Fc receptors

In order to understand the functional significance of the heterogeneity predicted by the three FcR cDNAs, we have sought to determine the pattern of FcR expression at the protein level in a variety of receptor-positive primary cells and continuous cell lines (T. Koch, H. Plutner, G. Healey, W. Hunziker & I. Mellman, unpublished results). Using synthetic mRNAs translated in the presence of dog pancreas microsomes, we have obtained the *in vitro* expression of protein corresponding to each of the three receptor cDNAs. A xenogeneic rabbit antiserum to mFcRII, which recognizes extracellularly oriented determinants, was found to immunoprecipitate the β-1, β-2, and α translation products. Each protein differed, as expected, in molecular weight (β-1 was 53K; β-2 was 47K; α was 45K). In contrast, the rat monoclonal antibody (C14, see above; Green *et al.* 1985) directed towards the receptor's cytoplasmic domain recognized β-1 and β-2 but not α, in accordance with the sequence differences between these receptor species (Fig. 3).

Having established that the three receptor isotypes could be distinguished on the basis of molecular weight and differential reactivity with anti-mFcRII antibodies, we next immunoprecipitated FcR from a variety of cell lines pulse-labelled with [^{35}S]methionine for 10 min, conditions which would label only immature RER forms corresponding exactly to those obtained by cell-free translation in the presence of microsomes. In the lymphocyte lines (A20/2J B cells; S49.1 T cells), and in the J774 macrophage line, β-1 was clearly the predominant receptor species synthesized although some lower molecular weight bands, including one corresponding in molecular weight to β-2, were also observed as minor components. In P388D$_1$ macrophages and in thioglycollate-elicited peritoneal macrophages, the predominant receptor species corresponded to β-2. By digesting the labelled microsomes with proteinase K prior to immunoprecipitation (Green *et al.* 1985), we were also able to show that the two receptor types differed only in the lengths of their cytoplasmic tails. The protease-protected fragments (i.e. extracellular and membrane-spanning domains) immunoprecipitated from digested microsomes of cells expressing β-1 or β-2 were of identical molecular weights. Importantly, all labelled bands irrespective of molecular weight were immunoprecipitated with equal efficiency by both antibodies; none corresponded in mobility to the translation product derived from the α cDNA. Thus, although the macrophages examined expressed transcripts that apparently contained α-specific sequences, functional expression of an α protein could not be detected. It is important to note that by analysing the precursor RER forms of the various receptors, these experiments should have detected intracellular α, even if it failed to be transported to the cell surface or was rapidly degraded after synthesis.

Although it is too early to conclude that the α-specific transcripts are 'sterile', i.e. unable to program the translation of protein, it is clear that the predominant form of mFcRII expressed by mouse macrophages and lymphocytes corresponds to either β-1 or β-2. Since macrophages and different macrophage cell lines were found to express either of the β-type proteins, it is conceivable that the presumptive splicing events leading to the production of one or the other FcR isoform is developmentally regulated.

The degree of heterogeneity observed in the cytoplasmic domains of these receptors is both striking and unprecedented. It was also unexpected since the involvement of FcR in endocytic and transmembrane signalling events suggested *a priori* that there might have been considerable selection pressure to conserve cytoplasmically oriented sequences. Determining the functional consequences of these naturally occurring site-directed mutagenesis 'experiments' will be of considerable interest (see below).

Functional expression of mFcRII

As mentioned earlier, it has been possible to obtain both transient and permanent expression of mFcRII using β-1 and β-2 cDNAs transfected into COS or CHO cells (H. Miettinen *et al.*, unpublished results). In the permanent CHO lines, cell surface expression is uniform and efficient ($2-8\times10^5$ per cell), approximating the quantities of receptor normally produced by macrophages. Importantly, the transfected receptor appears to be functionally active, at least with respect to endocytosis. When expressed in either CHO or COS cells, the β-2 form of the receptor is capable of mediating the binding, internalization, and delivery to lysosomes of immune complexes in a fashion similar to that observed in macrophages. Using permanently expressing cell lines, we have even been able to document that the kinetics of endocytosis of the receptor and ligand also appear normal. By showing that receptor binding and endocytosis can occur in fibroblast cell lines, which normally do not express FcR, these observations demonstrate that the functional mFcRII activity does not require the involvement of any other macrophage- or lymphocyte-specific proteins.

In an attempt to identify which domains are important for the various functional activities of the receptor, we have already begun generating a series of mutant and hybrid receptors using site-directed mutagenesis. A permanent CHO cell line has been generated using one such mutant, from which the entire cytoplasmic tail (following the first cytoplasmic lysine) was deleted. Using both immunofluorescence and quantitative assays for immune complex uptake, it appears that this deletion substantially interferes with the ability of the mutant receptor to mediate internalization and/or delivery to lysosomes. Thus, the FcR's cytoplasmic tail, although capable of considerable sequence heterogeneity, appears to be necessary for endocytosis. It is yet not clear, however, whether it is the initial internalization step or the subsequent transport from endosomes to lysosomes that is blocked in the mutant cell lines.

Structure and cDNA cloning of human Fc receptors (hFcR)

Given the unexpected heterogeneity observed among murine FcR, it has become of considerable interest to isolate and characterize cDNA clones encoding the homologous human FcR. Human monocytes, granulocytes, and lymphocytes are well known to express at least three distinct FcR types (Table 1) (Anderson & Looney, 1986). The first of these, hFcRI, is a 70K high-affinity receptor for monomeric IgG recognized by the monoclonal antibody 32 (Anderson, 1982; Cohen *et al.* 1983). It is found only on monocytes and macrophages and is thus thought to be directly homologous to mFcRI, i.e. the monomeric IgG2a receptor. hFcRII, like mFcRII, is more widely distributed and exhibits a low affinity for monomeric IgG. It is detected by two monoclonal antibodies (IV.3 and Ku67), which immunoprecipitate a narrow 40K glycoprotein (Looney *et al.* 1986; Vaughn *et al.* 1985). While there is no known human FcR homologous to the murine IgG3 receptor, a third hFcR (hFcR-N) has been identified on granulocytes and to a lesser extent on macrophages (Fleit *et al.*

Table 2. *Sequence homology between mouse and human Fc receptors by domain*

Mouse FcR isoform	Human FcR domain			
	Signal	Extracellular	Transmembrane	Cytoplasmic
Alpha cDNA	70%	65%	N.S.	N.S.
β-1 cDNA	N.S.	70%	50%	N.S.
IgG2b/1 FcR (β-2)	N.S.	70%	50%	N.S.

N.S., no statistically significant amino acid homology.

1982). This receptor exhibits a very low affinity for IgG and is immunoprecipitated by several monoclonal antibodies as a heterogeneous glycoprotein band of 40–70K (Perussia *et al.* 1984; Fleit *et al.* 1982).

Using the β-2 cDNA pFcR13 as a probe, we have recently isolated and characterized a cDNA encoding a highly homologous FcR from the U937 human monocyte cell line (Stuart *et al.* 1987). Expression of this cDNA (referred to as 16.2) by transfection in fibroblasts produces a 40K glycoprotein that reacts with the anti-hFcRII reagent IV.3. A monoclonal anti-peptide antibody specific to a synthetic peptide encoding a portion of the predicted amino acid sequence, recognizes IV.3-positive cells and not IV.3-negative cells.

The amino acid sequence deduced from this cDNA is strikingly similar to both the α and β forms of murine FcR (Table 2). The extracellular domain of the human FcR is 70% homologous to both murine sequences. The two immunoglobulin-like domains are exactly conserved, although two of the four *N*-linked glycosylation sites found in the murine sequences have been lost by amino acid substitution. At the same time, however, the human receptor is somewhat chimeric in nature. Its predicted signal sequence, as well as the 5′ untranslated region of clone 16.2, are decidedly 'α-like', although the membrane spanning domain is 50% homologous to murine β and thus completely distinct from α. Most interestingly, especially in view of the considerable sequence heterogeneity found amoung the murine FcR cDNAs, the cytoplasmic tail of the human FcR is completely unique, being unlike either α, β or any other known protein sequence.

While the expression data and the sequence of the extracellular and membrane spanning domains indicate that the human receptor encoded by clone 16.2 is directly homologous to mFcRII, the differences in their cytoplasmic domains suggest that these two molecules may be functionally distinct. Presumably, hFcRII and mFcRII should mediate more or less identical activities in human and murine monocytes. Thus, the divergence in sequence may indicate that considerable sequence plasticity can be tolerated in the FcR cytoplasmic domain or that other hFcRII-like cDNAs have yet to be isolated. While further attempts to isolate such cDNAs from the U937 library have proved unsuccessful, we have recently identified two additional cDNAs from a human placental cDNA library (S. Stuart, N. Simister *et al.*, unpublished results). Although originally screened to identify cDNAs corresponding to the syncytiotrophoblast FcR, which mediates the transcellular transport of maternal

IgG, the deduced sequences obtained are strikingly similar to sequences characteristic of macrophage-lymphocyte FcR. Presumably, these cDNAs were derived from placental macrophages (e.g. Hofbauer cells) or lymphocytes as opposed to placental epithelial cells. One of these predicts a sequence, which is very similar to that encoded by 16.2, with only a few amino acid substitutions, except that it has a distinct 3′ untranslated region. The second, however, is directly homologous to the murine β FcR sequences throughout, i.e. the cytoplasmic domains of the human and murine receptors are similar.

Further characterization of the expression of these molecules, as well as the analysis of the functional activities associated with them, will be needed to appreciate the significance of this extended but closely related family of membrane receptors. Such information will be of obvious importance to understand the functions of FcR on leukocytic cells. In addition, however, it will also provide some fundamental insights into the problems of receptor function in general, given the almost unprecedented variation in the cytoplasmic domains of this family of otherwise monotypic cell surface receptors.

This work was supported by grants from the National Institutes of Health (GM-29765; GM-33904 to IM). WH is a fellow of the Damon Runyon-Walter Winchell Cancer Fund. DV is the recipient of awards from the Leslie Warner and Argall Hull Foundations.

References

ADEREM, A., KEUM, M. M., PURE, E. & COHN, Z. A. (1986). Bacterial lipopolysaccharides, phorbol myristate acetate, and zymosan induce the myristoylation of specific macrophage proteins. *Proc. natn. Acad. Sci. U.S.A.* **83**, 5817–5821.

ANDERSON, C. L. (1982). Isolation of the receptor from a human monocyte cell line (U937) and from human peripheral blood monocytes. *J. exp. Med.* **156**, 1794–1805.

ANDERSON, C. L. & LOONEY, R. J. (1986). Human leukocyte IgG Fc receptors. *Immunol. Today* **7**, 264–266.

BALFOUR, A. H. & JONES, E. A. (1978). Properties of receptors for IgG on human placental cell membranes. *Int. Archs. Allergy* **56**, 435–442.

BARCLAY, A. N., JOHNSON, P., McCAUGHAN, G. W. & WILLIAMS, A. F. (1987). Immunoglobulin-related structures associated with vertebrate cell surfaces. In *The T-Cell Receptors* (ed. T. W. Mak). New York: Plenum Press (in press).

BIJSTERBOSCH, M. K. & KLAUS, G. G. B. (1985). Cross-linking of surface immunoglobulin and Fc receptors on B lymphocytes inhibits stimulation of inositol phospholipid breakdown via the antigen receptor. *J. exp. Med.* **162**, 1825–1836.

BOYLE, M. D. P. (1984). Applications of bacterial Fc receptors in immunotechnology. *Biotechniques* **Nov/Dec**, 334–339.

BRADTZAEG, P. (1981). Transport models for secretory IgA and secretory IgM. *Clin. exp. Immunol.* **44**, 221–232.

CIOCO, R. F., XUE, B., WALLACE, D., PERNIS, B., SISKIND, G. W. & THORBECKE, G. J. (1985). T cells with receptors for IgD. *Nature, Lond.* **316**, 744–746.

COHEN, L., SHARP, S. & KULCZYCKI, A. JR (1983). Human monocytes, B lymphocytes and non-B lymphocytes each have structurally unique Fc gamma receptors. *J. Immun.* **131**, 378–382.

CONRAD, D. H. & PETERSON, L. H. (1984). The murine lymphocyte receptor for IgE. I. Isolation and characterization of the murine B cell Fc epsilon receptor and comparison with Fc epsilon receptors from rat and human. *J. Immun.* **132**, 796–803.

COOPER, S. M. & SAMBRAY, Y. (1977). Characterization of the Fc receptors of the murine leukemia L1210. *J. supramolec. Struct.* **6**, 591–597.

COSTA, J., YEE, C., NAKAMURA, Y. & RABSON, A. (1978). Characteristics of Fc receptor induced by herpes simplex virus. *Intervirology* **10**, 32–39.

DIAMOND, B. & YELTON, D. E. (1981). A new Fc receptor on mouse macrophages binding IgG3. *J. exp. Med.* **153**, 514–519.

DICKLER, H. B. (1976). Lymphocyte receptors for immunoglobulin. *Adv. Immunol.* **24**, 167–213.

DIVIRGILIO, F., MEYER, B. C., GREENBURG, S. & SILVERSTEIN, S. C. (1988). Fc receptor-mediated phagocytosis occurs in macrophages at exceedingly low Ca^{2+} levels. *J. Cell Biol.* **106**, 657–666.

FLEIT, H. B., WRIGHT, S. D. & UNKELESS, J. C. (1982). Human neutrophil Fc g receptor distribution and structure. *Proc. natn. Acad. Sci. U.S.A.* **79**, 3275–3279.

FRIDMAN, W. H. & GOLSTEIN, P. (1974). Immunoglobulin-binding factor present on and produced by thymus-processes lymphocytes (T-cells). *Cell Immunol.* **11**, 442–455.

FRIDMAN, W. H., RABOURDIN-COMBE, C., NEAUPORT, SAUTES, C. & GISLER, R. H. (1984). Characterization and function of T cell Fc gamma receptor. *Immunol. Rev.* **56**, 51–88.

GREEN, S. A., PLUTNER, H. & MELLMAN, I. (1985). Biosynthesis and intracellular transport of the mouse macrophage Fc receptor. *J. biol. Chem.* **260**, 9867–9874.

HEALICON, R. M. & FOREMAN, J. C. (1984). Receptors for immunoglobulin E (IgE). In *The Receptors, Vol. I*, pp. 83–140. New York: Academic Press.

HELENIUS, A., MELLMAN, I., WALL, D. A. & HUBBARD, A. C. (1983). Endosomes. *Trends Biochem. Sci.* **8**, 245–250.

HEMPERLY, J. J., MURRAY, B. A., EDELMAN, G. M. & CUNNINGHAM, B. A. (1986). Sequence of a cDNA clone encoding the polysialic acid-rich and cytoplasmic domains of the neural cell adhesion molecule N-CAM. *Proc. natn. Acad. Sci. U.S.A.* **83**, 3037–3041.

HOOVER, R. G., DIECKGRAEFE, B. K. & LYNCH, R. G. (1981). T cells with Fc receptors for IgA: Induction of T alpha cells in vivo and in vitro by purified IgA. *J. Immun.* **127**, 1560–1563.

HOWE, C. L., GRANGER, B. L., HULL, M., GREEN, S. A., GABEL, C., HELENIUS, A. & MELLMAN, I. (1988). Protein sequence, oligosaccharides, and membrane insertion of Igp120: Identification of a highly conserved family of lysosomal membrane glycoproteins. *Proc. natn. Acad. Sci. U.S.A.* (in press).

ISHIZAKA, K. (1984). Regulation of IgE synthesis. *A. Rev. Immunol.* **2**, 159–182.

KIKUTANI, H., INUI, S., SATO, R., BARSUMIAN, E. L., OWAKI, H., YAMASAKI, K., KAISHO, T., UCHIBAYASHI, N., HARDY, R. R., HIRANO, T., TSUNASAWA, S., SAKIYAMA, F., SUEMURA, M. & KISHIMOTO, T. (1986). Molecular structure of human lymphocyte receptor for immunoglobulin E. *Cell* **47**, 657–665.

KINET, J.-P., METZGER, H., HAKIMI, J. & KOICHAN, J. (1987). A cDNA presumptively coding for the α subunit of the receptor with high affinity for IgE. *Biochemistry* **26**, 4605–4610.

KUHN, L. C. & KRAEHENBUHL, J.-P. (1982). The sacrificial receptor-translocation of polymeric IgA across epithelia. *Trends Biochem. Sci.* **7**, 299–302.

LANGONE, J. J. (1982). Protein A from staphylococcus aureus and related immunoglobulin receptors produced by streptococci & pneumococci. *Adv. Immunol.* **32**, 157–252.

LEWIS, V. A., KOCH, T., PLUTNER, H. & MELLMAN, I. (1986). Characterization of a cDNA clone for a mouse macrophage-lymphocyte Fc receptor. *Nature, Lond.* **324**, 372–375.

LITEPLO, R. G., SHAW, A. R. & SCHALAMOWITZ, M. (1982). Partial purification of fetal rabbit yolk sac membrane Fc receptor. *J. Immun.* **129**, 2573–2579.

LIU, F.-T., ALBRANDT, K., MENDEL, E., KULCZYCKI, A., JR & ORIDA, N. K. (1985). Identification of an IgE-binding protein by molecular cloning. *Proc. natn. Acad. Sci. U.S.A.* **82**, 4100–4104.

LOONEY, R. J., ABRAHAM, G. N. & ANDERSON, C. L. (1986). Human monocytes and U937 cells bear two distinct Fc receptors for IgG. *J. Immun.* **136**, 1641–1647.

LOUBE, S. R. & DORRINGTON, K. J. (1980). Isolation of biosynthetically labeled Fc-binding proteins from detergent lysates and spent culture fluid of a macrophage-like cell line (P388D$_1$). *J. Immun.* **125**, 970–975.

LYDYARD, P. M. & FANGER, M. W. (1982). Characteristics and function of Fc receptors on human lymphocytes. *Immunology* **47**, 1–17.

MARTENS, C. L., HUFF, T. F., JARDIEU, P., TROUNSTINE, M. L., COFFMAN, R. L., ISHIZAKA, K. & MOORE, K. W. (1985). cDNA clones encoding IgE-binding factors from a rat-mouse T-cell hybridoma. *Proc. natn. Acad. Sci. U.S.A.* **82**, 2460–2464.

MATRE, R., HAAHEIM, L. R. & TONDER, O. (1984). A monoclonal antibody inhibiting human placental Fc gamma-receptor activity. *Int. Archs. Allergy appl. Immun.* **75**, 227–229.

MELLMAN, I., FUCHS, R. & HELENIUS, A. (1986). Acidification of endocytic and exocytic pathways. *A. Rev. Biochem.* **55**, 663–700.

MELLMAN, I., HOWE, C. & HELENIUS, A. (1987). The control of membrane traffic on the endocytic pathway. *Curr. Top. membr. Transport* **29**, 255–288.

MELLMAN, I. & PLUTNER, H. (1984). Internalization and degradation of macrophage Fc receptors bound to polyvalent immune complexes. *J. Cell Biol.* **98**, 1170–1177.

MELLMAN, I., PLUTNER, H., STEINMAN, R. M., UNKELESS, J. C. & COHN, Z. A. (1983). Internalization and degradation of macrophage Fc receptors during receptor-mediated phagocytosis. *J. Cell Biol.* **96**, 887–895.

MELLMAN, I., PLUTNER, H. & UKKONEN, P. (1984). Internalization and rapid recycling of macrophage Fc receptors tagged with monovalent anti-receptor antibody: possible role of a prelysosomal compartment. *J. Cell Biol.* **98**, 1163–1169.

MELLMAN, I. & UNKELESS, J. C. (1980). Purification of a functional mouse Fc receptor through the use of a monoclonal antibody. *J. exp. Med.* **152**, 1048–1069.

METZGER, H. (1984). The receptor on mast cells and related cells with high affinity for IgE. *Contemp. Top. molec. Immunol.* **9**, 115–145.

MORETTA, L., FERRARINI, M., DURANTE, M. L. & MINGARI, M. C. (1975). Expression of a receptor for IgM by human T cells *in vitro. Eur. J. Immunol.* **5**, 565–569.

MOSTOV, K. E., FREIDLANDER, M. & BLOBEL, G. (1984). The receptor for transepithelial transport of IgA and IgM contains multiple Ig-like domains. *Nature, Lond.* **308**, 37–43.

NEAUPORT-SAUTES, C., RABOURDIN-COMBE, C. & FRIDMAN, W. H. (1979). T-cell hybrids bear Fcγ receptors and secrete suppressor immunoglobulin binding factors. *Nature, Lond.* **227**, 656–662.

NIEZGODKA, M., MIKULSKA, J., UGORSKI, M., BORATYNSKI, J. & LISOWSKI, J. (1981). Human placental membrane receptor for IgG: Studies on properties and solubilization of the receptor. *Molec. Immunol.* **18**, 163–172.

OGATA, M. & SIGETA, S. (1979). Appearance of IgG Fc receptors in cultured human cells infected with varicellazoster virus. *Infect. Immunol.* **26**, 770–776.

O'SULLIVAN, D. M., NOONAN, D. & QUARANTA, V. (1987). Four Ia invariant chain forms derive from a single gene by alternate splicing and alternate initiation of transcription/translation. *J. exp. Med.* **166**, 444–460.

PARA, M. F., BAUCKE, R. B. & SPEAR, P. G. (1980). IgG(Fc)-binding receptors on virions of herpes simplex virus type I and the transfer of these receptors to the cell surface by infection. *J. Virol.* **34**, 512–520.

PERUSSIA, B., ACUTO, O., TERHORST, C., FAUST, J. & LAZARUS, R. (1983). Human natural killer cells analyzed by B73.1, a monoclonal antibody blocking Fc receptor functions. *J. Immun.* **130**, 2142–2148.

PETER, H. H., PAVIE-FISCHER, J., FRIDMAN, W., AUBERT, C., CESARINI, J.-P., ROUBIN, R. & KOURILSKY, F. M. (1975). Cell-mediated cytotoxicity in vitro of human lymphocytes against a tissue culture melanoma cell line (IGR3). *J. Immun.* **115**, 539–548.

PFEFFERKORN, L. C. (1984). Transmembrane signaling: An ion-flux-independent model for signal transduction by complexed Fc receptors. *J. Cell Biol.* **99**, 2231–2240.

PHILLIPS, N. E. & PARKER, D. C. (1984). Cross-linking of B lymphocyte Fc-gamma receptors and membrane immunoglobulin inhibits blastogenesis. *J. Immun.* **132**, 627–632.

PITUCH-NOWOROLSKA, A., NOWOROLSKA, J., PRYJMA, J. & ZEMBALA, M. (1985). The role of shed Fc receptor in the regulation of lymphocyte response to phytohemagglutin (PHA). *Immunology* **55**, 693–701.

PURE, E., DURIE, C. J., SUMMERILL, C. K. & UNKELESS, J. C. (1984). Identification of soluble Fc receptors in mouse serum and the conditioned medium of stimulated B cells. *J. exp. Med.* **160**, 1836–1849.

PURE, E., WITMER, M. D., LUM, J. B., MELLMAN, I. & UNKELESS, J. C. (1987). Properties of a second epitope of the murine Fc receptor for aggregated IgG. *J. Immun.* (in press).

RAVETCH, J. V., LUSTER, A. D., WEINSHANK, R., KOCHAN, J., PAVLOVEC, A., PORTNOY, D. A., HULMES, J., PAN, Y.-C. E. & UNKELESS, J. C. (1986). Structural heterogeneity and functional domains of murine immunoglobulin G Fc receptors. *Science* **234**, 718–725.

RODEWALD, R., LEWIS, D. M. & KRAEHENBUHL, J.-P. (1983). IgG receptors of intestinal brush borders from neonatal rats. In *Brush Border Membranes* (Ciba Foundation Symposium No. 95), pp. 287–299. Pitman Books, Ltd.

ROUBIN, R. & ZOLLA-PAZNER, S. (1979). Markers of macrophage heterogeneity. I. Studies of macrophages from various organs of normal mice. *Eur. J. Immunol.* **19**, 972–978.

ROUZER, C. A., SCOTT, W. A., KEMPE, J. & COHN, Z. A. (1980). Prostaglandin synthesis by macrophages requires a specific receptor-ligand interaction. *Proc. natn. Acad. Sci. U.S.A.* **77**, 4279–4282.

SAKUMA, S., FURUKAWA, T. & PLOTKIN, S. A. (1977). The characterization of IgG receptor induced by human ctomegalovirus. *Proc. Soc. exp. Biol. Med.* **155**, 168–172.

SIMISTER, N. E. & REES, A. R. (1985). Isolation and characterization of an Fc receptor from neonatal rat small intestine. *Eur. J. Immunol.* **15**, 733–738.

SPIEGELBERG, H. L. (1981). Lymphocytes bearing Fc receptors for IgE. *Immunol. Rev.* **56**, 199–218.

STEINMAN, R. M., MELLMAN, I. S., MULLER, W. A. & COHN, Z. A. (1983). Endocytosis and the recycling of plasma membrane. *J. Cell Biol.* **96**, 1–27.

STUART, S. G., TROUNSTINE, M. L., VAUX, D. J. T., KOCH, T., MARTENS, C. L., MELLMAN, I. & MOORE, K. W. (1987). Isolation and expression of cDNA clones encoding a human receptor for IgG (FcRII). *J. exp. Med.* (in press).

UKKONEN, P., LEWIS, V., MARSH, M., HELENIUS, A. & MELLMAN, I. (1986). Transport of macrophage Fc receptors and Fc receptor-bound ligands to lysosomes. *J. exp. Med.* **163**, 952–971.

UNKELESS, J. C. (1977). The presence of two Fc receptors on murine macrophages: evidence from a varient cell line and differential trypsin sensitivity. *J. exp. Med.* **145**, 931–947.

UNKELESS, J. C. (1979). Characterization of a monoclonal antibody directed against mouse macrophage and lymphocyte Fc receptors. *J. exp. Med.* **150**, 580–596.

UNKELESS, J. C., FLEIT, H. & MELLMAN, I. S. (1981). Structural aspects and heterogeneity of immunoglobulin Fc receptors. *Adv. Immunol.* **31**, 247–270.

VAUGHN, M., TAYLOR, M. & MOHANAKUMAR, T. (1985). Characterization of human IgG Fc receptors. *J. Immun.* **135**, 4059–4065.

WIGER, D. & MICHAELSON, T. E. (1985). Binding site and subclass specificity of the herpes simplex virus type 1-induced Fc receptor. *Immunology* **54**, 565–572.

YEE, C., COSTE, J., HAMILTON, V., KLEIN, G. & RABSON, A. S. (1982). Changes in the expression of Fc receptors produced by induction of Epstein-Barr virus in lymphoma cell lines. *Virology* **120**, 376–381.

YOUNG, J. D.-E., KO, S. S. & COHN, Z. A. (1984). The increase in intracellular free calcium associated with Fc receptor-ligand interaction: role in phagocytosis. *Proc. natn. Acad. Sci. U.S.A.* **81**, 5430–5434.

YOUNG, J. D.-E., UNKELESS, J. C., YOUNG, T. M., MAURO, A. & COHN, Z. A. (1983). Role of mouse macrophage IgG Fc receptor as ligand-dependent ion channel. *Nature, Lond.* **306**, 186–189.

J. Cell Sci. Suppl. 9, 67–97 (1988)
Printed in Great Britain © The Company of Biologists Limited 1988

C3 receptors on macrophages

S. K. ALEX LAW

MRC Immunochemistry Unit, Department of Biochemistry, University of Oxford, South Parks Road, Oxford, OX1 3QU, UK

Summary

The complement receptors on macrophage are responsible for their binding and ingestion of opsonized targets. The two established receptors are CR1, which recognizes C3b, and CR3, which recognizes iC3b, the natural product of C3b from cleavage by the complement control protein factor I and its cofactors. CR1 belongs to a group of proteins that contain a structural element characterized by its size of 60–65 amino acids, and four conservatively positioned cysteines, which engage in a self-contained 1–3, 2–4 disulphide arrangement. This structural unit is called SCR (short consensus repeat) and is found in the complement proteins C1r, C1s, C2, factor B, factor H, C4BP, DAF, MCP and CR2, each of which interacts with some cleavage products of C3 and/or C4. CR1 has 30 SCR units accounting for its entire extracellular structure. It has a transmembrane segment and a small cytoplasmic domain. CR3 is a heterodimer containing an α and β subunit held together by non-covalent forces. The β subunit is also found in the two leukocyte antigens, LFA-1 and p150,95, which have α subunits distinct from that of CR3. The β subunit contains 56 cysteine residues, 42 of which lie in a span of 256 residues immediately adjacent to the transmembrane segment. It shares extensive sequence homology with subunits of membrane protein complexes that bind fibronectin and vitronectin, implicating that they all belong to an extended set of surface adhesion molecules not restricted to the immune system. p150,95 is also expressed on macrophages and it has iC3b binding activity. It also shares some functional properties with CR3 as an ahesion surface molecule.

Introduction

The complement proteins are the effector molecules of the humoral immune system. To date, more than 20 proteins have been identified and classified as members of this group. Apart from the nine classical components, C1–C9, other proteins include the activation components of the alternative pathway and the control proteins, which keep the complement system finely tuned to mediate and coordinate various processes in host defence and inflammation. Of all the components, C3 occupies the pivotal position in the system, for its activation to yield the anaphylatoxin, C3a, and C3b, which binds covalently to target cells, is the point at which the classical and the alternative pathways converge. (For a review on the activation of complement, see Reid, 1986.) Cells coated with C3b can either be lysed by the terminal components, C5–C9, or be ingested by phagocytic cells, which have specific receptors for C3b and its cleavage products. Two of these receptors have been characterized on the plasma membrane of macrophages. They are the complement receptor type 1 (CR1), earlier known as the C3b receptor or the C3b/C4b complement receptor, and complement receptor type 3 (CR3, also referred to by its antigenic properties as the Mac-1 or Mo1 antigen), which recognizes iC3b, the cleavage product of C3b by factor I and its cofactors.

The interaction between surface-bound complement components and membrane molecules on blood cells was first formalized in 1953 by R. A. Nelson, who used the term immune adherence to describe the attachment of microorganisms sensitized with antibody and complement to human erythrocytes. The complement-dependent adherence was also recognized to have an enhancing effect on the phagocytosis of the target. Subsequent work by Nelson and colleagues extended the term immune adherence to describe the attachment of complement-treated targets to primate erythrocytes and non-primate platelets (Siqueira & Nelson, 1961). This adherence phenomenon was not observed with non-primate erythrocytes and primate platelets. (For review of earlier work, see D. S. Nelson, 1963.) Clearly, some factors in the complement system and corresponding ones on erythrocyte and platelet surfaces were responsible for the phenomenon of immune adherence. The factor in the complement system was identified first.

Nishioka & Linscott (1963) reported a subcomponent of C'3 from guinea-pig serum as being essential for the immune adherence reaction. They called it C'3c in order to distinguish it from the other three subcomponents, C'3a, C'3b and C'3d. Two more subcomponents of C'3 were found when Nelson et al. (1966) purified the nine components of guinea-pig complement and delineated the activation steps of the classical pathway. C'3c was renamed as C'3 (see Müller-Eberhard, 1968) and later as C3. In the same period, the third component in the human complement system was identified as the β1C-glycoprotein (Müller-Eberhard & Nilsson, 1960; Müller-Eberhard et al. 1966).

Introduction of the rosetting technique to study the adherence of complement-coated sheep erythrocytes to different cell types allowed Lay & Nussenzweig (1968) to determine the presence or absence of C3 receptors on the surface of these cells. It also enabled them to identify functionally two distinct types of C3 receptors. The adherence of C3-bearing sheep erythrocytes to lymphocytes could take place in the presence of EDTA, whereas their adherence to monocytes required the presence of Mg^{2+}.

Progress towards the classification of C3 receptors was made in the early 1970s by studying their distribution on different classes of leukocytes and their roles in various physiological responses including phagocytosis (for review see Bianco & Nussenzweig, 1977). During this period there were parallel advances in the description of the molecular structure of C3 and its degradation products. The view that C3b was cleaved by factor I (then known as the C3b inactivator) into C3c and C3d was re-evaluated by establishing the existence of a stable intermediate product, iC3b (see below). The covalent nature of the bond between the labile binding site of C3b and cell surface structures was also clarified (Law & Levine, 1977). It was only then that cells bearing structurally defined C3 fragments could be prepared (Law et al, 1979; Carlo et al. 1979) and it was thus possible to demonstrate that receptors for C3b, iC3b and C3d were distinct (Carlo et al. 1979).

The investigation of receptors at the molecular level began with the purification of CR1 by Fearon (1979). Subsequently, the polypeptide structures of the receptors for C3d (Barel et al. 1981) and iC3b (Wright et al. 1983a), now known as CR2 and CR3, respectively, were identified (see Table 1). Techniques involving the use of monoclonal antibodies and recombinant DNA, as well as the availability of cell lines expressing various complement receptors, contributed much to the purification and structural characterization of these molecules. Other membrane proteins having an affinity for C3 were also discovered (see below and also Ross & Medof, 1985; Sim & Walport, 1987). Before discussing the details of the structure of the receptor molecules, however, it is essential to have an appreciation for the molecular structure of their ligands C3, C4 and their cleavage products.

The structure of C3, C4 and their cleavage products (Fig. 1)

C3

Native C3 in plasma consists of two disulphide cross-linked polypeptides α and β of molecular weights 115K and 75K ($K = 10^3 M_r$) respectively (Bokisch *et al.* 1975; Nilsson *et al.* 1975). An internal thioester is located in the α chain between the cysteine and glutamine residues in a sequence Cys–Gly–Glu–Gln (Tack *et al.* 1980). Upon activation, a fragment of 77 amino acids, C3a, is removed from the N terminus of the α chain (Müller-Eberhard *et al.* 1966; Hugli, 1975). The cleavage event induces a conformational change in the remainder of the protein, C3b, resulting in the exposure of the thioester, which becomes extremely reactive with hydroxyl nucleophiles. Thus if C3 is activated by a surface-bound enzyme, known as C3-convertase, in the complement system, a portion of the C3b generated will become covalently bound to the cell surface by reacting with surface-bound hydroxyl groups to form acyl ester bonds. For the majority of the activated C3b molecules, their thioester will be hydrolysed, thus yielding fluid-phase C3b. (For review of the covalent binding reaction, see Law, 1983.) The ratio between bound and fluid-phase C3b depends upon the type of cell surface on which activation takes place; both the surface density of the acceptor molecules and the reactivity of the hydroxyl groups on them play a role in the overall binding efficiency of C3b. Under artificial, experimental conditions, for example the binding of C3 to sheep erythrocytes or zymosan, a value of 10 % is generally accepted.

Both fluid-phase and surface-bound C3b are cleaved by factor I in the presence of cofactors. To date, three molecules are known to have the cofactor activity for this reaction. They are factor H (previously known as the β1H-globulin) (Whaley & Ruddy, 1976*a,b*; Pangburn *et al.* 1977), membrane cofactor protein (MCP, previously referred to as gp45–70) (Seya *et al.* 1986*a*), and CR1 (Fearon, 1979). Two sites on the α' chain of C3b, marked as I1 and I2 in Fig. 1A, are cleaved sequentially to generate fragments of sizes 63K, 3K, and 40K in that order from the N terminus (Harrison & Lachmann, 1980; Sim *et al.* 1981). The 3K fragment (C3f) is free and what remains is a three-chain disulphide cross-linked structure composed of the 63K and 40K polypeptides of the α' chain and the intact β chain. This molecule is referred to as iC3b (previously also referred to as C3b' or C3bi). If generated from surface-bound C3b, iC3b remains covalently linked to the cell surface *via* the 63K fragment (Law *et al.* 1979).

Table 1. *C3 receptors and other C3-binding membrane proteins*

Protein	Other names	Differentiation antigen nomenclature	$M_r \times 10^{-3}$	Ligand	Major human cell types[†]		References[‡]
					Positive	Negative	
CR1	C3b receptor, C3b/C4b receptor	CD35	220	C3b,C4b	E,B,G,M	P	Fearon (1985)
CR2	C3d receptor, EBV virus receptor	CD21	140	C3dg,iC3b	B	E,G,M,φ	Fingeroth et al. (1984), Tedder et al. (1984)
CR3	Mac-1 antigen, iC3b receptor	α, CD11b; β, CD18	α, 160; β, 95	iC3b	G,M,φ	E,B,T	Sanchez-Madrid et al. (1983)
CR4-1				C3dg,iC3b	B,N,P	T,M	Vik & Fearon (1987)
CR4-2	p150,95	α,CD11c; β, CD18	α, 150; β, 95	iC3b	G,M,φ	F,B,T	Hogg et al. (1986)
MCP	Membrane-cofactor protein, gp45-70		45–70	(C3b,C4b)§	B,T,N,M	E	Seya et al. (1987)
DAF	Decay accelerating factor		70	(C3b,C4b)§	E,L,P		Kinoshita et al. (1985)
H(M)	Membrane-bound Factor H		155	C3b	( )¶		Malhotra & Sim (1985), Schulz et al. (1984)
p90			90	iC3b	( )‖		Micklem & Sim (1985)

* From Appendix E, *Leukocyte Typing III: White Cell Differentiation Antigens* (ed. A. J. McMichael), p. 1029. Oxford, New York, Tokyo: Oxford University Press.

† Human cell types: E, erythrocytes; B, B lymphocytes; T, T lymphocytes; M, monocytes; φ, macrophages; G, granulocytes; N, neutrophils; L, leukocytes; P, platelets.

‡ The references are primarily for cell distributions. Others are quoted in the text.

§ By virtue of their activity either as a cofactor for factor I mediated breakdown of C3b and C4b or as a factor to accelerate the dissociation of the enzymes C3bBb and C4b2a.

¶ Found on cell lines Raji and U937 as well as tonsil lymphocytes.

‖ Found in detergent extract from spleen.

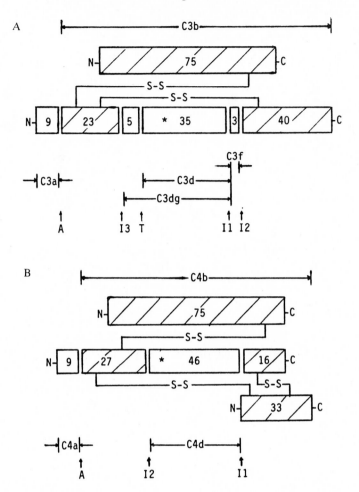

Fig. 1. C3, C4 and their cleavage products. A. C3, the two chains of C3, α and β, are shown with the interchain disulphide bonds as determined by Janatova (1986). Molecular weight of each fragment is expressed as $M_r \times 10^{-3}$ as derived from de Bruijn & Fey (1985). The thioester site is shown as an asterisk. The cleavage sites are marked: A, the convertase cleavage site to generate C3a and C3b; I1, I2, and I3, the factor I cleavage sites to generate iC3b′, iC3b and C3f, and C3c and C3dg; T, the trypsin cleavage site to produce C3d. The polypeptide chains of C3c are cross-hatched. B. C4, the three chains of C4, α, β and γ, are shown with the interchain disulphide bonds according to Janatova (1986) and Seya *et al.* (1986b). Molecular weight of each fragment ($M_r \times 10^{-3}$) as derived from Belt *et al.* (1984). The thioester site is shown as an asterisk. The cleavage sites are marked: A, the C1 cleavage site to generate C4a and C4b; I1, the factor I cleavage site to produce iC4b; I2, the factor I cleavage site to yield C4c and C4d. The polypeptide chains of C4c are cross-hatched.

iC3b can be further degraded into smaller fragments by different proteolytic enzymes. In serum, where protease inhibitors are in abundance, iC3b is relatively stable. In the laboratory, proteases such as trypsin are used to assist its subsequent cleavages. Two major fragments are generally obtained and are loosely referred to as

C3c and C3d. With most proteases, there are additional cleavage sites on C3c. Thus the structure of C3c, with a protease-dependent variable number of polypeptides held together as a single molecule by disulphide bonds and non-covalent forces, has usually not been analysed in detail. C3d, however, is invariably found as a single polypeptide containing both the covalent binding site and the classical D antigen (West *et al.* 1966; Law *et al.* 1979). Most relevant for the purpose of this review is the fact that C3d contains the recognition site for CR2. When generated with trypsin, C3d has a size of about 35K.

The physiological breakdown products of iC3b have been studied by prolonged incubation of blood or serum in which the complement system has been artificially activated by immune aggregates or cobra venom factor (Davis *et al.* 1984; Janatova & Gobel, 1985). The larger product of C3 degradation is again referred to as C3c, but the smaller one is called C3dg in order to distinguish it from C3d generated by exogenous enzymes. It is larger than the trypsin-generated C3d by 48 residues in the N terminus and is electrophoretically different (Lachmann *et al.* 1982). Presumably, C3dg is identical to the α_2D fragments described by West *et al.* (1966) (Lachmann *et al.* 1982; Davis *et al.* 1984). C3c generated this way contains three disulphide-linked polypeptides, the intact β chain, the N-terminal 23K fragment and C-terminal 40K fragment of the α' chain (Davis *et al.* 1984; Janatova & Gobel, 1985). Analysis of C3 fragments from the serum of a patient with circulating C3 cleavage products showed fragment sizes different from the above, suggesting the natural degradation of iC3b is likely to be more complicated (Davis *et al.* 1984). The enzyme(s) responsible for the conversion of iC3b to C3c and C3dg has not been identified. However, the extent of conversion is different in activated serum and activated whole blood. Whereas variable amounts of residual iC3b are found in activated serum, the generation of C3c and C3dg in activated blood always appears to proceed to completion. These observations suggest that the enzyme(s) mediating this reaction could be of cellular origin (Davis *et al.* 1984).

The degradation of surface-bound C3b is complicated by the fact that these molecules are covalently linked to a variety of cell surface molecules. The overall cell surface properties, such as surface charge and the nature of the acceptor molecules to which C3b is attached, may affect the rate and degree of degradation of C3b. In fact, it is precisely this property that distinguishes activating and non-activating surfaces of the alternative pathway of complement. Activating surfaces retard the degradation of some of the surface-bound C3b to iC3b, thus allowing the surface-bound C3b to form the C3-convertase with factor B to initiate the positive feedback loop of C3 activation (Fearon & Austen, 1977*a*,*b*). Recently, Newman & Mikus (1985) studied the kinetics of the deposition of C3b and its subsequent degradation to iC3b on a number of cell surfaces when treated with serum. Whereas the conversion of C3b to iC3b was virtually instantaneous and complete on sheep erythrocytes, a non-activator of the alternative pathway, a substantial fraction of C3b, ranging from 10% to 80%, remained unconverted on activating surfaces such as rabbit erythrocytes, yeast and five different strains of bacteria.

The conversion of surface-bound iC3b to C3dg in serum is at best slow on a number of surfaces including the erythrocytes of sheep (Law *et al*. 1979; Ross *et al*. 1982; Medicus *et al*. 1983), rabbit and guinea-pig (Medicus *et al*. 1983) as well as yeast and various bacteria (Newman & Mikus, 1985). Although soluble iC3b was thought not to be degraded by factor I with any of the three known cofactors under physiological conditions, CR1 appeared to be able to act as a cofactor for a factor-I-mediated cleavage of bound iC3b (reaction I3 in Fig. 1A) to C3c and C3dg on immune aggregates (Medof *et al*. 1982*a,b*), and human and sheep erythrocytes (Ross *et al*. 1982; Medicus *et al*. 1983). Different results have also been reported (Malhotra & Sim, 1984). It is possible that the rate and extent of the breakdown of surface-bound iC3b are different from the breakdown of fluid-phase iC3b. However, a systematic study of this aspect has not been reported.

C4

The structure and function of C4 resemble those of C3 in a variety of ways (for review see Reid, 1986; Campbell *et al*. 1988). Both are synthesized as a single polypeptide (for review see Colten, 1986) with the individual chains found in the mature molecule arranged in the order of $\beta-\alpha-\gamma$ for C4 and $\beta-\alpha$ for C3 (Belt *et al*. 1984; de Bruijn & Fey, 1985). The inter-chain sites on the pro-molecules are marked by stretches of tetrabasic residues which are probably removed by a common set of enzymes. The pro-C4 and pro-C3 are of similar molecular sizes and their primary amino acid sequences, as derived from their cDNA sequences, show an identity of about 25 % after alignment. Both are activated similarly by the removal of the N-terminal 77 amino acid residues of their respective α chains, and they both bind to cell surfaces by an acyl-transfer reaction between the internal thioester and surface-bound nucleophilic groups. They play corresponding roles in the activation of the classical and alternative pathways, where C4b and C3b serve as the non-catalytic component of the C3-convertases of the classical and alternative pathways respectively, and they do so by interacting with the two homologous proteins, C2 and factor B. Both are under the similar regulatory control of factor I with an overlapping set of cofactors. The three cofactors for the degradation of C4b are C4BP (Shiraishi & Stroud, 1975; Fujita *et al*. 1978; Fujita & Nussenzweig, 1979), CR1 (Iida & Nussenzweig, 1981; Medof & Nussenzweig, 1984), and MCP (Seya *et al*. 1986*a*). Factor I cleaves C4b at sites on either side of the thioester (marked I1 and I2 in Fig. 1B) to yield C4c and C4d. The relative efficiency of the cofactors in the I1 and I2 cleavages has been studied and found to be different; CR1 is effective in mediating both I1 and I2 cleavages for both surface-bound and fluid-phase C4b (Medof & Nussenzweig, 1984), whereas MCP is only active in mediating the I1 cleavage (Seya *et al*. 1986*a*). The intermediate, iC4b, which exists in laboratory conditions (Nagasawa *et al*. 1980; Seya *et al*. 1986*a*), may not be a stable product in serum or blood. The affinity of C4b for CR1 is demonstrated by the immune adherence reaction between C4b-coated sheep erythrocytes and human erythrocytes (Cooper, 1969). Receptors for iC4b or C4d have not been described.

The C3 receptors and other membrane C3-binding proteins

A list of membrane proteins having an affinity for various C3 fragments is found in Table 1. Three of them, CR1, CR2 and CR3, have been established as receptors, the numerical order given to them reflects the chronological order of establishment of the molecular structure of their respective major ligands, C3b, C3d and iC3b. Two proteins have been described as CR4. They are referred to in this article as CR4-1 (Vik & Fearon, 1985) and CR4-2 (also known as p150,95, see Ross & Medof, 1985), and they are distinct both in their ligand specificity and their divalent cation requirement. Whereas the binding of iC3b and C3dg to CR4-1 takes place in the presence of EDTA (Vik & Fearon, 1985), the interaction between iC3b and CR4-2 requires divalent cations (Micklem & Sim, 1985; Malhotra *et al.* 1986). It is to be hoped that the nomenclature will be standardized in the near future. Other C3-binding proteins are not called receptors, probably because their major known functions do not include the triggering of a cellular response upon interaction with ligand. The major ligands for these molecules, the apparent molecular weight of their component polypeptides, and the distribution of their expression among major cell types are also included in Table 1.

Except for two, the proteins listed in Table 1 can be divided into two groups according to their structural similarity to either CR1 or CR3. Proteins belonging to the CR1 group contain repeating structural units each of about 60 amino acid residues known as SCR. This structure was first described in some soluble components of complement and later in proteins outside the complement system. All proteins in the CR1 group that contain this structural unit interact with C3 and/or C4. CR2, which is found predominantly on B lymphocytes (Tedder *et al.* 1984), also belong to this group (Weis *et al.* 1986). The CR3 group includes CR3 and CR4-2. Together with the LFA-1 antigen found on lymphocytes, granulocytes, and activated macrophages, the three proteins form the leukocyte adhesion glycoprotein family of the immune system. They are probably a subgroup of a more extensive family of cell adhesion glycoproteins including the receptors for fibronectin and vitronectin.

The two proteins that do not belong to either the CR1 or the CR3 group are CR4-1 and p90. No structural data are available for CR4-1, and p90 has been reported as a protein in spleen extract that shows binding affinity for iC3b at low ionic strength (Micklem & Sim, 1985). Neither will be discussed further in this article. More detailed structural information regarding CR1, CR3 and related proteins, is presented below.

CR1 and related proteins

The SCR-containing proteins

Investigation of the activation of the alternative pathway (Fearon & Austen, 1977*a*,*b*) led Fearon (1979) to postulate a factor on the surface of human erythrocyte membranes that could inhibit the formation of the surface-bound C3-convertase, thus accounting for the finding that human erythrocytes fail to activate the alternative pathway even after the removal of surface sialic acid residues. The factor was shown to be a protein with the ability to accelerate the decay of cell-bound C3-convertase of the alternative pathway (reaction 3D, Table 2). Using this property as an assay, a protein was purified from human erythrocyte membranes; it was also found to have the cofactor activity for the factor-I-mediated cleavage of C3b. Its affinity for C3 was demonstrated in the purification procedure in which a key step was the affinity chromatography of the partially purified protein on a C3–Sepharose column. Subsequently, its identity as the C3b receptor was firmly established when antibodies against this protein were found to inhibit C3b receptor functions in both peripheral blood leukocytes and erythrocytes (Fearon, 1980).

Data on the primary structure of CR1 were obtained by protein and cDNA sequencing (Wong *et al.* 1985; Klickstein *et al.* 1987*a*). The protein was found to contain an array of a structural element found in complement proteins that interact with C3b and C4b (for review see Reid *et al.* 1986; Kristensen *et al.* 1987*a*). This element is now known as SCR (for short consensus repeat, as distinct from LHR for long homologous repeat, see below).

SCRs were first observed in factor B (Morley & Campbell, 1984). Sequence analysis showed that the N-terminal residues of factor B could be arranged into three repeating units, each about 60 residues in length. The possible role of these units in binding C4b or C3b was suggested when eight similar repeats were found in the monomeric subunit of the C4-binding protein, C4BP, accounting for the major part of the primary structure of that protein (Chung *et al.* 1985). Subsequently, these units were found in other complement proteins as well as membrane proteins that interact with C3 and/or C4. A list of these proteins and their functions is shown in Table 2.

A problem in analysing tandem repeating structures is to determine the boundaries that mark the end of one unit and the beginning of the next. The first suggestive evidence in defining an SCR unit came from the study of the exon/intron organization of the factor B gene (Campbell *et al.* 1984). Each of the second, third, and fourth exons was found to code for a region that could be regarded as a repeating unit. This appears to be a general rule because data from the exon/intron structure of other SCR-containing proteins support this contention (see Reid *et al.* 1986; Kristensen et *al.* 1987*a*). However, exceptions are also found; the second SCRs of the C4BP (Barnum *et al.* 1987) and factor H (Vik *et al.* 1987) of the mouse appear to be coded in two exons.

Extensive analysis of the primary structure of the SCRs available to date clearly shows a consensus sequence built around the four cysteine residues. The consensus structure is shown in Fig. 2, along with the number and arrangement of SCRs for each protein.

The view that each SCR, as defined by primary and genomic structural analysis, represents an individual domain at the protein level, also found support from the limited information on the arrangement of the disulphide bonds in C4BP (Janatova *et al.* 1987) and factor H (Day *et al.* 1987), as well as in the non-complement protein β_2-glycoprotein I (Lozier *et al.* 1984). The four cysteine residues in each SCR were

Table 2. *Function of proteins in the complement system with the short consensus repeat (SCR) units*

Protein	No. of SCR	C3, C4 proteolysis		Decay[b] acceleration	Adherence ligand	References[c]
		Reaction[a]	Accessory proteins			
C1r	2	4A[d]	C1s			13,27
C1s	2	4A	C1q, C1r			27,31
C2	3	3A	C4b			2,27
B	3	3A	C3b			22,27
H	20	3I1, 3I2 (4I1, 4I2)[e]	I	3D		5,11,25,24,34
C4BP	8(*7)[f]	4I1, 4I2[g] (3I1, 3I2)[e]	I	4D		8,9,10,16,23,29
CR1	30	3I1, 3I2, 3I3 4I1, 4I2	I	3D, 4D	C3b, C4b	4,6,12,16,17,24,29
CR2	(15/16)[h]	3I3	I		C3dg, iC3b	1,7,20,21,32,33
DAF	4[g]			3D, 4D[j]		3,14,18,19,26
MCP	4[g]	3I1, 3I2, 4I1	I			30
H(M)	(?)[j]	3I1[k]	I		C3b	15,28

[a] C3, C4 proteolysis reactions: 3A, C3→C3a+C3b; 3I1, C3b→iC3b'; 3I2, iC3b'→iC3b+C3f; 3I3, iC3b→C3c+C3dg; 4A, C4→C4a+C4b; 4I1, C4b→iC4b; 4I2, iC4b→C4c+C4d.

[b] Decay acceleration reactions: 3D, C3bBb→C3b+Bb; 4D, C4b2a→C4b+C2a.

[c] References: (1) Barel et al. (1981); (2) Bentley & Campbell (1986); (3) Caras et al. (1987); (4) Cooper (1969); (5) Crossley & Porter (1980); (6) Fearon (1979); (7) Frade et al. (1985); (8) Fujita & Nussenzweig (1979); (9) Fujita et al. (1978); (10) Gigli et al. (1979); (11) Harrison & Lachmann (1980); (12) Iida & Nussenzweig (1981); (13) Journet & Tosi (1986); (14) Kinoshita et al. (1986); (15) Malhotra & Sim (1985); (16) Medof & Nussenzweig (1984); (17) Medof et al. (1982a); (18) Medof et al. (1984); (19) Medof et al. (1987); (20) Mitomo et al. (1987); (21) Moore et al. (1987); (22) Morley & Campbell (1984); (23) Nagasawa et al. (1980); (24) Nicholson-Weller et al. (1982); (25) Pangburn et al. (1977); (26) Pangburn et al. (1983); (27) Reid (1986); (28) Schulz et al. (1984); (29) Seya et al. (1985); (30) Seya et al. (1986a); (31) Tosi et al. (1987); (32) Weis et al. (1984); (33) Weis et al. (1987); (34) Whaley & Ruddy (1976a).

[d] Does not mediate this reaction directly but participates in the overall C1 cleavage of C4.

[e] Weaker activity.

[f] Seven identical subunits each with 8 SCRs in human. The monomeric unit of the mouse C4BP has only six SCR units (Kristensen et al. 1987b); the number of subunits in the mouse protein is not known.

[g] 4I2 not effective on membrane bound C4b.

[h] See Fig. 2.

[i] Detected only when C3bBb and C4b2a are on the same cell as DAF.

[j] Not characterized but presumed to be factor H-like.

[k] 3I2 not characterized.

shown to engage in disulphide bonds in a self-contained 1–3, 2–4 fashion. Inter-SCR disulphide bonds have not been found. The current model for the unit structure appears to be a 'triple-loop' hinged at two disulphide bonds (Klickstein *et al.* 1987*a*). The fourth cysteine residue and the first cysteine residue of the adjacent SCR is, on the average, separated by four residues. The engagement of the cysteine residues in different disulphide bonds suggests that adjacent SCRs are tightly packed against each other. This is in agreement with the appearance of the C4BP as a 'spider-like' structure in electron micrographs (Dahlback *et al.* 1983). The seven identical subunits form the 'legs' of the spider extending from a small central core, presumably formed by the non-SCR region of the subunits. Each 'leg' of the spider is interpreted to be a stack of the eight SCRs (Chung *et al.* 1985) with a dimension of 30×330 Å; thus each SCR is more or less globular with a diameter of about 35 Å (Dahlback *et al.* 1983; Perkins *et al.* 1986).

The significance of the SCR in C3/C4 binding proteins is not certain. It is attractive to postulate that each SCR is a C3/C4 binding unit, with each unit contributing to the combined affinity of the protein for either C3 or C4. This conjecture, however, is not supported by experiments. C4BP and factor H have specificities for C4 and C3, respectively, and cross activities are weak if positive. Furthermore, the cofactor activities of both factor H (Alsenz *et al.* 1984) and C4BP (Chung & Reid, 1985; Fujita *et al.* 1985) are associated with particular proteolytic fragments of the respective proteins. Currently, the SCRs are thought of as the building blocks of the C3/C4 binding proteins with one or a few from each protein containing an active binding site.

Family studies of the genes specifying SCR-containing proteins, either by allotypic polymorphism at the protein level or by restriction fragment length polymorphism (RFLP) at the nucleic acid level, showed that those for CR1, factor H, C4BP and DAF are found to be closely linked (Rodriguez de Cordoba *et al.* 1985; Rey-Campos *et al.* 1987; Lublin *et al.* 1987). The gene cluster is referred to as the RCA (regulators for complement activation) linkage group and has been localized to the q32 region of chromosome 1 (Wong *et al.* 1985; Lublin *et al.* 1987). Using pulse-field electrophoresis, a genomic fragment of 950 kb was shown to contain the genes for CR1, DAF, C4BP and CR2 (Carroll *et al.* 1987). The gene for factor H, however, is not in this genomic fragment. It is not known whether the remaining regulatory protein, MCP, belongs to this linkage group.

CR1

CR1 is the longest polypeptide of this family of proteins and it contains the greatest number of SCRs reported to date. Klickstein *et al.* (1987*a*) described a partial cDNA clone coding for about 80 % of CR1 inclusive of the C terminus, and the predicted structure included 23 SCRs, a transmembrane segment of 25 amino acid residues, and a cytoplasmic domain of 43 amino acid residues. A higher order of organization was found among the first 21 SCRs, which could be broken down into groups of seven SCRs to give three long homologous repeat (LHR) units. Anticipating that an extra LHR would account for the missing 5' end of the clone, Klickstein *et al.*

(1987a) called the three units LHR-B, LHR-C, and LHR-D. The LHRs are highly homologous, with the lowest pairwise post-alignment identity of 67% between LHR-B and LHR-D. LHR-C appears to be a composite of LHR-B and LHR-D. Its first four SCRs can be aligned with the corresponding ones of LHR-B at 99% and those of LHR-D at 61% homology. The remaining three SCRs, however, showed 76% and 91% homology with the corresponding SCRs in LHR-B and LHR-D, respectively. It is interesting to note that the gene segment for LHR-C could not have been generated by unequal crossing over between pre-existing gene segments for LHR-B and LHR-D but could possibly have arisen by gene conversion. Two other partial cDNA clones were reported by Hourcade *et al.* (1987) and Klickstein *et al.* (1987b). Both clones contain a signal peptide at the 5' end with a 3' end extending into the clone previously described by Klickstein *et al.* (1987a). The derived amino acid sequence indicated that they contain the postulated LHR-A unit. Of the seven SCRs, the five C-terminal ones share 99% homology with the corresponding SCRs of LHR-B, whereas the two N terminal are at a lower level of about 60% homology.

Another unusual structural feature of CR1 is its size polymorphism. CR1 is coded for by a single gene, and four allotypes of different sizes have been identified. They are designated as types A (190K), B (220K), C (160K) and D (250K) in the descending order of their gene frequencies of 0·83, 0·16, 0·01 and 0·002 respectively (Holers *et al.* 1987). The two most abundant forms are also known as the F and S allotypes (Dykman *et al.* 1983; Wong *et al.* 1983). The structure described by Klickstein *et al.* (1987a,b) and Hourcade *et al.* (1987) is that of the A allotype. The polymorphism has been indicated to lie in the length of the polypeptide structure since the size differences between the allotypes is unlikely to be caused by differential glycosylation (Lublin *et al.* 1986), and the mRNA size differences are found to

---

Fig. 2. The schematic structure of short consensus repeats (SCRs) and their arrangement in complement proteins. A. Three contiguous SCRs are shown with conserved residues marked in the middle SCR (see Reid *et al.* 1986; Kristensen *et al.* 1987a; Klickstein *et al.* 1987a). The two disulphide bonds within each unit are also shown. The consensus structure is generated from data obtained from the complement proteins as well as non-complement proteins including β_2-glycoprotein I (Lozier *et al.* 1984), factor XIIIb (Ichinose *et al.* 1986), haptoglobin (Kurosky *et al.* 1980), and interleukin-2 receptor (Leonard *et al.* 1985). Amino acids are encircled and represented by their single letter codes: C, cysteine; F, phenylalanine; G, glycine; I, isoleucine; L, leucine; P, proline; S, serine; T, threonine; V, valine; W, tryptophan; Y, tyrosine. Circles enclosing more than one letter show the possible alternatives. B. The arrangement of SCRs, each represented by a circle, in ten complement proteins is shown. C1r, C1s, C2 and factor B also contain a serine protease (SP) domain at the C-terminal end of the protein (see Reid, 1986). C4BP contains seven identical subunits each with eight SCRs. They are disulphide bonded together via the non-SCR structure at the C terminus. The CR1 structure shown represents the most common allelic form, CR1-A, with 30 SCRs (see text). Two CR2 structures had been reported in the XIIth International Complement Workshop; the one from tonsil lymphocytes contains 15 SCRs (Weis *et al.* 1987) and one from Raji cells contains 16 SCRs (Moore *et al.* 1987). Both CR1 and CR2 have a hydrophobic transmembrane segment and a relatively small cytoplasmic domain. DAF anchors to the membrane by a lipid tail in the form of a phosphatidylinositol. MCP contains four SCR units (J. P. Atkinson, personal communication), but the remainder of its structure is not known.

correlate with the size of the allotypes (Holers *et al*. 1987). The different sizes of the allotypes could be accounted for by the assumption that they differ from each other by the addition or the removal of discrete numbers of LHRs (Klickstein *et al*. 1987*a*). Supportive evidence is found in the analysis of genomic clones covering the gene encoding the B allotype (Wong *et al*. 1987), which appears to contain five LHRs, one more than the A allotype.

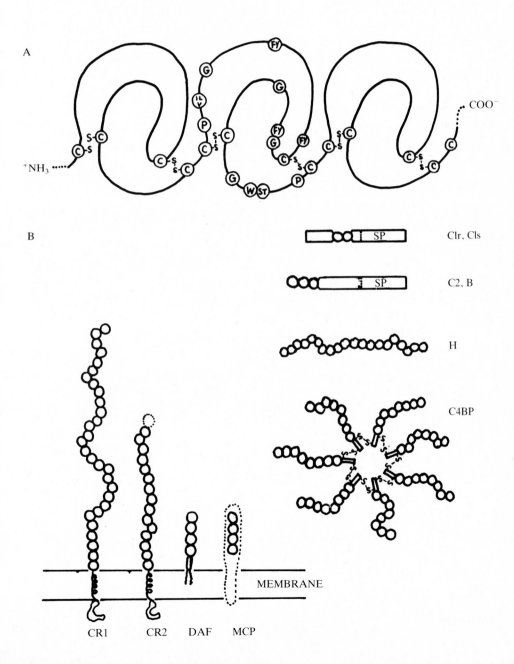

Based on the presumably rigid structure conferred by the linear array of 30 SCRs and the previous finding of Abrahamson & Fearon (1983), who observed that ferritin-conjugated anti-CR1 antibodies bound to neutrophils were frequently 500 Å away from the plasma membrane, Klickstein et al. (1987a) proposed that CR1 could be a structure whose extension from the membrane increases its efficiency to interact with C3b-coated targets. This proposal is in line with the postulate of Hourcade et al. (1987), who suggested that the active site of CR1 resides in the first two SCRs, based on the fact that these two SCRs are more divergent in their primary structure than the corresponding ones in other LHRs. The interaction of C3b (C4b) with CR1 mediates the known functions of CR1, all of which lead to the processing of the C3b bearing targets (for review see Fearon, 1985). The regulatory activity of CR1 in the complement cascade has been discussed extensively with respect to both its capacity to act as a cofactor for factor-I-mediated cleavage of C3b and in its decay-accelerating activity in dissociating, and hence inactivating, the C3bBb enzyme complex. In addition, CR1 on primate erythrocytes may have an important role in the traffic and clearance of immune complexes. Apparently, immune complexes bind to the erythrocytes via a C3b–CR1 interaction and are removed from the erythrocytes during their passage through liver and spleen (Medof & Oger, 1982; Cornacoff et al. 1983; Waxman et al. 1984). CR1 on platelets of non-primates may have an equivalent function. CR1 can exist in two states on macrophages and other phagocytes. In its passive state it promotes adherence of the phagocytes to C3b-coated targets, thus enhancing the occurrence of ingestion mediated by other receptors, e.g. Fc receptor (Mantovani et al. 1972; Bianco et al. 1975; Griffin et al. 1975; Newman et al. 1980). Upon treatment of macrophages with T lymphokines (Griffin & Griffin, 1979), phorbol esters (Wright & Silverstein, 1982), or extracellular matrix proteins such as fibronectin (Wright et al. 1983b), CR1 is promoted to an active state and the C3b–CR1 interaction appears to be sufficient to trigger the phagocytic process. Changelian & Fearon (1986) studied the phosphorylation of cell surface receptors and demonstrated the phosphorylation of CR1 on phagocytic cells upon stimulation with phorbol myristate acetate (PMA). Phosphorylation did not occur without stimulation or on non-phagocytic cells with or without stimulation. Thus the activity state of the phagocytic cell correlates well with the phosphorylation of CR1. A possible site for protein kinase C mediated phosphorylation has been identified on the putative cytoplasmic domain (Klickstein et al. 1987a).

CR3 and related proteins

CR3

Before the polypeptide structures of C3 and its breakdown products were clarified, the only C3 receptor having an identifiable ligand was CR1. The major reason was that C3b-coated sheep erythrocytes could be easily prepared from purified complement components for immune adherence or rosetting assays. Although receptors distinct from CR1 had been described (Lay & Nussenzweig, 1968; Ross et al. 1973), their ligand specificities required a re-examination when the conversion of surface-bound C3b to C3d was found to have a stable intermediate, iC3b (Law *et al*. 1979). Receptor activity specific for iC3b was established by the demonstration that the rosetting pattern of iC3b-coated sheep erythrocytes with different leukocytes was different from those of C3b- or C3d-coated cells (Carlo *et al*. 1979; Ross & Lambris, 1982). However, the receptor for iC3b continued to escape identification because most leukocytes bear more than one type of C3 receptor on their surfaces, and these receptors cross-react with the three ligands, C3b, iC3b and C3d. CR3 was finally distinguished from CR1 and CR2, functionally by its requirement for divalent cations (Wright & Silverstein, 1982; Ross *et al*. 1983), and structurally by its identification with specific monoclonal antibodies (Beller *et al*. 1982; Wright *et al*. 1983*a*). CR2 was found to have binding affinity for both C3d and iC3b in the absence of divalent cations (Ross *et al*. 1983). It was also found to be the receptor for the Epstein Barr virus on B lymphocytes (Fingeroth *et al*. 1984; Nemerow *et al*. 1985).

The function of CR3 on phagocytes was found to be similar to that of CR1 (Newman *et al*. 1980) except for its requirement for divalent cations (Wright & Silverstein, 1982; Ross *et al*. 1983). Both CR1 and CR3 appear to respond to similar stimulants for transition from passive to active mediators of phagocytosis (Wright & Silverstein, 1982; Wright *et al*. 1983*b*). Release of toxic oxygen metabolites is not coupled to phagocytosis mediated by active CR1 and CR3 in contrast to the IgG–FcR-mediated activity (Wright & Silverstein, 1983). CR3 is also found to possess divalent cation dependent binding to unopsonized zymosan (Ross *et al*. 1985*a*) and β glucan (Ross *et al*. 1987). This interaction differs from that between CR3 and iC3b by its ability to trigger a phagocytic response and respiratory burst from unstimulated neutrophils and monocytes. Furthermore, two monoclonal anti-CR3 antibodies, anti-Leu-15 and OKM1, were found to block iC3b and β-glucan binding to CR3, respectively, without reciprocal blocking activity (Ross *et al*. 1985*a*), suggesting that iC3b and β-glucan bind to different sites on CR3.

The molecular structure of mouse CR3 was first established when Beller *et al*. (1982) observed that the binding of iC3b-coated erythrocytes to macrophages is inhibited by a monoclonal antibody against the macrophage surface marker, Mac-1, thus demonstrating that CR3 and Mac-1 are the same molecule. The molecular structure of Mac-1 was already known. It contains two non-covalently associated subunits with apparent molecular weights for the α and β subunits at 160K and 95K respectively (Springer *et al*. 1979). The human CR3 was later shown to have a similar structure by Wright *et al*. (1983*a*) and Sanchez-Madrid *et al*. (1983).

Leukocyte adhesion glycoproteins

In characterizing surface molecules that mediate T lymphocyte functions, Davignon *et al*. (1981) described a set of antigens that is required for T cell adhesion to target cells. One of the antigens was named LFA-1 (lymphocyte-function-associated antigen-1). Like Mac-1, it is also a heterodimer with apparent molecular weights for its two subunits of 180K and 95K. Although the LFA-1 and Mac-1 antigens apparently have different α subunits, their β subunits have a very similar, if not

identical two-dimensional tryptic peptide map (Kurzinger *et al*. 1982). Using a panel
of monoclonal antibodies, Sanchez-Madrid *et al*. (1983) showed that the β subunits
of LFA-1 and CR3 are identical with respect to their antigenicity, apparent
molecular weights and isoelectric points. A third antigen with the same β subunit was
also identified by these authors. In the absence of a known function, it was referred to
as p150,95 by the molecular weight of its subunits.

Later work by Micklem & Sim (1985) and Malhotra *et al*. (1986) demonstrated the
affinity of p150,95 for iC3b. Iodinated membrane proteins were passed through an
iC3b–Sepharose column at low ionic strength. The bound material eluted with
EDTA was shown to contain CR3 and p150,95 by specific monoclonal antibodies as
well as by SDS–polyacrylamide gel electrophoresis. The high level of p150,95
antigen on the surface of tissue macrophages led to the suggestion that it may be the
iC3b receptor on these cells (Hogg *et al*. 1986). This is supported by recent results
(Myones *et al*. 1987; Keizer *et al*. 1987) indicating that p150,95 may function as an
iC3b phagocytic receptor.

Human LFA-1 was initially defined by monoclonal antibodies which inhibit cell
killing by cytolytic T lymphocytes and natural killer cells (Sanchez-Madrid *et al*.
1982; Hildreth *et al*. 1983) at the Mg^{2+}-dependent adherence stage prior to the
delivery of the lethal hit (Springer *et al*. 1982). It was subsequently shown also to
partake in a wide range of T-lymphocyte-mediated adherence activities including
antigen presentation to both T and B cells as well as antigen-independent aggregation
of leukocytes (for review see Springer *et al*. 1987). Springer *et al*. (1987) proposed a
unified scheme for various LFA-1-mediated adherence reactions by suggesting that
they require the promotion of LFA-1 to an active state. In the case of antigen-
dependent adherence, the triggering signal comes from the antigen–receptor
interaction, whereas in the case of antigen-independent adherence, the signal is
provided for by non-specific agents such as phorbol esters.

In LFA-1-mediated aggregation of leucocytes, LFA-1-negative cells can co-
aggregate with LFA-1-positive cells, thus LFA-1-dependent cell adhesion is not
mediated by a 'like–like' recognition between LFA-1 molecules on different cells
(Rothlein & Springer, 1986), suggesting the existence of ligand molecules for LFA-1.
One molecule that satisfies the functional criteria of a ligand for LFA-1 is ICAM-1
(intercellular adhesion molecule-1). Monoclonal antibodies against ICAM-1 inhibit
LFA-1-dependent cell adhesion. The adherence of T lymphocytes (LFA-1-positive,
low ICAM-1 expression) and fibroblasts (LFA-1-negative, ICAM-1-positive) can be
inhibited by either the pre-treatment of T cells with antibodies against LFA-1 or by
the pre-treatment of the fibroblasts with antibodies against ICAM-1. Furthermore,
the inhibition is not additive since either treatment effectively inhibits aggregation to
an extent significantly greater than 50 %. These observations thus provide strong
evidence that ICAM-1 and LFA-1 are receptor–ligand counterparts (Dustin *et al*.
1986). ICAM-1 may not be the only ligand for LFA-1, however, since the
LFA-1-dependent homotypic aggregation of SKW-3, the T lymphoma line with low
ICAM-1 expression, is not inhibited by an anti-ICAM-1 antibody (Rothlein *et al*.
1986).

Although CR3, LFA-1 and possibly p150,95 have their respective distinct functions, they also have a common adherence activity with unopsonized microorganisms. Wright & Jong (1986) demonstrated the divalent cation dependent binding of the rough strains of *Escherichia coli* and *Salmonella typhimurium* to macrophages *via* the interaction between the bacterial lipopolysaccharide and each of the three adhesion proteins. The binding was not observed with the smooth strains of these bacteria, which have the additional O antigen on their lipopolysaccharide. The significance of this binding is not known, but it may be a general property of macrophages with respect to a selected spectrum of microorganisms. This binding may be related to that of *Histoplasma capsulatum* to macrophages (Bullock & Wright, 1987) and of *Staphylococcus epidermidis* to neutrophils (Ross *et al*. 1985*b*). Since all three proteins can mediate this activity, it is likely that they do so *via* their common β subunit. It should be pointed out, however, that this binding is distinct from that of CR3 to unopsonized yeast and zymosan, which is not mediated by LFA-1 (Ross *et al*. 1985*a*).

Patients who lack CR3, LFA-1 and p150,95 on their leukocyte surfaces suffer from recurrent infections (for review see Anderson & Springer, 1987). The failure to express these antigens is associated with the failure to produce a mature form of the β subunit (Springer *et al*. 1984; Dana et *al*. 1987; Kishimoto *et al*. 1987*a*) and consequently the maturation of the α subunits is affected. The deficiency is inherited as an autosomal recessive trait and the gene encoding the β subunit had been mapped to region q22.1–qter of chromosome 21 (Marlin *et al*. 1986; Solomon *et al*. 1988).

The primary structure of the β subunit derived from cDNA was obtained by a combination of protein and cDNA sequencing (Law *et al*. 1987; Kishimoto *et al*. 1987*b*). It contains 747 amino acid residues, six possible *N*-glycosylation sites, a transmembrane segment of 23 residues, and a cytoplasmic domain of 47 residues. The most striking feature is an abundance of cysteine residues, 56, accounting for 7·6 % of the total number of residues. Of the cysteine residues, 42 lie within a span of 256 residues immediately N-terminal to the transmembrane segment. Sequence analysis indicates that the cysteine-rich region may be grouped into three or four repeating structures, each containing eight cysteine residues. However, the boundaries of these units are not known. By comparing their N-terminal sequences, the three α subunits appear to share a significant amount of homology (Pierce *et al*. 1986; Miller *et al*. 1987*a*). Furthermore, homology between the N-terminal sequences of the α subunit of LFA-1 and α interferon has been observed, the significance of which is not clear (Springer *et al*. 1985).

High cysteine content is a characteristic of a number of receptors including the epidermal growth factor (EGF) (Ullrich *et al*. 1984), low-density lipoprotein (LDL) (Yamamoto *et al*. 1984) and insulin receptors (Ullrich *et al*. 1985). No significant homology was found between the β subunit of the leukocyte adhesion glycoproteins and these proteins by the ALIGN program (Dayoff *et al*. 1983), although a high degree of homology was found between the β subunit and the subunits of two other receptors, both having affinity for the active site tripeptide, Arg–Gly–Asp, of fibronectin. They are the IIIa component of the glycoprotein IIb/IIIa on human platelets (Pytela *et al.* 1986; Fitzgerald *et al.* 1987) and a subunit of the integrin complex from chicken fibroblasts (Horwitz *et al.* 1985; Tamkun *et al.* 1986). An Arg–Gly–Asp tripeptide is located in the primary structure of C3 (de Bruijn & Fey, 1985) and the region around this tripeptide is found to share significant sequence homology with the Arg–Gly–Asp region of fibronectin and vitronectin (Wright *et al.* 1987). Indeed, a synthetic peptide covering the C3 sequence in this region inhibited the iC3b-mediated binding of erythrocyte to macrophages (Wright *et al.* 1987). However, the specificity for Arg–Gly–Asp is apparently lost in CR3. A hexapeptide, Gly–Arg–Gly–Asp–Ser–Pro, highly reactive with the fibronectin receptors (Pierschbacher & Ruoslahti, 1984; Pytela *et al.* 1986), was not inhibitory to the iC3b–CR3 interaction. Furthermore, mouse C3, which mediates equivalent functions to those of human C3, has a leucine in place of arginine in the tripeptide (Wetsel *et al.* 1984). It is possible that the iC3b–CR3 interactive site has evolved along a course different from that between fibronectin and its receptors, although some of their features remain identifiably related.

When the amino acid sequences of the β subunit of the leukocyte adhesion glycoproteins and the related subunits of the fibronectin-binding proteins are compared, the aligned structures show a pairwise identity of over 40 % including all 56 cysteine residues (Tamkun *et al.* 1986; Law *et al.* 1987; Kishimoto *et al.* 1987b; Fitzgerald *et al.* 1987). An analysis of their homology, based in part on the combined strategy used by the ALIGN (Dayhoff *et al.* 1983) and DIAGON (Staden, 1982) programs, is shown in Fig. 3. The pairwise aligned sequences were adjusted to generate consensus alignment of the three proteins. Alignment scores for each position similar to the DIAGON program were generated for the three sequences in the pairwise fashion. Three values were obtained for each position and their geometric mean was taken. The final score as a function of sequence position is shown as the upper curve in Fig. 3 (for details see Fig. 3 legend). This manipulation is useful in comparing sequences in a semi-quantitative fashion. The composite comparison tends to exaggerate the similarity common to all three sequences. Four homologous regions, I, II, III and IV are identified, in which III is the cysteine-rich region and IV is the transmembrane region extending to the cytoplasmic domain. The high degree of homology in the transmembrane–cytoplasmic region may emphasize the similarity between these proteins in their interaction with cytoskeletal and cytoplasmic proteins. The two N-terminal regions may be responsible for their interaction with the presumably homologous partner subunits.

Since cysteine matches in sequence comparison are given a high score in the Mutation Data Matrix (Dayhoff *et al.* 1983), scores obtained from sequences with high cysteine content could be biased and require adjustment. Assuming that the cysteine residues in the extracellular domain are engaged in disulphide bonds and they are conserved solely for that reason, their contribution is accounted for by the alignment of the sequences. Hence, further analysis of the homology between the sequences could be made without the score from the cysteine matches. By this criteria, a new score was obtained for each position and the result is shown as the

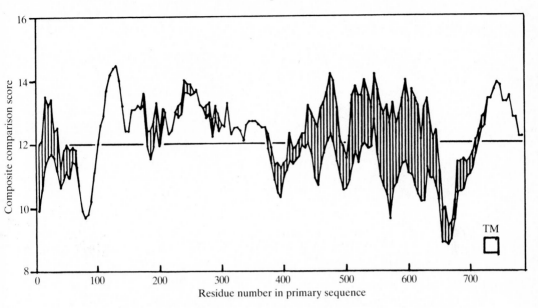

Fig. 3. Composite analysis on the primary structure homology of the β subunit of the human leukocyte adhesion glycoproteins, the IIIa subunit of the human IIb/IIIa glycoprotein on platelets and the corresponding subunit of the integrin complex from chicken fibroblasts. This analysis is based in part on the strategies employed by the sequence analysis programs ALIGN and DIAGON. The three sequences were first aligned pairwise by ALIGN and a consensus alignment was generated by minor adjustments. Three scores were obtained at each position by pairwise comparison of the three aligned sequences using the alogarithm of DIAGON, using a bias of +10 to the Mutation Data Matrix. An unmatched gap was given a score of 6 and a matched gap a score of 12. A window of 25, with 12 on each side of the residue of interest, was used and the score was normalized for each residue. The value of 12 would be the default cut-off value in DIAGON. The geometric mean of the three comparison scores is plotted against the sequence and is shown as the upper curve. The lower curve was generated in the same way except the contributions from matching cysteine residues were nullified. The differential between the two curves is shaded. The position of the transmembrane segment (TM) is marked.

lower curve in Fig. 3. It is clear that the scores for regions I, II and IV remain high but those for region III drop to below the level of significance. Thus, the cysteine-rich region may only be important in providing a rigid structure so that other domains of the molecule may be held and presented in the desired spatial configuration.

General discussion

In the past two years a substantial amount of information along with an abundance of questions have been obtained for the structure of CR1 and CR3. The complete primary structure of CR1 can be deduced from the combined work of two research groups (Klickstein *et al*. 1987*a,b*; Hourcade *et al*. 1987), and its overall structure on the cell surface has been interpreted as a proteinaceous 'skyscraper' with the active site on top. The protein is anchored to the membrane with a hydrophobic segment linked to a cytoplasmic domain of 43 residues inclusive of a possible phosphorylation site. Except for the first two SCRs, where the binding site presumably resides, the remaining 28 SCRs may simply be playing a structural role to extend the active site from the plasma membrane so as to enhance its effectiveness. The binding signal has to be communicated to the cell to initiate functional activities. Two transmission mechanisms are possible. First, the linear array of SCRs may act as a conduit by which the signal is transmitted to the cytoplasmic domain. Since the 28 SCR units are not simply structural elements in this case, they must also possess the capacity to transmit information from one SCR to another along the rod-like structure. (If the LHRs confer a higher order of tertiary structure, they may be the unit signal transmission element.) Second, the signal may be transmitted by mobilizing CR1 laterally on the plasma membrane. The aggregation of the cytoplasmic domains could be the signal to initiate a cellular response. If this is correct, the 28 structural SCRs could be replaced by any other 28, or, to within certain limits, by a different number of SCR units. Michl *et al.* (1979) and Griffin & Mullinax (1981) observed that the lateral mobility of CR1 (and CR3) on the plasma membrane is correlated with the ability of the macrophages to bind and ingest C3b- (and iC3b-) coated particles, thus lending support to the proposed second mechanism. How the mobility of the receptor correlates with its phosphorylation and ultimately with its ability to mediate phagocytosis, is not known.

The CR1 structure described here is for the most common allotype, CR1-A. The next frequent allotype, CR1-B, is larger by about 30K and presumably by one LHR unit of seven SCRs (Wong *et al.* 1987). Extrapolation from the estimated length of CR1-A of 1140 Å, the active site of CR1-B would be about 1350 Å from the cell surface. However, whether this structural extension has a functional advantage is not clear. The efficiency of CR1-B in mediating decay acceleration and cofactor activity is not appreciably different from that of CR1-A (Seya *et al.* 1985) and its efficiency in mediating receptor function has not been evaluated quantitatively.

Though we lack a knowledge of the structure of the α subunit of CR3, our knowledge of the structure of the β subunit allows us to speculate on the structure and function of CR3 as a whole, as well as that of some of its related molecules. The region adjacent to the transmembrane segment contains 20 % cysteine and predictably has a very tightly knotted tertiary structure. The three or four repeating units have not been defined in terms of their boundaries; the exon/intron organization of the gene may, however, provide indicative information in this regard. Because of the high density of cysteines, determination of disulphide bonds is at best difficult. Phosphorylation of CR3 has not been observed (Changelian & Fearon, 1986). However, the activation of CR3 by PMA treatment of phagocytes led to the speculation that a protein kinase C type of phosphorylation may be involved and that the reason why receptor-bound phosphates have not been detected is because of dephosphorylation. In line with this argument are the observations of Wright & Meyer (1986), who showed that the activated state of CR3 in polymorphonuclear leukocytes was transient in nature. In addition, by introducing to their experiments the phosphate analogue, thio-phosphate, which can be incorporated into proteins but is resistant to subsequent hydrolysis by phosphatases, they were able to prolong the activated state of CR3. The activated state of CR1 has also been shown to be reversible. However, its deactivation appeares to follow a slower kinetics (Wright & Meyer, 1986), thus providing a plausible explanation for the detection of CR1 but not CR3 phosphorylation on PMA-treated phagocytes (Changelian & Fearon, 1986).

Comparison of the N-terminal sequences for the α subunits of CR3, p150,95 and LFA-1 reveal significant homology between the three subunits (Pierce *et al.* 1986; Miller *et al.* 1987*a*). They are also found to be related to the corresponding subunits of fibronectin receptors and platelet gpIIb/IIIa. This latter finding suggests that the leukocyte adhesion glycoproteins belong to the immune system branch of a more extended family of proteins involved in cell adhesion and cell migration whose members are characterized, at least in part, by their heterodimeric structure (Hynes, 1987; Kishimoto *et al.* 1987*c*).

CR1 and CR3, although structurally very different, are surprisingly similar in their role and regulation in phagocytosis. They are passive receptors until the phagocytes are stimulated. Their lateral mobility in the plasma membrane and phosphorylation may be important in the elevation to an active state. Furthermore, unlike Fc-receptor-mediated phagocytosis, phagocytosis *via* active CR1 and CR3 is not coupled to the release of toxic oxygen metabolites. The expression of CR1 and CR3 on polymorphonuclear leukocytes and monocytes is also under another type of regulation. A latent pool of receptors could be mobilized to the surface upon stimulation with chemotactic factors such as C5a and *N*-formyl-methionyl–leucyl–phenylalanine (fMLP), resulting in an increase by several fold of receptor molecules on the cell surface (Fearon & Collins, 1983; Miller *et al.* 1987*b*). Since CR1 and CR3 recognize different cleavage products of C3 and have different divalent cation requirements, it is not surprising that their extracellular structures are different. Their cytoplasmic domains, however, should show some resemblance to each other because either directly or indirectly, they have to link to the cytoskeleton to initiate the ingestion process. Treatment of phagocytes with drugs that disrupt actin filaments, such as cytochalasin B, prevents ingestion of targets but not binding (Axline & Reaven, 1974). Similar features can be found in the activities mediated by other cell adhesion proteins: functions of LFA-1 are also inhibited by cytochalasin B (Rothlein *et al.* 1986), and integrin, the fibronectin binding protein on chicken fibroblasts, has been shown to have affinity for the cytoskeletal protein talin (Horowitz *et al.* 1986). However, CR1 and the β subunit of CR3 do not share any structural homology inclusive of the cytoplasmic domain. The key may lie, of course, in the α subunit of CR3. Work is in progress to study the α subunit of CR3 as well as those of LFA-1 and p150,95. Their structures will shed light on the functions of the leukocyte adhesion glycoproteins and will contribute to our general understanding of the functions of the extended group of adhesion molecules, their interaction with structures on cells, microorganisms and extracellular matrix, and their communication with cytoskeletal and cytoplasmic proteins during cell mobility and differentiation.

I thank Dr K. B. M. Reid and Professor R. P. Levine for critical comments and Ms C. Brooks for preparation of the manuscript.

References

ABRAHAMSON, D. R. & FEARON, D. T. (1983). Endocytosis of the C3b receptor of complement with coated pits in human polymorphism of leukocytes and monocytes. *Lab. Invest.* **48**, 162–168.

ALSENZ, J., LAMBRIS, J. D., SCHULTZ, T. F. & DIERICH, M. P. (1984). Localization of the complement-component C3b-binding site and the cofactor activity for factor 1 in the 38 kDa tryptic fragment of factor H. *Biochem. J.* **244**, 389–398.

ANDERSON, D. C. & SPRINGER, T. A. (1987). Leukocyte adhesion deficiency: an inherited defect in Mac-1, LFA-1 and p150,95 glycoproteins. *A. Rev. Med.* **38**, 175–194.

AXLINE, S. G. & REAVEN, E. P. (1974). Inhibition of phagocytosis and plasma membrane mobility of the cultivated macrophage by cytochalasin B: role of subplasmalemmal microfilament. *J. Cell Biol.* **62**, 647–659.

BAREL, M., CHARRIAUT, C. & FRADE, R. (1981). Isolation and characterisation of a C3b-receptor-like molecule from membranes of a human B lymphoblastoid cell line (Raji). *FEBS Lett.* **136**, 111–116.

BARNUM, S., KENNEY, J., KRISTENSEN, T., NOACK, D., SELDON, M., E'DUSTACHIO, P., CHAPLIN, D. & TACK, B. (1987). Chromosomal location and structure of the mouse C4BP gene. *Complement* **4**, 131 (abs).

BELLER, D. I., SPRINGER, T. A. & SCHREIBER, R. D. (1982). Anti-Mac-1 selectively inhibits the mouse and human type three complement receptor. *J. exp. Med.* **156**, 1000–1009.

BELT, K. T., CARROLL, M. C. & PORTER, R. R. (1984). The structural basis of the multiple forms of human complement component C4. *Cell* **36**, 907–914.

BENTLEY, D. R. & CAMPBELL, R. D. (1986). C2 and factor B: Structure and genetics. *Biochem. Soc. Symp.* **51**, 7–18.

BIANCO, C., GRIFFIN, F. M. JR & SILVERSTEIN, S. C. (1975). Studies of the macrophage complement receptor: alteration of receptor function upon macrophage activation. *J. exp. Med.* **141**, 1278–1290.

BIANCO, C. & NUSSENZWEIG, V. (1977). Complement receptors. *Contemp. Top. Molec. Immun.* **6**, 145–176.

BOKISCH, V. A., DIERICH, M. P. & MÜLLER-EBERHARD, H. J. (1975). Third component of complement (C3): structural properties in relation to functions. *Proc. natn. Acad. Sci. U.S.A.* **72**, 1989–1993.

BULLOCK, W. E. & WRIGHT, S. D. (1987). Role of the adherence-promoting receptor, CR3, LFA-1, and p150,95 in binding of Histoplasma capsulatum by human macrophages. *J. exp. Med.* **165**, 195–210.

CAMPBELL, R. D., BENTLEY, D. R. & MORLEY, B. J. (1984). The factor B and C2 genes. *Phil. Trans. R. Soc. Lond.* B **306**, 367–378.

CAMPBELL, R. D., LAW, S. K. A., REID, K. B. M. & SIM, R. B. (1988). Structure, organisation, and regulation of the complement genes. *A. Rev. Immun.* **6**, 161–195.

CARAS, I. W., DAVITZ, M. A., RHEE, L., WEDDELL, G., MARTIN, D. W. & NUSSENZWEIG, V. (1987). Cloning of decay-accelerating factor suggests novel use of splicing to generate two proteins. *Nature, Lond.* **325**, 545–549.

CARLO, J. R., RUDDY, S., STUDER, E. & CONRAD, D. H. (1979). Complement receptor binding of C3b-coated cells treated with C3b-inactivator, β1H globulin and trypsin. *J. Immun.* **123**, 523–528.

CARROLL, M. C., ALICOT, E. A., KATZMAN, P., KLICKSTEIN, L. B. & FEARON, D. T. (1987). Organisation of the genes encoding CR1, CR2, DAF and C4bp in the RCA locus on human chromosome 1. *Complement* **4**, 141 (abs).

CHANGELIAN, P. S. & FEARON, E. T. (1986). Tissue-specific phosphorylation of complement receptors CRI and CR2. *J. exp. Med.* **163**, 101–115.

CHUNG, L. P., BENTLEY, D. R. & REID, K. B. M. (1985). Molecular cloning and characterisation of the cDNA-coding for C4b binding protein. *Biochem. J.* **230**, 133–141.

CHUNG, L. P. & REID, K. B. M. (1985). Structural and functional studies on C4b-binding protein, a regulatory component of human complement system. *Biosci. Rep.* **5**, 855–865.

COLTEN, H. (1986). Genetics and synthesis of components of the complement system. In *Immunobiology of the complement system: an introduction for research and clinical medicine* (ed. G. D. Ross), pp. 163–181. London: Academic Press.

COOPER, N. R. (1969). Immune adherence by the fourth component of complement. *Science* **165**, 396–398.

CORNACOFF, J. B., HEBERT, L. A., SMEAD, W. L., VANAMAN, M. E., BIRMINGHAM, D. J. & WAXMAN, F. J. (1983). Primate erythrocyte immune-complex clearing mechanism. *J. clin. Invest*, **71**, 236–247.

CROSSLEY, L. G. & PORTER, R. R. (1980). Purification of the human complement control protein C3b inactivator. *Biochem. J.* **191**, 173–182.

DAHLBACK, B., SMITH, C. A. & MÜLLER-EBERHARD, H. J. (1983). Visualization of human C4bp-binding protein and its complexes with vitamin K-dependent protein S and complement protein C4b. *Proc. natn. Acad. Sci. U.S.A.* **80**, 3461–3465.

DANA, N., CALYTON, L. K., TENNON, D. G., PIERCE, M. W., LACHMANN, P. J., LAW, S. A. & ARNAOUT, M. A. (1987). Leukocytes from four patients with complete or partial Leu-CAM deficiency contain the common β-subunit precursor and β-subunit messenger RNA. *J. clin. Invest.* **79**, 1010–1015.

DAVIGNON, D., MARTZ, E., REYNOLDS, T., KURZINGER, K. & SPRINGER, T. A. (1981). Lymphocyte function-associated antigen 1 (LFA-1).: a surface antigen distinct from Lyt-2,3 that participates in T lymphocyte-mediated killing. *Proc. natn. Acad. Sci. U.S.A.* **78**, 4535–4539.

DAVIS, A. E. III, HARRISON, R. A. & LACHMANN, P. J. (1984). Physiologic inactivation of fluid phase C3b: isolation and structural analysis of C3c, C3d,g (A2D) and C3g. *J. Immun.* **132**, 1960–1966.

DAY, A. J., RIPOCHE, J., WILLIS, A. C. & SIM, R. B. (1987). Structure and polymorphism of human factor H. *Complement* **4**, 147–148 (abs).

DAYHOFF, M. O., BARKER, W. C. & HUNT, L. T. (1983). Establishing homologies in protein sequences. *Meth. Enzymol.* **91**, 524–545.

DE BRUIJN, M. H. L. & FEY, G. H. (1985). Human complement component C3: cDNA coding sequence and derived primary structure. *Proc. natn. Acad. Sci. U.S.A.* **82**, 708–712.

DUSTIN, M. L., ROTHLEIN, R., BHAN, A. K., DINARELLO, C. A. & SPRINGER, T. A. (1986). Induction by IL 1 and interferon-Y, tissue distribution, biochemistry, and function of a natural adherence molecule (ICAM-1). *J. Immun.* **137**, 245–254.

DYKMAN, T. R., COLE, J. L., IIDA, K. & ATKINSON, J. P. (1983). Polymorphism of the human erythrocyte C3b-C4b receptor. *Proc. natn. Acad. Sci. U.S.A.* **80**, 1698–1702.

FEARON, D. T. (1979). Regulation of the amplification C3 convertase of human complement by an inhibitory protein isolated from human erythrocyte membrane. *Proc. natn. Acad. Sci. U.S.A.* **76**, 5867–5871.

FEARON, D. T. (1980). Identification of the membrane glycoprotein that is the C3b receptor of the human erythrocyte, polymorphonuclear leukocyte, B lymphocyte and monocyte. *J. exp. Med.* **152**, 20–30.

FEARON, D. T. (1985). The human C3b receptor. In *Complement* (ed. H. J. Müller-Eberhard & P. A. Miescher), pp 101–114. New York: Springer Verlag.

FEARON, D. T. & AUSTEN, K. F. (1977*a*). Activation of the alternative complement pathway due to resistance of zymosan-bound amplification convertase to endogenous regulatory mechanisms. *Proc. natn. Acad. Sci. U.S.A.* **74**, 1683–1687.

FEARON, D. T. & AUSTEN, K. F. (1977*b*). Activation of the alternative pathway with rabbit erythrocytes by circumvention of the regulatory action of endogenous control proteins. *J. exp. Med.* **146**, 22–33.

FEARON, D. T. & COLLINS, L. A. (1983). Increased expression of C3b receptors on polymorphonuclear leukocytes induced by chemotactic factors and by purification procedures. *J. Immun.* **130**, 370–375.

FINGEROTH, J. D., WEIS, J. J., TEDDER, T. F., STOMINGER, J. L., BIRD, P. A. & FEARON, D. T. (1984). Epstein-Barr virus receptor of human B lymphocytes is also the C3d receptor CR2. *Proc. Natn. Acad. Sci. U.S.A.* **81**, 4510–4514.

FITZGERALD, L. A., STEINER, B., RALL, S. C. JR, LO, S-S. & PHILLIPS, D. R. (1987). Protein sequence of endothelial glycoprotein IIIa derived from a cDNA clone: Identity with platelet glycoprotein IIIa and similarity to 'integrin'. *J. biol. Chem.* **262**, 3936–3939.

FRADE, R., BAREL, M., EHLIN-HENRIKSSON, B. & KLEIN, G. (1985). gp140, the C3d receptor of human B lymphocytes, is also the Epstein-Barr virus receptor. *Proc. natn. Acad. Sci. U.S.A.* **82**, 1450–1493.

FUJITA, T., KAMATO, T. & TAMURA, N. (1985). Characterisation of functional properties of C4-binding protein by monoclonal antibodies. *J. Immun.* **134**, 3320–3324.

FUJITA, T. & NUSSENZWEIG, V. (1979). The role of C4 binding protein and B1H in proteolysis of C4b and C3b. *J. exp. Med.* **150**, 267–276.

FUJITA, T., GIGLI, I. & NUSSENZWEIG, V. (1978). Human C4-binding protein. II. Role in proteolysis of C4b by C3b-inactivator. *J. exp. Med.* **148**, 1044–1051.

GIGLI, I., FUJITA, T. & NUSSENZWEIG, V. (1979). Modulation of the classical pathway C3 convertase by plasma proteins C4 binding protein and C3b inactivator. *Proc. natn. Acad. Sci. U.S.A.* **76**, 6596–6600.

GRIFFIN, F. M. JR & GRIFFIN, J. A. (1980). Augmentation of macrophage complement receptor function in vitro. II. Characterization of the effects of a unique lymphokine upon the phagocytic capabilities of macrophages. *J. Immun.* **125**, 884–849.

GRIFFIN, F. M. JR & MULLINAX, P. J. (1981). Augmentation of macrophage complement receptor function in vitro. III. C3b receptors that promote phagocytosis migrate within the plane of the macrophage plasma membrane. *J. exp. Med.* **154**, 291–305.

GRIFFIN, F. M. JR, BIANCO, C. & SILVERSTEIN, S. C. (1975). Characterization of the macrophage receptor for complement and demonstration of its functional independence from the receptor for the Fc portion of immunoglobulin G. *J. exp. Med.* **141**, 1269–1277.

GRIFFIN, J. A. & GRIFFIN, F. M. JR (1979). Augmentation of macrophage complement receptor function in vitro. I. Characterization of the cellular interactions required for the generation of a T-lymphocyte product that enhances macrophage complement receptor function. *J. exp. Med.* **150**, 653–675.

HARRISON, R. A. & LACHMANN, P. J. (1980). The physiological breakdown of the third component of human complement. *Molec. Immun.* **17**, 9–20.

HILDRETH, J. E. K., GOTCH, F. M., HILDRETH, P. D. K. & MCMICHAEL, A. H. (1983). A human lymphocyte-associated antigen involved in cell-mediated lympholysis. *Eur. J. Immun.* **13**, 202–208.

HOGG, N., TAKACS, L., PALMER, D. G., SALVENDRAN, Y. & ALLEN, C. (1986). The p150,95 molecule is a marker of human mononuclear phagocytes: a comparison with expression of class II molecules. *Eur. J. Immun.* **16**, 240–248.

HOLERS, V. M., CHAPLIN, D. D., LEYKAM, J. F., GRUNER, B. A., KUMAR, V. & ATKINSON, J. P. (1987). Human CR1 mRNA polymorphism correlates with the CR1 allelic molecular weight polymorphism. *Proc. natn. Acad. Sci. U.S.A.* **84**, 2459–2463.

HORWITZ, A., DUGGAN, K., BUCK, C., BECKERLE, M. C. & BURRIDGE, K. (1986). Interaction of plasma membrane fibronectin receptor with talin, a transmembrane linkage. *Nature, Lond.* **320**, 531–533.

HORWITZ, A., DUGGAN, K., GREGGS, R., DECKER, C. & BUCK, C. (1985). The cell substrate attachment (CSAT) antigen has properties of a receptor for laminin and fibronectin. *J. Cell Biol.* **101**, 2134–2144.

HOURCADE, D., MIESNER, D. R., ATKINSON, J. P. & HOLERS, V. M. (1987). Structural analysis of the C3b/C4b receptor: the amino terminus. *Complement* **4**, 171–172 (abs).

HUGLI, T. E. (1975). Human anaphylatoxin (C3a) from the third component of complement: Primary structure. *J. biol. Chem..* **250**, 8293–8301.

HYNES, R. O. (1987). Integrins: A family of cell surface receptors. *Cell* **48**, 549–554.

ICHINOSE, A., MCMULLEN, B. A., FUJIKAWA, K. & AVIE, E. W. (1986). Amino acid sequences of b-subunit of human factor XIII, a protein composed of ten repetitive segments. *Biochemistry* **25**, 4633–4638.

IIDA, K. & NUSSENZWEIG, V. (1981). Complement receptor is an inhibitor of the complement cascade. *J. exp. Med.* **153**, 1138–1150.

JANATOVA, J. (1986). Detection of disulphide bonds and localization of intrachain linkages in the third (C3) and the fourth (C4) components of human complement. *Biochem. J.* **233**, 819–825.

JANATOVA, J. & GOBEL, R. J. (1985). Activation and fragmentation of the third (C3) and the fourth (C4) components of complement: generation and isolation of physiologically relevant fragments C3c and C4c. *J. immun. Methods* **85**, 17–26.

JANATOVA, J., REID, K. B. M. & WILLIS, A. C. (1987). Implications of disulphide bonds in the structure of C4BP. *Complement* **4**, 173–174 (abs).

JOURNET, A. & TOSI, M. (1986). Cloning and sequencing of full length cDNA encoding the precursor of human complement component C1r. *Biochem. J.* **240**, 783–787.

KEIZER, G. D., TE VELDE, A. A., SCHWARTING, R., FIGDOR, C. G. & DE VRIES, J. E. (1987). Role of p150,95 in adhesion, migration, chemotaxis and phagocytosis of human monocytes. *Eur. J. Immun.* **17**, 1317–1322.

KINOSHITA, T., MEDOF, M. E. & NUSSENZWEIG, V. (1986). Endogenous association of decay-accelerating factor (DAF) with C4b and C3b on cell membranes. *J. Immun.* **136**, 3390–3395.

KINOSHITA, T., MEDOF, M. E., SILBER, R. & NUSSENZWEIG, V. (1985). Distribution of decay-accelerating factor in the peripheral blood of normal individuals and patients with paroxysmal noctural hemoglobinuria. *J. exp. Med.* **162**, 75–92.

KISHIMOTO, T. K., HOLLANDER, N., ROBERTS, T. M., ANDERSON, D. C. & SPRINGER, T. A. (1987a). Heterogenous mutations in the β-subunit common to the LFA-1, Mac-1, and p150,95 glycoproteins cause leukocyte adhesion deficiency. *Cell* **50**, 193–202.

KISHIMOTO, T. K., MILLER, L. J. & SPRINGER, T. A. (1987c). Homology of LFA-1, Mac-1, and p150,95 with the extracellular matrix receptors defines a novel supergene family of adhesion proteins. In *Leucocyte Typing III: white cell differentiation antigens* (ed. A. J. McMichael), pp. 896–898. Oxford, New York, Tokyo: Oxford University Press.

KISHIMOTO, T. K., O'CONNER, K., LEE, A., ROBERTS, T. M. & SPRINGER, T. A. (1987b). Cloning of the β subunit of the leukocyte adhesion proteins: homology to an extracellular matrix receptor defines a novel supergene family. *Cell* **48**, 681–690.

KLICKSTEIN, L. B., RABSON, L. D., WONG, W. W., SMITH, J. A. & FEARON, D. T. (1987a). CRI 5′ cDNA sequences contain a fourth long homologous repeat (LHR) and identify a new B cell-specific mRNA. *Complement* **4**, 180 (abs).

KLICKSTEIN, L. B., WONG, W. W., SMITH, J. A., WEIS, J. H., WILSON, J. G. & FEARON, D. T. (1987a). Human C3b/C4b receptor (CR1): Demonstration of long homologous repeating domains that are composed of short consensus repeats characteristic of C3/C4 binding proteins. *J. exp. Med.* **165**, 1095–1112.

KRISTENSEN, T., D'EUSTACHIO, P., OGATA, R. T., CHUNG, L. P., REID, K. B. M. & TACK, B. F. (1987a). The superfamily of C3b/C4b-binding proteins. *Fedn Proc. Fedn Am. Socs exp. Biol.* **46**, 2463–2469.

KRISTENSEN, T., OGATA, R. T., CHUNG, L. P., REID, K. B. M. & TACK, B. F. (1987b). cDNA structure of murine C4b-binding protein, a regulatory component of the serum complement system. *Biochemistry* **26**, 4668–4674.

KUROSKY, A., BARNETT, D. R., LEE, T. H., TOACHSTONE, B., HAY, R. E., ARNOTT, M. S., BOWMAN, B. H. & FITCH, W. M. (1980). Covalent structure of human haptoglobin: a serine protease homolog. *Proc. natn. Acad. Sci. U.S.A.* **77**, 3388–3392.

KURZINGER, K., HO, M. K. & SPRINGER, T. A. (1982). Structural homology of a macrophage differentiation antigen and an antigen involved in T-cell-mediated killing. *Nature, Lond.* **296**, 668–670.

LACHMANN, P. J., PANGBURN, M. K. & OLDROYD, R. G. (1982). Breakdown of C3 after complement activation: identification of a new fragment, C3g, using monoclonal antibodies. *J. exp. Med.* **156**, 205–216.

LAW, S. K., FEARON, D. T. & LEVINE, R. P. (1979). Action of the C3b-inactivator on cell-bound C3b. *J. Immun.* **122**, 750–765.

LAW, S. K. & LEVINE, R. P. (1977). Interaction between the third complement protein and cell surface macromolecules. *Proc. natn. Acad. Sci. U.S.A.* **74**, 2701–2705.

LAW, S. K. A. (1983). The covalent binding reaction of C3 and C4. *Ann. N.Y. Acad. Sci.* **421**, 246–258.

LAW, S. K. A., GAGNON, J., HILDRETH, J. E. K., WELLS, C. E., WILLIS, A. C. & WONG, A. J. (1987). The Primary Structure of the β-subunit of the Cell Surface Adhesion Glycoproteins LFA-1, CR3 and p150,95 and its relationship to the fibronectin receptor. *EMBO J.* **6**, 915–919.

LAY, W. H. & NUSSENZWEIG, V. (1968). Receptors for complement on leukocytes. *J. exp. Med.* **128**, 991–1010.

LEONARD, W. J., DEPPER, J. M., KANEHISA, M., KRONKE, M., PEFFER, N. J., SVETLIK, P. B., SULLIVAN, M. & GREENE, W. C. (1985). Structure of the interleukin-2 receptor gene. *Science* **230**, 633–639.

LOZIER, J., TAKAHASHI, N. & PUTNAM, F. W. (1984). Complete amino acid sequence of human plasma β2-glycoprotein I. *Proc. natn. Acad. Sci. U.S.A.* **81**, 3640–3644.

LUBLIN, D. M., GRIFFITH, R. C. & ATKINSON, J. P. (1986). Influence of glycosylation on allelic and cell specific Mr variation, receptor processing and ligand binding of the human complement C3b/C4b receptor. *J. biol. Chem.* **261**, 5736–5744.

LUBLIN, D. M., LEMONS, R. S., LE BEAU, M. M., HOLERS, V. M., TYKOCINSKI, M. L., MEDOF, M. E. & ATKINSON, J. P. (1987). The gene encoding decay-accelerating factor (DAF) is located in the complement-regulatory locus on the long arm of chromosome 1. *J. exp. Med.* **165**, 1731–1736.

MALHOTRA, V., HOGG, N. & SIM, R. B. (1986). Ligand binding by the p150,95 antigen of U937 cells: properties in common with CR3. *Eur. J. Immun.* **16**, 1117–1123.

MALHOTRA, V. & SIM, R. B. (1984). Role of complement receptor CR1 in the breakdown of soluble and zymosan-bound C3b. *Biochem. Soc. Trans.* **12**, 781–782.

MALHOTRA, V. & SIM, R. B. (1985). Expression of complement factor H on cell surface of the human monocytic cell line U937. *Eur. J. Immun.* **15**, 935–941.

MANTOVANI, B., RABINOVITCH, M. & NUSSENZWEIG, V. (1972). Phagocytosis of immune complexes by macrophages: different roles of the macrophage receptor sites for complement (C3) and for immunoglobulin (IgG). *J. exp. Med.* **135**, 780–792.

MARLIN, S. D., MORTON, C. C., ANDERSON, D. C. & SPRINGER, T. A. (1986). LFA-1 immunodeficiency disease: definition of the genetic defect and chromosomal mapping of the α and β subunits of the lymphocyte function associated antigen 1 (LFA-1) by complementation in hybrid cells. *J. exp. Med.* **164**, 855–867.

MEDICUS, R. G., MELAMED, J. & ARNAOUT, M. A. (1983). Role of human factor I and C3b receptor in the cleavage of surface-bound C3bi molecules. *Eur. J. Immun.* **13**, 465–470.

MEDOF, M. E., IIDA, K., MOLD, C. & NUSSENZWEIG, V. (1982a). Unique role of the complement receptor CR1 in the degradation of C3b associated with immune complexes. *J. exp. Med.* **156**, 1739–1754.

MEDOF, M. E., KINOSHITA, T. & NUSSENZWEIG, V. (1984). Inhibition of complement activation on the surface of cells after incorporation of decay accelerating factor (DAF) into their membranes. *J. exp. Med.* **160**, 1558–1578.

MEDOF, M. E., LUBLIN, D. M., HOLERS, V. M., AYERS, D. J., GETTY, R. R., LEYKAM, J. F., ATKINSON, J. P. & TYCOCINSKI, M. L. (1987). Cloning and characterisation of cDNAs encoding the complete sequence of decay accelerating factor. *Proc. natn. Acad. Sci. U.S.A.* **84**, 2007–2011.

MEDOF, M. E. & NUSSENZWEIG, V. (1984). Control of the function of substrate-bound C4b-C3b by the complement receptor CR1. *J. exp. Med.* **159**, 1669–1685.

MEDOF, M. E. & OGER, J. J-F. (1982). Competition for immune complexes by red cells in human blood. *J. lab. clin. Immun.* **7**, 7–13.

MEDOF, M. E., PRINCE, G. M. & MOLD, C. (1982b). Release of soluble immune complexes from immune adherence receptors on human erythrocytes is mediated by C3b inactivator independently of B1H and is accompanied by generation of C3c. *Proc. natn. Acad. Sci. U.S.A.* **79**, 5047–5051.

MICHL, J., PIECZONDA, M., UNKELESS, J. C. & SILVERSTEIN, S. C. (1979). Effects of immobilized immune complexes on Fc- and complement-receptor function in resident and thioglycollate-elicited mouse peritoneal macrophages. *J. exp. Med.* **150**, 607–621.

MICKLEM, K. J. & SIM, R. B. (1985). Isolation of complement-fragment iC3b-binding proteins by affinity chromatography: the identification of p150,95 as an iC3b-binding protein. *Biochem. J.* **231**, 233–236.

MILLER, L. J., BAINTON, D. F., BORNEGAARD, N. & SPRINGER, T. A. (1987*b*). Stimulated mobilization of monocyte Mac-1 and p150,95 adhesion proteins from an intracellular vascular compartment to the cell surface. *J. clin. Invest.* **80**, 535–544.

MILLER, L. J., WIEBE, M. & SPRINGER, T. A. (1987*a*). Purification and α-subunit N-terminal sequences of human Mac-1 and p150,95 leukocyte adhesion proteins. *J. Immun.* **138**, 2381–2383.

MITOMO, K., FUJITA, T. & IIDA, K. (1987). Functional and antigenic properties of complement receptor type 2, CR2. *J. exp. Med.* **165**, 1424–1429.

MOORE, M. D., COOPER, N. R. & NEMEROW, G. R. (1987). Molecular cloning and sequence of a cDNA clone encoding the entire EBV/C3d receptor, CR2. *Complement* **4**, 197 (abs).

MORLEY, B. J. & CAMPBELL, R. D. (1984). Internal homologies of the Ba fragment from human complement component factor B, a class III MHC antigen. *EMBO J.* **3**, 153–157.

MÜLLER-EBERHARD, H. J. (1968). Chemistry and reaction mechanisms of complement. *Adv. Immunol.* **8**, 1–80.

MÜLLER-EBERHARD, H. J., DALMASSO, A. P. & CALCOTT, M. A. (1966). The reaction mechanism of B1C-globulin (C′3) in immune hemolysis. *J. exp. Med.* **124**, 33–54.

MULLER-EBERHARD, H. J. & NILSSON, U. (1960). Relation of a β1-glycoprotein of human serum to the complement system. *J. exp. Med.* **111**, 217–234.

MYONES, B. L., DALZALL, J. G., HOGG, N. & ROSS, G. D. (1987). CR4 is p150,95 (CD11c), the third member of the LFA-1/CR3 (CD11a/CD11b) glycoprotein family (CD18). *Complement* **4**, 199 (abs).

NAGASAWA, S., ICHIHARA, C. & STROUD, R. M. (1980). Cleavage of C4b by C3b inactivator: production of a nicked form of C4b, C4b′, as an intermediate cleavage product of C4b by C3b inactivator. *J. Immun.* **125**, 578–582.

NELSON, D. S. (1963). Immune adherence. *Adv. Immunol.* **3**, 131–180.

NELSON, R. A. JR, (1953). The immune adherence phenomenon. An immunologically specific reaction between microorganism and erythrocytes leading to enhanced phagocytosis. *Science* **118**, 733–737.

NELSON, R. A. JR, JENSEN, J., GIGLI, I. & TAMURA, N. (1966). Methods for the separation, purification and measurement of nine components of guinea pig complement. *Immunochemistry* **3**, 111–135.

NEMEROW, G. R., WOLFERT, R., MCNAUGHTON, M. E. & COOPER, N. R. (1985). Identification and characterization of the Epstein-Barr virus receptor on human B lymphocytes and its relationship to the C3d complement receptor (CR2). *J. Virol.* **55**, 347–351.

NEWMAN, S. L. & MIKUS, L. K. (1985). Deposition of C3b and iC3b onto particulate activators of the human complement system: quantitation with monoclonal antibodies to human C3. *J. exp. Med.* **161**, 1414–1431.

NEWMAN, S. L., MUSSON, R. A. & HENSON, P. M. (1980). Development of functional complement receptors during in vitro maturation of human monocytes into macrophages. *J. Immun.* **125**, 2236–2244.

NICHOLSON-WELLER, A., BURGE, J., FEARON, D. T., WELLER, P. F. & AUSTEN, K. F. (1982). Isolation of a human erythrocyte membrane glycoprotein with decay accelerating activity for C3 convertases of the complement system. *J. Immun.* **129**, 184–189.

NILSSON, U. R., MANDLE, R. J. & MCCONNELL-MAPES, J. A. (1975). Human C3 and C5: Subunit structure and modifications by trypsin and C42–C423. *J. Immun.* **114**, 815–822.

NISHIOKA, K. & LINSCOTT, W. D. (1963). Components of guinea pig complement. I. Separation of a serum fraction essential for immune hemolysis and immune adherence. *J. exp. Med.* **118**, 767–793.

PANGBURN, M. K., SCHREIBER, R. D. & MÜLLER-EBERHARD, J. H. (1977). Human complement C3b inactivator: isolation, characterization, and demonstration of an absolute requirement for the serum protein B1H for cleavage of C3b and C4b in solution. *J. exp. Med.* **146**, 257–270.

PANGBURN, M. K., SCHREIBER, R. D. & MÜLLER-EBERHARD, J. H. (1983). Deficiency of an erythrocyte membrane protein with complement regulatory activity in paroxysmal nocturnal hemoglobinuria. *Proc. natn. Acad. Sci. U.S.A.* **80**, 5430–5434.

PERKINS, S. J., CHUNG, L. P. & REID, K. B. M. (1986). Unusual ultrastructure of complement-component C4b-binding protein of human complement by synchrotron x-ray scattering and hydrodynamic analysis. *Biochem. J.* **233**, 799–807.

PIERCE, M. W., REMOLD-O'DONNELL, E., TODD, R. F. III & ARNAOUT, M. A. (1986). N-terminal sequence of human leukocyte glycoprotein Mo1: Conservation across species and homology to platelet IIb/IIIa. *Biochim. Biophys. Acta* **874**, 368–371.

PIERSCHBACHER, M. D. & RUOSLAHTI, E. (1984). The cell attachment activity of fibronectin can be duplicated by small synthetic fragments of the molecule. *Nature* **309**, 30–33.

PYTELA, R., PIERSHCBACHER, M. D., GINSBERG, M. H., PLOW, E. F. & RUOSLAHTI, E. (1986). Platelet membrane glycoprotein IIb/IIIa: member of a family of arg-gly-asp-specific adhesion receptors. *Science* **231**, 1559–1562.

REID, K. B. M. (1986). Activation and control of the complement system. *Essays Biochem.* **22**, 27–68.

REID, K. B. M., BENTLEY, D. R., CAMPBELL, R. D., CHUNG, L. P., SIM, R. B., KRISTENSEN, T. & TACK, B. F. (1986). Complement system proteins which interact with C3b or C4b. *Immun. Today* **7**, 230–233.

REY-CAMPOS, J., RUBINSTEIN, P. & RODRIGUEZ DE CORDOBA, S. (1987). Decay accelerating factor: genetic polymorphism and linkage to the RCA (regulator of complement activation) gene cluster in humans. *J. exp. Med.* **166**, 246–252.

RODRIGUEZ DE CORDOBA, S., LUBLIN, D. M., RUBINSTEIN, P. & ATKINSON, J. P. (1985). Human genes for three complement components that regulate the activation of C3 are tightly linked. *J. exp. Med.* **161**, 1189–1195.

ROSS, G. D., CAIN, J. A. & LACHMANN, P. J. (1985*a*). Membrane complement receptor type three (CR3) has lectin like properties analogous to bovine conglutinin and functions as a receptor for zymosan and rabbit erythrocytes was well as a receptor for iC3b. *J. Immun.* **134**, 3307–3315.

ROSS, G. D., CAIN, J. A., MYONES, B. L., NEWMAN, S. L. & LACHMANN, P. J. (1987). Specificity of membrane complement receptor type three (CR3) for β-glycans. *Complement* **4**, 61–74.

ROSS, G. D. & LAMBRIS, J. D. (1982). Identification of a C3bi-specific membrane complement receptor that is expressed on lymphocytes, monocytes, neutrophils and erythrocytes. *J. exp. Med.* **155**, 96–110.

ROSS, G. D., LAMBRIS, J. D., CAIN, J. A. & NEWMAN, S. (1982). Generation of three different fragments of bound C3 with purified factor I or serum: I. Requirements for factor H vs CR1 cofactor activity. *J. Immun.* **129**, 2051–2060.

ROSS, G. D. & MEDOF, M. E. (1985). Membrane complement receptors specific for bound fragments of C3. *Adv. Immunol.* **37**, 217–267.

ROSS, G. D., NEWMAN, S. L., LAMBRIS, J. D., DEVERY-POCIUS, J. E., CAIN, J. A. & LACHMANN, P. J. (1983). Generation of three different fragments of bound C3 with purified factor I in serum. II. Location of binding sites in the C3 fragments for factor B and H, Complement receptors, and bovine conglutinin. *J. exp. Med.* **158**, 334–352.

ROSS, G. D., POLLEY, M. J., RABELLINO, E. M. & GREY, H. M. (1973). Two difference complement receptors on human lymphocytes; one specific for C3b and one specific for C3b inactivator-cleaved C3b. *J. exp. Med.* **138**, 798–811.

ROSS, G. D., THOMPSON, R. A., WALPORT, M. J., SPRINGER, T. A., WATSON, J. V., WARD, R. H. R., LIDA, J., NEWMAN, S. L., HARRISON, R. A. & LACHMANN, P. J. (1985*b*). Characterisation of patients with an increased susceptibility to bacterial infections and a genetic deficiency of leukocyte membrane complement receptor type 3 and related membrane antigen LFA-1. *Blood* **66**, 882–890.

ROTHLEIN, R., DUSTIN, M. L., MARLIN, S. D. & SPRINGER, T. A. (1986). A human intercellular adhesion molecule (ICAM-1) distinct from LFA-1. *J. Immun.* **137**, 1270–1274.

ROTHLEIN, R. & SPRINGER, T. A. (1986). The requirement for lymphocyte function associated antigen 1 in homotypic leukocyte adhesion stimulated by phorbal ester. *J. exp. Med.* **163**, 1132–1149.

SANCHEZ-MADRID, F., KRENSKY, A. M., WARE, C. F., ROBBINS, E., STROMINGER, J. L., BURAKOFF, S. J. & SPRINGER, T. A. (1982). Three distinct antigens associated with human T lymphocyte-mediated cytolysis, LFA-1, LFA-2, and LFA-3. *Proc. natn. Acad. Sci. U.S.A.* **79**, 7489–7493.

SANCHEZ-MADRID, F., NAGY, J. A., ROBBINS, E., SIMON, P. & SPRINGER, T. A. (1983). A human leukocyte differentiation antigen family with distinct β-subunits and a common β-subunit: the lymphocyte function-associated antigen (LFA-1), the C3bi complement receptor (OKM1/Mac-1), and the p150,95 molecule. *J. exp, Med.* **158**, 1785–1803.

SCHULZ, T. F., SCHIENER, O., ALSENZ, J., LAMBRIS, J. D. & DIERICH, M. P. (1984). Use of monoclonal antibodies against factor H to investigate the role of a membane-associated protein antigenically related to H in C3b-receptor function. *J. Immun.* **132**, 392–398.

SEYA, T., BALLARD, L., BORA, N., McNEARNEY, T. & ATKINSON, J. P. (1987). Membrane Cofactor Protein (MCP or gp45–70): a distinct complement regulatory protein with a wide tissue distribution. *Complement* **4**, 225 (abs).

SEYA, T., HOLERS, V. M. & ATKINSON, J. P. (1985). Purification and functional analysis of the polymorphic variants of CR1 and comparison with H, C4bp and DAF. *J. Immun.* **135**, 2661–2667.

SEYA, T., NAGASAWA, S. & ATKINSON, J. P. (1986*b*). Location of the interchain disulfide bonds of the fourth component of human complement (C4): evidence based on the liberation of fragments secondary to thiol-disulfide interchange reactions. *J. Immun.* **136**, 4152–4156.

SEYA, T., TURNER, J. R. & ATKINSON, J. P. (1986*a*). Purification and characterisation of a membrane protein (gp45–70) that is a cofactor for cleavage of C3b and C4b. *J. exp. Med.* **163**, 837–855.

SHIRAISHI, S. & STROUD, R. M. (1975). Cleavage products of C4b produced by enzymes in human serum. *Immunochemistry* **12**, 935–939.

SIM, E., WOOD, A. B., HSIUNG, L. M. & SIM, R. B. (1981). Pattern of degradation of human complement fragment C3b. *FEBS Lett.* **132**, 55–60.

SIM, R. B. & WOLPORT, M. J. (1987). C3 receptors. In *Complement in health and disease* (ed. K. Whaley), pp. 125–161. Lancaster, UK: MTP Press.

SIQUEIRA, M. & NELSON, R. A. (1961). Platelet agglutination by immune complexes and its possible role in hypersensitivity. *J. Immun.* **86**, 516–525.

SOLOMON, E., PALMER, R., HING, S. & LAW, S. K. A. (1988). Regional localization of CD18, the *β*-subunit of the cell surface adhesion molecule LFA-1, on human chromosome 21 by *in situ* hybridization. *Ann. human Genetics* (in press).

SPRINGER, T. A., DAVIGNON, D., HO, M. K., KURZINGER, K., MARTZ, E. & SANCHEZ-MADRID, F. (1982). LFA-1 and Lyt-2,3 molecules associated with T. lymphocyte-mediate killing; and Mac-1, and LFA-1 homologue associated with complement receptor. *Immun. Rev.* **68**, 111–135.

SPRINGER, T. A., DUSTIN, M. L., KISHIMOTO, T. K. & MARLIN, S. D. (1987). The lymphocyte function-associated LFA-1, CD2, and LFA-3 molecules: cell adhesion receptors of the immune system. *A. Rev. Immun.* **5**, 223–252.

SPRINGER, T., GALFRÉ, G., SECHER, D. S. & MILSTEIN, C. (1979). Mac-1: a macrophage differentiation antigen identified by monoclonal antibody. *Eur. J. Immun.* **9**, 301–306.

SPRINGER, T. A., TEPLOW, D. B. & DREYER, W. J. (1985). Sequence homology of the LFA-1 and Mac-1 leukocyte adhesion glycoproteins and unexpected relation to leukocyte interferon. *Nature, Lond.* **314**, 540–542.

SPRINGER, T. A., THOMPSON, W. S., MILLER, L. J., SCHMALSTIEG, F. C. & ANDERSON, D. C. (1984). Inherited deficiency of the Mac-1, LFA-1, p150.95 glycoprotein family and its molecular basis. *J. exp. Med.* **160**, 1901–1918.

STADEN, R. (1982). An interactive graphic program for comparing and aligning nucleic acid and amino acid sequences. *Nucl. Acids Res.* **10**, 2951–2961.

TACK, B. F., HARRISON, R. A., JANATOVA, J., THOMAS, M. L. & PRAHL, J. W. (1980). Evidence for the presence of an internal thiolester bond in the third component of human complement. *Proc. natn. Acad. Sci. U.S.A.* **77**, 5764–5768.

TAMKUN, J. W., DeSIMONE, D. W., FONDS, D., PATEL, R. S., BUCK, C., HORWITZ, A. F. & HYNES, R. O. (1986). Structure of integrin, a glycoprotein involved in the transmembrane linkage between fibronectin and actin. *Cell* **46**, 271–282.

TEDDER, T. F., CLEMENT, L. T. & COOPER, M. D. (1984). Expression of C3d receptors during human B cell differentiation: immunofluorescence analysis with the HB-5 monoclonal antibody. *J. Immun.* **133**, 678–683.

TOSI, M., DUPONCHE, C., MEO, T. & JULIER, C. (1987). Complete cDNA sequence of human C1s and close physical linkage of the homologous genes C1s and C1r. *Biochemistry* **26**, 8516–8524.

ULLRICH, A., BELL, J. R., CHEN, E. Y., HERRERA, R., PETRUZZELLI, L. M., DULL, T. J., GRAY, A., COSSENS, L., LIAO, Y. C., TSUBIKAWA, M., MASON, A., SEEBURG, P. H., GRUNFELD, C., ROSEN, O. M. & RAMACHANDRAN, J. (1985). Human insulin receptor and its relationship to the tyrosine kinase family of oncogenes. *Nature, Lond.* **313**, 756–761.

ULLRICH, A., COUSSENS, L., HAYFLICK, J. S., DULL, T. J., GRAY, A., TAM, A. W., LEE, J., YARDEN, Y., LIBRERMANN, T. A., SCHLESSINGER, J., DOWNWARD, J., MAYES, E. L., WHITTLE, N., WATERFIELD, M. D. & SEEBURG, P. H. (1984). Human epidermal growth factor receptor cDNA sequence and aberrant expression of the amplified gene in A431 spidermoid carcinoma cells. *Nature, Lond.* **309**, 418–425.

VIK, D. P. & FEARON, D. T. (1985). Neutrophils express a receptor for iC3b, C3dg, and C3d that is distinct from CR1, CR2, and CR3. *J. Immun.* **134**, 2571–2579.

VIK, D. P. & FEARON, D. T. (1987). Cellular distribution of complement receptor type 4 (CR4).: expression on human platelets. *J. Immun.* **138**, 254–258.

VIK, D. P., KEENEY, J. B., BRONSON, S., WESTLUND, B., KRISTENSEN, T., CHAPLIN, D. D. & TACK, B. F. (1987). Analysis of the murine factor H gene and related DNA. *Complement* **4**, 235 (abs).

WAXMAN, F. J., HEBERT, L. A., CORNACOFF, J. B., VANAMAN, M. E., SMEAD, W. L., KRAUT, E. H., BIRMINGHAM, D. J. & TAGUIAM, J. M. (1984). Complement depletion accelerates the clearance of immune complexes from the circulation of primates. *J. clin. Invest.* **74**, 1329–1340.

WEIS, J. J., FEARON, D. T., KLICKSTEIN, L. B., WONG, W. W., RICHARDS, S. A., DE BRUYN KOPS, A., SMITH, J. A. & WEIS, J. H. (1986). Identification of a partial cDNA clone for the C3d/Epstein Barr Virus receptor of human B lymphocytes: homology with the receptor for fragments C3b and C4b of the third and fourth components of complement. *Proc. natn. Acad. Sci. U.S.A.* **83**, 5639–5642.

WEIS, J. J., TEDDER, T. F. & FEARON, D. T. (1984). Identification of a 145,000 Mr membrane protein as the C3d receptor (CR2) of human B lymphocytes. *Proc. natn. Acad. Sci. U.S.A.* **81**, 881–885.

WEIS, J. J., TOOTHAKER, L. E., BURROW, S. R., WEIS, J. H. & FEARON, D. T. (1987). Human CR2 is comprised of linked groups of SCRs. *Complement* **4**, 238 (abs).

WEST, C. D., DAVIS, N. C., FORRISTAL, J., HERBST, J. & SPITZEL, R. (1966). Antigenic determinants of human B1C and B1G globulin. *J. Immun.* **96**, 650–658.

WETSEL, R. A., LUNDWALL, A., DAVIDSON, F., GIBSON, T., TACK, B. F. & FEY, G. H. (1984). Structure of murine complement component C3: II. Nucleotide sequence of cloned complementary DNA coding for the chain. *J. biol. Chem.* **259**, 13857–13862.

WHALEY, K. & RUDDY, S. (1976a). Modulation of C3b haemolytic activity by a plasma protein distinct from C3b-inactivator. *Science* **193**, 1011–1013.

WHALEY, K. & RUDDY, S. (1976b). Modulation of the alternative complement pathway by B1H globulin. *J. exp. Med.* **144**, 1147–1163.

WONG, W., CAHILL, J., KENNEDY, C., BENACCIO, E., WILSON, J., KLICKSTEIN, L., RABSON, L. & FEARON, D. (1987). Analysis of genomic polymorphisms in the human CR1 gene. *Complement* **4**, 240 (abs).

WONG, W. W., KLICKSTEIN, L. B., SMITH, J. A., WEIS, J. H. & FEARON, D. T. (1985). Identification of a partial cDNA clone for the human receptor for complement fragments C3b/C4b. *Proc. natn. Acad. Sci. U.S.A.* **32**, 7711–7715.

WONG, W. W., WILSON, J. G. & FEARON, D. T. (1983). Genetic regulation of a structural polymorphism of human C3b receptor. *J. clin. Invest.* **72**, 685–693.

WRIGHT, S. D., CRAIGMYLE, L. S. & SILVERSTEIN, S. C. (1983b). Fibronectin and serum amyloid P component stimulates C3b- and C3bi-mediated phagocytosis in cultured human monocytes. *J. exp. Med.* **158**, 1338–1343.

WRIGHT, S. D. & JONG, M. T. C. (1986). Adhesion-promoting receptors on human macrophages recognise Escherichia coli by binding to lipopolysaccharide. *J. exp. Med.* **164**, 1876–1888.

WRIGHT, S. D. & MEYER, B. C. (1986). Phorbol esters cause sequential activation and deactivation of complement receptors on polymorphonuclear leukocytes. *J. Immun.* **136**, 1759–1764.

WRIGHT, S. D., RAE, P. E., VAN VOORHIS, W. C., CRAIGMYLE, L. S., IIDA, K., TALLE, M. A., WESTBERG, E. F., GOLDSTEIN, G. & SILVERSTEIN, S. C. (1983a). Identification of the C3bi receptor of human monocytes and macrophages by using monoclonal antibodies. *Proc. natn. Acad. Sci. U.S.A.* **80**, 5699–5703.

WRIGHT, S. D., REDDY, P. A., JONG, M. T. C. & ERICKSON, B. W. (1987). C3bi receptor (complement receptor type 3) recognizes a region of complement protein C3 containing the sequence Arg-Gly-Asp. *Proc. natn. Acad. Sci. U.S.A.* **84**, 1965–1968.

WRIGHT, S. D. & SILVERSTEIN, S. C. (1982). Tumor-promoting phorbol esters stimulate C3b and C3b′ receptor-mediated phagocytosis in cultured human monocytes. *J. exp. Med.* **156**, 1149–1164.

WRIGHT, S. D. & SILVERSTEIN, S. C. (1983). Receptors for C3b and C3bi promote phagocytosis but not the release of toxic oxygen from human phagocytes. *J. exp. Med.* **158**, 2016–2023.

YAMAMOTO, T., DAVIS, C. G., BROWN, M. S., SCHNEIDER, W. J., CASEY, M. L., GOLDSTEIN, J. L. & RUSSELL, D. W. (1984). The human LDL receptor: a cysteine-rich protein with multiple Alu sequences in its mRNA. *Cell* **39**, 27–38.

Notes added in proof

Recent publications on the primary structure of the α subunits of mouse CR3 (Pytela, 1988) and human p150,95 antigen (Corbi *et al*. 1987) showed that they are highly homologous, each with a hydrophobic transmembrane segment and several Ca^{2+}-binding domains on the extracellular portion. They also share extensive sequence homology with the corresponding subunits of the matrix adhesion proteins (Argraves *et al*. 1987; Poncz *et al*. 1987; Suzuki *et al*. 1987).

References

ARGRAVES, W. S., SUZUKI, S., ARAI, H., THOMPSON, K., PIERSCHBACHER, M. D. & RUOSLAHTI, E. (1987). Amino acid sequence of the human fibronectin receptor. *J. Cell Biol.* **105**, 1183–1190.

CORBI, A. L., MILLER, L. J., O'CONNOR, K., LARSON, R. S. & SPRINGER, T. A. (1987). cDNA cloning and complete primary structure of the α subunit of a leukocyte adhesion glycoprotein, p150,95. *EMBO J.* **6**, 4023–4028.

PONCZ, M., EISMAN, R., HEIDENREICH, R., SILVER, S. M., VILAIRE, G., SURREY, S., SCHWARTZ, E. & BENNETT, J. S. (1987). Structure of the platelet membrane glycoprotein IIb. *J. biol. Chem.* **262**, 8476–8482.

PYTELA, R. (1988). Amino acid sequence of the murine Mac-1 α chain reveals homology with the integrin family and an additional domain relate to von Willebrand factor. *EMBO J.* **7**, 1371–1378.

SUZUKI, S., ARGRAVES, W. S., ARAI, H., LANGUINO, L. R., PIERSCHBACHER, M. D. & RUOSLAHTI, E. (1987). Amino acid sequence of the vitronectin receptor α subunit and comparative expression of adhesion receptor mRNAs. *J. biol. Chem.* **262**, 14080–14085.

J. Cell Sci. Suppl. 9, 99–120 (1988)
Printed in Great Britain © The Company of Biologists Limited 1988

Adhesion-promoting receptors on phagocytes

SAMUEL D. WRIGHT AND PATRICIA A. DETMERS

Laboratory of Cellular Physiology and Immunology, The Rockefeller University,
1230 York Avenue, New York, NY 10021, USA

Summary

Phagocytes express a family of structurally related receptors, LFA-l, CR3, and p150,95, that mediate adhesion of leukocytes to a variety of cells and surfaces. LFA-l mediates the binding of killer T cells to targets, CR3 mediates binding of phagocytes to iC3b-coated surfaces and to endothelial cells, and LFA-l, CR3, and p150,95 each mediate the binding of bacterial lipopolysaccharide. Here we review the structure and function of each of these receptors and present evidence that they are related to a larger class of adhesion-promoting receptors called integrins. Of particular emphasis are observations that the capacity of these receptors to promote adhesion is strongly and reversibly modulated by both soluble and surface-bound stimuli. We review this form of regulation and present evidence that changes in the binding activity of adhesion-promoting receptors is accomplished by changes in the two-dimensional distribution of receptors in the plane of the membrane. Inactive receptors are randomly distributed in the membrane, and their ability to bind a ligand-coated surface is enabled by a ligand-independent movement into small clusters. The implications of these structural features are discussed.

Introduction

Adhesion between phagocytes and other cells, particles, or the extracellular matrix is crucial for a variety of functions such as phagocytosis, diapedesis, and positioning of phagocytes in the liver, lungs, and other tissues. It has long been assumed that specific receptors mediate cellular adhesions, but only recently have such receptors been isolated and characterized. We describe here a newly recognized class of receptors that mediate cell–cell and cell–substratum adhesion, and we review the functions of these receptors on phagocytes.

Leukocyte adhesion deficiency (LAD)

The notion that a few receptors could be responsible for a wide range of adhesion events first arose with the discovery of a class of patients that exhibit recurrent life-threatening infections with gram-positive, gram-negative and fungal pathogens (reviewed in Anderson & Springer, 1987; Todd & Freyer, 1988). These patients exhibit extreme leukocytosis but a failure to form pus at sites of infection. *In vitro* experiments showed that polymorphonuclear leukocytes (PMN) from these patients are defective in adhesion to iC3b-coated erythrocytes, to protein-coated glass or plastic surfaces (Anderson *et al.* 1984), and to endothelial cells (Harlan *et al.* 1985), and that failure to adhere results in the failure to display chemotactic responses. Thus, susceptibility to infection probably results both from an inability to bind and ingest opsonized pathogens and a failure to recruit cells to sites of infection. More importantly, these observations suggest that the leukocytes of LAD patients fail to extravasate and are retained in the vasculature by a failure to adhere to endothelial cells. Characterization of the proteins missing from the patients' leukocytes have amply confirmed their role in adhesion to endothelium and in several other adhesion events.

A family of adhesion-promoting receptors

The phenotype of LAD patients is caused by a failure of leukocytes to express three related proteins, LFA-1, CR3, and p150,95 (Springer *et al.* 1984). Each of these cell-surface glycoproteins consists of an $\alpha_1\beta_1$ dimer composed of a 150–190K ($K = 10^3 M_r$) α chain and a 95K β chain, schematically depicted in Fig. 1. The β chain is identical in each of these three proteins (Sanchez-Madrid *et al.* 1983), and has been given the designation CD18 by the International Leukocyte Antigen Workshop. The α chains, on the other hand, are structurally and antigenically distinct. Thus a monoclonal antibody against the α chain of CR3 (OKM1 for example) will bind and precipitate CR3, but not LFA-1 or p150,95, while a monoclonal against the common β chain (IB4 for example) will precipitate all three of these dimeric proteins (Wright *et al.* 1983*a*). The α chains of LFA-1, CR3, and p150,95 are termed CD11a, CD11b, and CD11c, respectively, and CR3 may thus be referred to as CD11b/CD18.

LAD patients are deficient in all three of these proteins because of an inherited defect in the β chain (Springer *et al.* 1984). Cells from LAD patients do synthesize normal precursors of the α chains, but these precursors are very rapidly degraded and do not appear on the cell surface. The α chains can, however, be 'rescued' in cells fused with a murine partner that expresses normal β chain (Marlin *et al.* 1986). Here the human α chain appears on the cell surface joined with a murine β chain.

The cellular distribution of LFA-1, CR3, and p150,95 is outlined in Table 1. Lymphocytes express abundant LFA-1, but neither CR3 nor p150,95 can be detected. PMN express abundant CR3, and LFA-1 and p150,95 are minor but easily

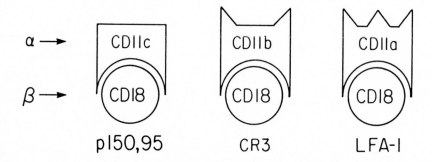

Fig. 1. Schematic representation of the LFA-1, CR3, p150,95 family of leukocyte antigens. Each protein is a dimer composed of a unique α chain in association with a β chain that is identical in all three proteins.

Table 1. *Adhesion-promoting receptors of leukocytes*

Receptor	mABs against α chain	Cellular distribution	Function	Reference
CR3 (CD11b/CD18)	OKM1, OKM10 M1/70 44a	Monocyte, macrophage, PMN, NK cells	iC3b receptor LPS receptor	Wright *et al.* (1983*a*) Beller *et al.* (1982) Arnaout *et al.* (1983)
LFA-1 (CD11a/CD18)	TS1/22 TA-1	Monocyte, macrophage, PMN, T and B cells NK cells	NK–target binding T cell–target binding Macrophage–tumour binding LPS receptor	Sanchez-Madrid *et al.* (1982) LeBien & Kersey (1980)
p150,95 (CD11c/CD18)	LeuM5 3·9	Monocyte, macrophage, PMN	? LPS receptor	Lanier *et al.* (1985) Hogg *et al.* (1986)

Antibodies against the β chain are IB4 (Wright *et al.* 1983*a*), 60·3 (Beatty *et al.* 1983), and TS1/18 (Sanchez-Madrid *et al.* 1982). See text for further details and references.

detectable components. Macrophages express large amounts of all three of these proteins. Expression of these antigens appears restricted to leukocytes, and they are not found on other mammalian cell types.

Function of LFA-1, CR3, and p150,95

The role of the individual receptors has been dissected primarily with the use of monoclonal antibodies against the individual α chains. Some of the principal antibodies that have been used are listed in Table 1.

CR3

The first molecule shown to be deficient from LAD patients (Arnaout *et al.* 1982) had been previously identified as a receptor for a cell-bound fragment of complement (Beller *et al.* 1982; Wright *et al.* 1983*a*), and the name CR3 (complement receptor type three) derives from the nomenclature of complement receptors (see the chapter in this volume by S. K. A. Law for more detailed discussion of complement and other complement receptors). CR3 has also been referred to as Mac-1 and Mo1 because it is the first phagocyte-specific antigen identified by monoclonal antibodies in mouse and man respectively. CR3 functions as an opsonic receptor, and promotes the binding of iC3b-coated cells and particles by monocytes, macrophages, and PMN (Wright & Silverstein, 1982; Wright & Meyer, 1986). In appropriately stimulated cells, binding is followed by phagocytosis of the particle. The credentials of CR3 as an adhesion-promoting receptor are thus well established.

   CR3 recognizes surface-bound iC3b but does not recognize either the precursor, C3b, or the product of further cleavage, C3dg (Carlo *et al.* 1979; Wright & Silverstein, 1982; Ross & Lambris, 1982). (C3b is recognized by a separate receptor, CRl, and this receptor is described by Law (1988).) Binding of monomeric or dimeric iC3b to CR3 has not been reported, presumably because of a low binding affinity, and the above statements on the specificity of the receptor rest primarily on studies using particles coated with defined complement fragments to measure binding to CR3-bearing cells. These particles, usually sheep erythrocytes, bear from 10^4 to 10^5 iC3b per red cell, and the resulting multivalent interaction with phagocytes is very avid. By analogy, it is likely that LFA-1 and p150,95 also bind their target ligands with low affinity and that adhesion events mediated by these receptors are driven by multivalent interactions. As described below, a functional consequence of this low affinity is a potential to reverse adhesion and promote detachment.

   CR3 is composed of two non-covalently linked polypeptides, an α chain of 185K and a β chain of 95K, both of which are exposed at the cell surface (Sanchez-Madrid *et al.* 1983; Wright *et al.* 1983*a*). Two lines of evidence suggest that the binding site for iC3b is located, at least in part, on the α polypeptide. First, monoclonal antibodies directed against the α polypeptide have been raised, and a subset of these block the binding of iC3b, while antibodies against the β chain do not (Wright *et al.*

1983*a*). Further evidence for the role of the α chain in the binding of iC3b comes from observations of the β chain in dimeric association with alternative α chains. Neither LFA-1 nor p150,95 recognizes iC3b (Wright & Jong, 1986) and since both of these receptors express β chain, it is unlikely that the β chain binds iC3b.

CR3 requires relatively high concentrations of divalent cations (about 0·5 mM-Ca^{2+} and Mg^{2+}) in order to interact effectively with ligand (Wright & Silverstein, 1982). This behaviour contrasts with that of other opsonic receptors (CRl, and receptors for the Fc domain of IgG (FcR)), which do not require divalent cations for binding activity. In addition, the binding capacity of CR3 is temperature dependent, and is absent in cells held at 0°C (Wright & Jong, 1986), again distinguishing CR3 from other opsonic receptors (CRl, FcR) which bind well at 0°C.

The region of the iC3b molecule that is recognized by CR3 has recently been defined by the use of synthetic peptides (Wright *et al.* 1987). CR3 binds particles coated with a 21 amino acid peptide that spans residues 1383–1403 of C3. This peptide contains the triplet Arg–Gly–Asp (RGD) in its midsection. As discussed below, RGD serves as a recognition structure for many receptors involved in cell adhesion events, and CR3 thus appears to be a member of a larger family of adhesion-promoting receptors.

Molecules other than iC3b may also serve as ligands for CR3. As noted above, CR3 is the principal adhesion-promoting receptor of PMN, and PMN from LAD patients fail to adhere to endothelial cells both *in vitro* (Harlan *et al.* 1985) and *in vivo* (reviewed in Anderson & Springer, 1987; Todd & Freyer, 1988). Moreover, antibodies against CR3 block the binding of phagocytes to endothelial cells *in vivo* (Arfors *et al.* 1987; Rosen & Gordon, 1987; K.-E. Arfors & S. D. Wright, unpublished observations) and *in vitro* (Wallis *et al.* 1986). Thus, CR3 is likely to recognize a structure on endothelial cells and to mediate diapedesis.

LFA-1

Monoclonal antibodies against LFA-1 were identified by screening clones for the ability to block T-cell-mediated cytolysis (Sanchez-Madrid *et al.* 1982). These studies identified three 'lymphocyte function-associated antigens', LFA-1, LFA-2, and LFA-3, which are required for efficient cytolysis. LFA-2 and LFA-3 are structurally and functionally distinct from the proteins under consideration in this review and will not be discussed further.

Several studies indicate that anti-LFA-1 antibodies block cytolysis by blocking adhesion of the killer cell to the target. The step that is blocked by binding of the antibody to LFA-1 on the killer cell had previously been described as a Mg^{2+}-dependent, temperature-dependent adhesion event (reviewed in Martz, 1986). Anti-LFA-1 antibodies also block natural killer-mediated cytotoxicity (Mentzer *et al.* 1986*a*), macrophage-mediated tumour cytotoxicity (Strassman *et al.* 1986), and PMN-mediated antibody-dependent cytotoxicity (Miedema *et al.* 1984; Kohl *et al.* 1984). In all of these cases, the inhibition is caused by binding of the antibody to LFA-1 on the killer cell (not on the target), and thereby blocking adhesion to the target cells. Consistent with these data are results that show that T cells, NK cells, and PMN from LAD patients all show defects in cytotoxicity assays (Kohl *et al.* 1984; Mentzer *et al.* 1986*b*).

It is important to point out in this context that LFA-1 does not provide the specificity for the cytotoxic cells. Rather, targets are selected by separate recognition molecules (T3Ti for example) on the killer, which bind to structures on the target. The bond created by these recognition molecules, however, is weak and LFA-1 functions to strengthen the adhesion (Martz, 1986).

LFA-1 also participates in adhesion events that are unrelated to cytotoxicity. Anti-LFA-1 blocks both the spontaneous (Mentzer *et al.* 1985) and the PMA-stimulated aggregation of B lymphocyte cell lines (Rothlein *et al.* 1986), and very recent data indicate that LFA-1 is involved in strengthening the adhesion between T cells and dendritic cells (Inaba & Steinman, 1987). Effective adhesion with a dendritic cell appears to be a prerequisite for stimulation of resting T cells (Steinman *et al.* 1986).

The ligand that LFA-1 recognizes on target cells has long eluded investigators, but recent studies have identified a molecule, intercellular adhesion molecule-1 (ICAM-1), that serves as a ligand in at least some instances. ICAM-1 is recognized by a monoclonal antibody that blocks LFA-1-dependent aggregation of lymphoblastoid cell lines (Rothlein *et al.* 1986). This inhibition is additive with that caused by anti-LFA-1. While the aggregation of some cell lines is strongly inhibited by anti-ICAM-1 antibody, the LFA-1-dependent aggregation of other lines cannot be inhibited. Thus, it appears that ICAM-1 is not the only ligand for LFA-1.

ICAM-1 is a membrane-bound polypeptide of 90K (Rothlein *et al.* 1986) found on epithelial cells, endothelial cells, B cells, and macrophages (Dustin *et al.* 1986). By homology one would postulate that ICAM-1 contains an RGD sequence similar to that recognized by CR3 in C3bi, but sequence data on ICAM-1 are not yet available.

p150,95

A unique function for p150,95 has not yet been described and its name reflects only the molecular weight of its constituent polypeptide chains. Nevertheless, it does appear to function in adhesion events. p150,95 participates in binding of unopsonized bacteria (Wright & Jong, 1986) and fungi (Bullock & Wright, 1987), a function shared with LFA-1 and CR3 (see below). Further, certain cytotoxic T cell clones express appreciable levels of p150,95, and the killing mediated by these cell lines can be blocked by anti-p150,95 antibodies (Keizer *et al.* 1987). As observed with anti-LFA-l antibodies, the anti-p150,95 antibodies block formation of conjugates of killer and target. A unique ligand for p150,95 has not yet been identified.

Antibodies against p150,95 were first obtained by immunizing mice with cells from patients with hairy cell leukaemia (Schwarting *et al.* 1985). Hairy cells express very abundant p150,95 and very little CR3 or LFA-1 (S. D. Wright, unpublished observations), but the significance of this observation is not clear. p150,95 is also expressed in high abundance on tissue macrophages (Hogg *et al.* 1986), and may thus be expected to serve a major function of these cells.

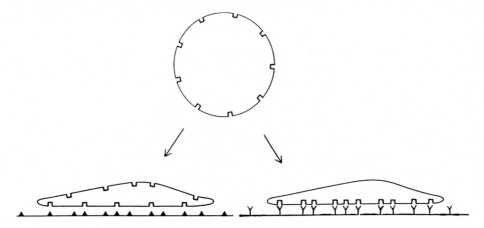

Fig. 2. Clearing receptors from the apical portion of the plasma membrane by surface-bound anti-receptor antibodies. Macrophages spread on serum albumin-coated surfaces exhibit cell surface receptors that are distributed around the entire cell perimeter (left-hand side). In contrast, macrophages spread on surfaces coated with anti-receptor monoclonal antibodies exhibit depletion of receptors from the apical membrane (right-hand side). This clearing of receptors from the apical surface occurs by diffusion of receptors in the plane of the membrane to the basal surface where they are trapped by interaction with a specific antibody. A single monoclonal antibody only clears its target antigen, not other receptors on the cell surface.

LFA-1, CR3, and p150,95 recognize microbes without the aid of complement

Several workers have noted that antibodies against CR3 not only inhibited the binding of iC3b-coated particles but also partially inhibited binding of particles such as zymosan (Ezekowitz *et al.* 1984; Ross *et al.* 1985*a*), *Leishmania* (Blackwell *et al.* 1985; Mosser & Edelson, 1985), and *Staphylococcus* (Ross *et al.* 1985*b*). Since these binding experiments were performed in the absence of a source of complement, it was proposed that CR3 interacts not with C3bi but with the particles directly. Further support for this idea came from the observation that cells from LAD patients exhibit defective recognition of zymosan (Ross *et al.* 1985*b*) and *Escherichia coli* (S. D. Wright, unpublished observations), again in the absence of serum opsonins.

More detailed experiments have indicated that CR3, LFA-1, and p150,95 each share the capacity to bind directly the microbes *Histoplasma capsulatum* (Bullock & Wright, 1987) and *E. coli* (Wright & Jong, 1986). In these experiments, individual receptors were cleared from the apical surface of the macrophage membrane by allowing the cells to spread on surfaces derivatized with specific anti-receptor monoclonal antibodies. The receptors diffuse in the plane of the membrane and are trapped by antibody at the basal surface of the macrophage (Fig. 2). By this means it was shown that clearing all three receptors, CR3, LFA-1, and p150,95, inhibits the binding of microbes, but binding is still observed if any one of these receptors is present. Thus, each of these homologous receptors is individually capable of binding to *H. capsulatum* and *E. coli*.

The capacity of CR3, LFA-1, and p150,95 to bind directly to microbes without the intervention of antibody or complement represents a mechanism by which macrophages may recognize potential pathogens before the onset of adaptive immunity. Consistent with this notion is the observation that LAD patients suffer frequent life-threatening infections primarily in the first 2 years of life. Those patients that survive the first years, however, may live to adulthood in relatively good health.

CR3, LFA-1, and p150,95 recognize bacterial lipopolysaccharide (LPS)

What is the nature of the ligand on the surface of microbes that is recognized by adhesion-promoting receptors? Recent work indicates that the chemical structure of the ligands on *E. coli* is very different from the proteins, iC3b or ICAM-1. Macrophages bind *E. coli* by recognizing lipopolysaccharide (LPS), the most prevalent molecule on the surface of the bacterium (Wright & Jong, 1986). The portion of the LPS molecule that is recognized is the Lipid A region, which consists of a fatty-acylated diglucosamine bisphosphate. Since the fatty acids of Lipid A are buried in the outer membrane of the bacterium, it is likely that the diglucosamine phosphate provides the recognition structure bound by CR3, LFA-1, and p150,95. It is also likely that sugar phosphates on the surface of *H. capsulatum*, zymosan, and *Leishmania* may account for their recognition by these receptors.

Bacterial LPS (endotoxin) causes profound physiological effects in man and animals. These include fever, shock, and the induction of the acute phase response (Morrison & Ulevitch, 1978). The cell type primarily responsible for these effects is the macrophage, which synthesizes large amounts of interleukin-1 and cachectin (TNFα) in response to LPS (Beutler *et al.* 1985; Durum *et al.* 1985). The studies described above indicate that CR3, LFA-1, and p150,95 can bind LPS, but whether these receptors directly mediate the many biological effects of LPS is not yet certain.

How can adhesion-promoting receptors bind ligands as different as iC3b and LPS? Ross *et al.* (1985a) originally suggested that CR3 has two distinct binding sites, one site for iC3b and another for microbes, and recent data support this claim. The binding site for iC3b can be blocked by certain monoclonal anti-α chain antibodies (OKM10 for example), which do not block binding of LPS (S. D. Wright, unpublished results) or the CR3-dependent spreading of PMN on protein-coated plastic (Dana *et al.* 1986). Conversely, binding of LPS (S. D. Wright, unpublished results) and spreading on plastic (Dana *et al.* 1986) can be blocked by an anti-α chain antibody (mAb 904) that does not block the binding of iC3b. These data suggest that CR3 has two binding sites, one for iC3b and another for LPS. It is of interest to note that LPS is a common contaminant of all laboratory solutions, binds avidly to tissue culture plastic (Wright & Jong, 1986), and may thus contribute to the avid adhesion of phagocytes to artificial substrata *in vitro*.

CR3, LFA-1, and p150,95 are related to adhesion-promoting receptors on other cells

Work from several laboratories indicates that CR3, LFA-1, and p150,95 are members of a large, broadly distributed family of proteins that promote cell adhesion

(Ruoslahti & Pierschbacher, 1986; Hynes, 1987). This class of receptors, recently termed 'integrins' by Hynes (1987), includes the fibronectin receptor, vitronectin receptor, gp IIb/IIIa of platelets (the fibrinogen receptor), the VLA antigen series, and several others. Sequence data show extensive homology among α chains and among β chains of all the integrins sequenced. A detailed description of the structural properties of integrins and their relation to one another is presented by Law (1988) and will not be covered here. Rather, we will point out several functional similarities among integrins, which allow a unified view of their actions.

A summary of the properties of several integrins is shown in Table 2. While not all properties have been documented for all receptors, the consensus emerges that each integrin is a large dimeric surface protein that promotes relatively weak adhesion either to ligand-coated cells or substrata. Effective adhesion requires warm temperatures and divalent cations. The requirement for divalent cations is explained by the presence of tandem repeats of a cation-binding domain in the α chain of all integrins thus far sequenced. The requirement for warm temperatures remains to be explained.

Integrins appear capable of binding to two types of ligands. The first and best characterized are protein in nature. These ligands show far less sequence homology than the receptors, but nearly all contain the amino acid sequence, Arg-Gly-Asp (RGD), at the recognition site (Ruoslahti & Pierschbacher, 1986). For example, the fibronectin receptor recognizes the sequence *GRGD*S in fibronectin, the vitronectin receptor recognizes *TRGD*V in vitronectin, and CR3 recognizes *YRGD*Q in C3bi. Nevertheless, integrins do not cross react with each others' ligands. For example, CR3 does not bind fibronectin, nor does the fibronectin receptor bind iC3b (Wright & Meyer, 1985). A likely explanation for this is that the amino acids flanking RGD exhibit only weak similarity, thus providing a possible basis for discrimination (Wright *et al.* 1987).

A second type of ligand for integrins is glycolipid. Ganglioside GD2 co-localizes with the vitronectin receptor in adhesion plaques and co-purifies with the vitronectin receptor in detergent solutions, indicating the presence of a binding site on this integrin for glycolipid (Cheresh *et al.* 1987). As detailed above, CR3, LFA-1, and p150,95 each recognize LPS, another glycolipid (Wright & Jong, 1986). It is not clear at present whether the binding site for LPS on the CD18 complex is

Table 2. *Integrins, a family of adhesion-promoting receptors*

Receptor	Ligands	Requires divalents	Temperature dependent
CR3	iC3b (*YRGD*Q), LPS	+	+
LFA-1	ICAM-1, LPS	+	+
p150,95	LPS, ?	+	+
Fn receptor	Fibronectin (*GRGD*S), GD2	+	+
Vn receptor	Vitronectin (*TRGD*V), GD2	+	?
gpIIb/IIIa	Fibrinogen, fibronectin (*GRGD*S)	+	?

All the above receptors are $\alpha_1\beta_1$ dimers. Additional integrins that have been less well characterized are the VLA antigen family (Hemler *et al.* 1987) and position specific antigens of *Drosophila* (Wilcox & Leptin, 1985). See Hynes (1987) for a review of these findings.

homologous with the binding site for GD2 on the vitronectin receptor, since, in the former case, the receptors bind LPS that is anchored in an adjacent bilayer, and in the latter, receptors bind GD2 that is anchored in the same bilayer. It is also not known if other integrins bind glycolipids, but it appears likely since cell types that do not express CR3, LFA-1 or p150,95, such as endothelial cells, do show marked physiological responses to LPS (Schleimer & Rutledge, 1986).

Integrins appear not to be involved in the strong, long-term adhesions found between cells in tissues. Thus, integrins appear unrelated to proteins of gap junctions, tight junctions, or desmosomes. Rather, integrins mediate relatively weak adhesions that may be readily broken.

The reversible nature of adhesions caused by integrins is illustrated by several findings. (1) Cells bearing fibronectin receptors can migrate rapidly across surfaces coated with fibronectin (Rovasio et al. 1983), indicating that sequential, transient attachments are made between fibronectin receptors and ligand. (2) The LFA-1-mediated binding of killer T cells to targets can be as short as 10 min, ending when the killer detaches and moves to another target (Sanderson, 1976). (3) The iC3b receptor mediates the binding of polymorphonuclear leukocytes (PMN) to endo-thelial cells, which must be short-lived to enable diapedesis to occur. (4) High concentrations of synthetic peptides bearing the RGD sequence, which competi-tively block the action of several integrins (Ruoslahti & Pierschbacher, 1986), prevent normal migration of cells in avian, amphibian (Boucaut et al. 1984), and insect embryos (Naidet et al. 1987), a process for which transient adhesions are obviously required.

One can imagine two models of receptor behaviour that could be used to generate transient adhesions. In the first model, cells would deliver adhesion-promoting receptors to the cell surface only at the place and time required, and after they had functioned, either the receptor or the ligand would be proteolytically inactivated to break the adhesion. In a second model, adhesions are made or broken by allosteric alteration of the receptors, which effectively turn them on or off. An important prediction of this second model is that receptors may be left on the cell surface in the 'off' state such that they can be turned on when and where needed. We present evidence below that supports the second of these two hypotheses, and demonstrates that CR3 is expressed on the cell surface in a form that is unable to bind ligand. We believe that this property of on/off regulation will prove to be a general feature of integrins.

The function of adhesion-promoting receptors is regulated

Several observations suggest that integrins might exist on the cell surface in an inactive state. Transformed fibroblasts fail to bind fibronectin despite apparently normal levels of fibronectin receptors (Hirst et al. 1986; Chen et al. 1986). LFA-1 may also exist in an inactive form, since the LFA-1- dependent aggregation of B cells or lymphoblastoid cell lines is not observed unless the stimulant phorbol myristate acetate (PMA) is added (Rothlein & Springer, 1986). The most detailed studies of on/off behaviour, however, are available for CR3 on macrophages and PMN. We review here the evidence for regulation of binding and phagocytosis by CR3 in phagocytes and discuss the agents that mediate the regulation. We will first discuss regulation of the binding capacity of CR3.

CR3 on resting human monocytes and macrophages avidly mediates binding of iC3b-coated erythrocytes with half-maximal binding at about 5000 iC3b per erythrocyte (Wright & Silverstein, 1982). Culture of the phagocytes for 48 h with interferon (IFN)γ (but not IFNα) causes a striking decrease in the binding capacity of C3 receptors: half-maximal binding of erythrocytes is not obtained even with 120 000 iC3b per erythrocyte (Wright *et al.* 1986). This result contrasts with the behaviour of Fc receptors in that IFNγ causes dramatically enhanced expression of FcγR$_{p72}$ (Guyre *et al.* 1983) and enhanced binding of IgG-coated erythrocytes (Wright *et al.* 1986).

The reduced binding activity of CR3 in IFNγ-treated cells is not associated with changes in the number of cell surface receptor molecules, nor is it associated with proteolytic inactivation of the receptors (Wright *et al.* 1986). Rather, CR3 appears to be reversibly disabled. This point is emphasized by the observation that the binding capacity of CR3 can be fully restored in minutes by allowing the phagocytes to interact with surfaces coated with the extracellular matrix protein, fibronectin (see below).

The physiological significance of this 'deactivation' of CR3 by IFNγ is not currently clear, but IFNγ can be expected to diminish complement receptor activity on all macrophages except those in contact with the appropriate extracellular matrix components. Since IFNγ-treated macrophages possess extremely potent cytolytic activity, lowered capacity to adhere may control inappropriate cytolysis.

The binding activity of CR3 on granulocytes is also regulated but in a manner different from that seen in mononuclear cells (Wright & Meyer, 1986). Resting PMN have a *low* capacity to bind C3-coated particles. This binding activity is very rapidly up-regulated by several agents including PMA and C5a. Though PMA is not a physiological stimulus, its activities are the best characterized and are described in detail below.

Stimulation of PMN with PMA produces a biphasic response (Wright & Meyer, 1986). During the first 20 min, the capacity of CR3 to bind and phagocytose iC3b-coated erythrocytes is dramatically enhanced. During the following 30 min, the capacity to bind and phagocytose is depressed to levels below those shown by resting cells. Treatment of PMN with PMA causes a rapid rise in the expression of CR3 on the cell surface (Berger *et al.* 1984; O'Shea *et al.* 1985; Wright & Meyer 1986). Specific granules (Todd *et al.* 1984; O'Shea *et al.* 1985), granules identified by the presence of gelatinase (Petrequin *et al.* 1987), and granules identified by the presence of alkaline phosphatase (Borregaard *et al.* 1987) have all been implicated as a source of the newly expressed CR3. Though increased expression of CR3 is temporally associated with the enhanced capacity to bind and ingest C3-coated particles caused by PMA, an increased number of receptors is unlikely to be responsible for either the increased binding or phagocytosis. During activation of adherent PMN by PMA, the attachment of iC3b-coated erythrocytes increases 8- to 10-fold and phagocytosis increases 30- to 40-fold while the number of CR3 per cell increases only threefold (Wright & Meyer, 1986). More strikingly, the capacity of CR3 to bind ligand and signal phagocytosis is eliminated during incubation with PMA from 20 to 65 min, but the expression of CR3 does not change in this time. Increasing the expression of CR3 on the cell surface is clearly not sufficient to induce ligand binding, since treating PMN with the chemotactic peptide *N*-formyl-methionyl–leucyl–phenylalanine (fMLP) causes a twofold increase in the amount of CR3 on the cell surface (Berger *et al*. 1984) but does not affect the binding activity of this receptor (Detmers *et al*. 1987). The capacity of CR3 to bind ligand must therefore be controlled in another way.

What biochemical events could explain the transient changes in CR3 activity? Several observations suggest that phosphorylation may provide an answer. (1) The time course and reversibility of C3 receptor activation are consistent with the hypothesis that phosphorylation controls receptor activity. (2) PMA is a potent activator of a ubiquitous Ca^{2+}-activated, phospholipid-dependent protein kinase (Castagna *et al*. 1982). (3) Loading PMN with inorganic thiophosphate (thioP) allows irreversible activation of C3 receptors (Wright & Meyer, 1986). ThioP resembles phosphate and is incorporated into nucleotides and phosphoproteins, but the resulting thiophosphoproteins are resistant to phosphatases. One would thus expect that in a cell loaded with thioP, phosphorylation caused by stimulation of a kinase would result in a pool of thiophosphorylated proteins, which are resistant to dephosphorylation. It is thus likely that the irreversible activation of receptors observed in loaded cells is a consequence of irreversible thiophosphorylation. (4) Very recent data show that CR3 is a phosphoprotein, and its state of phosphorylation is regulated by PMA (S. D. Wright, unpublished results).

How could phosphorylation of CR3 alter its capacity to bind ligand? Our recent work indicates that CR3 aggregates in the plane of the membrane in response to PMA, and such aggregation appears to be a prerequisite for ligand binding (Detmers *et al*. 1987). When the surfaces of resting PMN are labelled with monoclonal anti-CR3 (OKM1) and colloidal gold and viewed by transmission electron microscopy, the gold particles depicting CR3 are present in a random distribution, with many as individuals (Fig. 3A). After PMN are treated with PMA for 25 min, which dramatically enhances binding activity, clusters of receptors are apparent (Fig. 3B). The time course of aggregation corresponds precisely with the time course of enhancement of binding. Aggregation is high at 25 min in PMA, and there is disaggregation by 50 min in PMA, by which time binding declines to levels comparable to those observed in resting cells (Fig. 4). Other surface antigens on

---

Fig. 3. Clustering of CR3 on the surface of PMN in response to PMA. A, Resting PMN and B, PMN treated for 25 min at 37°C with 33 ng ml^{-1} PMA were labelled with biotin-OKM1 and 10-nm streptavidin-conjugated colloidal gold as previously described (Detmers *et al*. 1987). Whereas most gold particles are present on resting cells as individual particles, distinct clusters of receptors are apparent after treatment with PMA (see text for details). Bar, 0·2 μm.

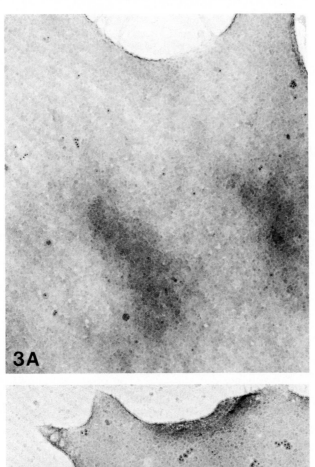

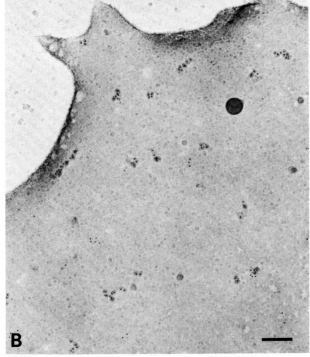

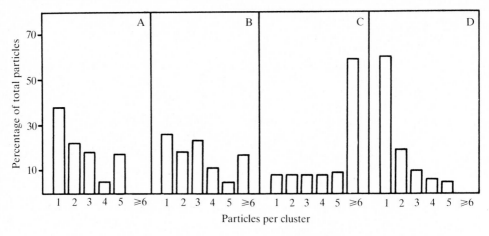

Fig. 4. Transient aggregation of CR3 on the surface of PMN treated with PMA. PMN were incubated for 50 min at 37 °C with 33 ng ml^{-1} PMA added for 0 (A), 10 (B), 25 (C) or 50 (D) min. Cells were labelled with biotin-OKM1 and 10-nm streptavidin gold, and the gold particles in each size of cluster were quantitated as previously described (Detmers *et al.* 1987). Aggregation increases from 0 to 25 min, and disaggregation occurs from 25 to 50 min (see text for details).

PMN (FcR, HLA) do not exhibit changes in their aggregation state in response to PMA, indicating that this is not a general property of membrane proteins. As mentioned above, treating PMN with the chemotactic peptide fMLP causes increased expression of CR3 on the cell surface (Berger *et al.* 1984) but does not enhance the binding activity of the receptor (Detmers *et al.* 1987). fMLP also does not cause aggregation of CR3, again supporting the idea that clustering of CR3 is required for binding ligand.

A possible mechanism by which clustering of receptors may endow them with enhanced binding activity is suggested by studies on the spatial distribution of the ligand, iC3b, on the surface of ligand-coated particles (A. Hermanowski-Vasotka, P. A. Detmers, D. Goetze, S. C. S. Iverstein & S. D. Wright, unpublished results). When C3 is deposited as random monomers, the resulting C3bi-coated erythrocytes are not bound by macrophages. However, if an equivalent number of C3bi molecules are deposited in clusters, binding to macrophages is avid. Similar results are observed with PMN. Even stimulated cells, in which CR3 is clustered on the surface of the phagocyte, are incapable of binding erythrocytes with randomly deposited iC3b, and avid binding is only observed when both the iC3b on the erythrocyte and the CR3 on the PMN are both clustered. Since the size of the clusters of iC3b (>5) is similar to the size of the clusters of CR3 (6–10), it is likely that clusters of ligand interact with clusters of receptors to mediate effective binding between cells.

Why does clustering of receptors and ligand promote the interaction of cells? Though we cannot rule out the possibility that clustering causes conformational changes in the proteins, we prefer the hypothesis that the multivalent binding between clusters stabilizes cell–cell interaction. To disassociate a cluster of ligands from a cluster of receptors, each of the individual receptor–ligand interactions would need to be simultaneously broken. The unlikelihood of this event could prevent the detachment of a iC3b-coated cell.

The observation that clustering of CR3 is required to mediate adhesion suggests a mechanism by which cells could detach from a ligand-coated surface or cell. Receptors that are actively mediating adhesion are held in position by two types of bonds, those among components of a receptor cluster and those between receptor and the opposing ligand. To reverse adhesion, these two bonds may be broken sequentially. The bond tethering a receptor to other members of a cluster appears to involve phosphorylation of the receptor and may thus be broken by the action of a phosphatase. Since the binding affinity of the second bond (between an individual receptor and an individual ligand) is very low, the 'off rate' will be high and receptors will release ligand often. Upon releasing ligand, untethered receptors would be free to diffuse in the plane of the membrane away from the cluster and away from ligand, thus reducing the chance of rebinding to ligand. Effective adhesion of a cluster of receptors with a cluster of ligands may thus be broken by sequentially breaking the individual receptor–ligand bonds and removing the receptors from the cluster.

Responses of cells to ligation of adhesion-promoting receptors

Secretion

The behaviour of CR3 differs from that of other opsonic receptors in two respects. During Fc-receptor-mediated phagocytosis, phagocytes release large amounts of oxygen metabolites (superoxide and hydrogen peroxide) and arachidonic acid metabolites (prostaglandins and leukotrienes). These substances act to kill the coated target and to promote inflammation. In contrast, CR3 triggers neither release of hydrogen peroxide (Wright & Silverstein, 1983; Yamamoto & Johnston, 1984) nor arachidonic acid metabolites (Aderem *et al*. 1985). The observation that C3 receptors do not promote secretion of these inflammatory compounds suggests that C3 receptor-mediated phagocytosis may provide a means of clearing opsonized particles without initiating or perpetuating an inflammatory response. They also emphasize how well suited CR3 is for its role in cell migration, which is not associated with killing of cells *en route*.

Adhesion-promoting receptors may, however, play a role in potentiating secretion events mediated by other receptors. The agonists fMLP and TNFα cause PMN to secrete enormous amounts of hydrogen peroxide, but secretion only occurs if the cells are allowed to adhere to surfaces (Nathan, 1987). Preliminary experiments suggest that the actions of CR3, LFA-1, and p150,95 are needed for this adhesion-dependent potentiation of secretion (C. F. Nathan & S. D. Wright, unpublished observations). Such an activity of adhesion-promoting receptors is ideally suited for use by cytotoxic cells such as T cells or NK cells. These cells do not secrete toxins constitutively, rather, secretion only occurs when the killers are attached to targets in an LFA-1-dependent manner.

Movement

The best appreciated function of adhesion-promoting receptors is to initiate elaboration of pseudopodia. Cells employ pseudopods in a similar way to accomplish spreading, phagocytosis, and locomotion, and we presume similar intracellular signals are used in all of these processes. While the nature of the intracellular signals used to cause movement of pseudopodia is unknown, recent experiments indicate that, like the binding activity, the signalling function of CR3 is regulated in phagocytic leukocytes. These studies have used phagocytosis of C3bi-coated erythrocytes as an assay, but the results are likely to apply to integrin-mediated migration as well.

Regulation of signalling by components of the extracellular matrix

Macrophages that are spread on human serum albumin or collagen exhibit low resting levels of CR3-mediated phagocytosis. However, when they spread on surfaces coated with fibronectin (Wright *et al.* 1983*b*; Pommier *et al.* 1983), or laminin (Bohnsack *et al.* 1985), their receptors are 'activated' and they promote phagocytosis. Several aspects of this type of activation of CR3 are worthy of note. First, fibronectin that is covalently bound to the substratum can activate the phagocytosis-promoting capacity of CR3 located on the apical portion of the phagocyte (Wright *et al.* 1983*b*). Thus, it is clear that fibronectin is not acting as an opsonin. Rather, it acts to regulate the activity of receptors for opsonins. Second, in order for fibronectin to activate C3 receptors, it must be bound to a substratum: soluble fibronectin is not capable of activating C3 receptors (Wright *et al.* 1983*b*; Wright & Meyer, 1985).

Fibronectin exerts its effect on CR3 by interacting with a receptor on macrophages which is also an integrin. Surface-bound synthetic peptides of fibronectin that contain the sequence RGD readily activate CR3 on macrophages, and soluble, monomeric peptides competitively inhibit activation by surface-bound fibronectin (Wright & Meyer, 1985). These experiments indicate that the activating effect of fibronectin is mediated by a receptor that recognizes the sequence RGD, and that fibronectin receptors must be crosslinked or immobilized in order to activate CR3. These data demonstrate that ligation of one member of the integrin family (the fibronectin receptor) may alter the behaviour of another integrin (CR3). It is worth noting that CR3 is not the only receptor that is regulated in this way. Macrophages express a structurally distinct C3 receptor, CR1, and the binding and signalling activity of CR1 is regulated by fibronectin exactly as is that of CR3 (Wright & Silverstein, 1982; Wright *et al.* 1983*b*, 1984, 1986).

Regulation of signalling activity by soluble molecules

The phagocytosis-promoting activity of CR3 on human macrophages can be strongly enhanced by the pleiotropic compound, PMA. Within minutes of being exposed to PMA, macrophages become capable of rapidly ingesting iC3b-coated red cells

(Wright & Silverstein, 1982). PMA affects only the ability of CR3 to signal phagocytosis, not the ability to bind ligand.

Complement receptors on macrophages may also be activated by soluble factors that are generated by stimulated T lymphocytes. Griffin & Griffin (1979, 1980) have described a novel lymphokine of approximately 10K, which activates the phagocytosis-promoting capacity of C3 receptors on murine peritoneal macrophages. A unique sequence of cellular interactions initiates release of this lymphokine. Upon ingestion of IgG-coated particles, macrophages elaborate a factor, which in turn causes T lymphocytes to secrete the lymphokine. The lymphokine appears to be different from other lymphokines such as IFNγ and interleukin-2, and cannot be elicited by classical mechanisms of lymphokine production such as antigenic stimulation of appropriate T cell clones (Griffin & Griffin, 1979). The receptor for the lymphokine has not been characterized.

Mechanisms by which signalling activity is regulated

How does ligation of one type of receptor (the receptor for lymphokine, fibronectin, or PMA) alter the capacity of a second type of receptor (CRl or CR3) to generate an intracellular signal? The answer to this question is not in hand, but several possibilities can be ruled out. Activation of C3 receptors for phagocytosis does not require protein synthesis since activation by either lymphokine or PMA occurs in the presence of inhibitors of protein synthesis (Griffin & Griffin, 1979; Wright & Silverstein, 1982). Thus, the manufacture of new receptors does not explain activation. Activation is not accompanied by changes in the number of cell surface receptors since neither PMA nor fibronectin causes changes in the expression of C3 receptors on the cell surface (Wright *et al.* 1984). This observation suggests that activation is caused by a structural change in existing C3 receptors. Activation of C3 receptors is reversible. Observations with lymphokine, PMA, and fibronectin all show that receptors can be switched from inactive to active and back in the course of an hour (Griffin & Griffin, 1979; Wright *et al.* 1984). Thus, activation is not the result of irreversible modifications such as proteolysis. We speculate that, as with binding activity, the signalling activity of receptors may also be regulated through reversible phosphorylation events, perhaps at sites separate from those that control binding.

Other responses to ligation of adhesion-promoting receptors

Students of embryology have long suspected that interactions of cells with matrix material or certain other cell types may influence the course of differentiation of that cell. Indeed, interaction of cells with fibronectin appears capable of altering their course of differentiation (West *et al.* 1979; Sieber-Blum *et al.* 1981; Loring *et al.* 1982). Since CR3, LFA-1, and p150,95 are structurally related to fibronectin receptors, one might expect that they would also direct differentiation events in leukocytes. Recent experiments by Ding *et al.* (1987) have shown that macrophages incubated for 2 days with a monoclonal antibody against murine CR3 exhibited the differentiative changes normally observed in response to IFNγ. Control experiments indicated that this was not caused by contaminating T cells or through autocrine production of IFNγ. These observations suggest a new facet of the function of adhesion-promoting receptors, which may have broad significance in understanding the interactions of cells.

Conclusion

We describe here one family of receptors that mediates a variety of adhesion events in leukocytes. These receptors are part of a larger group of receptors, integrins, which function in a great variety of adhesion events in many cell types. We wish to point out, however, that the search for receptors that mediate cell–cell adhesion is far from complete. We can expect that in the coming years many additional receptors will be discovered that deserve to be called 'adhesion-promoting.'

Supported by USPHS grant AI-22003 and a Grant-in-Aid from the American Heart Association with funds contributed in part by the American Heart Association Florida Affiliate. S.D.W. is an Established Investigator of the American Heart Association. P.A.D is an Arthritis Foundation Investigator.

References

ADEREM, A. A., WRIGHT, S. D., SILVERSTEIN, S. C. & COHN, Z. A. (1985). Ligated complement receptors do not activate the arachidonic acid cascade in resident peritoneal macrophages. *J. exp. Med.* **161**, 617–622.

ANDERSON, D. C., SCHMALSTIEG, F. C., ARNAOUT, M. A., KOHL, S., TOSI, M. F., DANA, N., BUFFONE, G. J., HUGHES, B. J., BRINKLEY, B. R., DICKEY, W. D., ABRAMSON, J. S., SPRINGER, T. A., BOXER, L. A., HOLLERS, J. M. & SMITH, C. W. (1984). Abnormalities of polymorphonuclear leukocyte function associated with a heritable deficiency of high molecular weight surface glycoproteins (GP138): Common relationship to diminished cell adherence. *J. clin. Invest.* **74**, 536–551.

ANDERSON, D. C. & SPRINGER, T. A. (1987). Leukocyte adhesion deficiency: an inherited defect in the Mac-1, LFA-1, and p150,95 glycoproteins. *A. Rev. Med.* **38**, 175–194.

ARFORS, K.-E., LUNDBERG, C., LINDBLOM, L., LUNDBERG, K., BEATTY, P. G. & HARLAN, J. M. (1987). A monoclonal antibody to the membrane glycoprotein complex CD18 inhibits polymorphonuclear leukocyte accumulation and plasma leakage in vivo. *Blood* **69**, 338–340.

ARNAOUT, M. A., PITT, J., COHEN, H. J., MELAMED, J., ROSEN, F. S. & COLTEN, H. R. (1982). Deficiency of a granulocyte-membrane glycoprotein (gp150) in a boy with recurrent bacterial infections. *New Engl. J. Med.* **306**, 693–699.

ARNAOUT, M. A., TODD, R. F. III, DANA, N., MELAMED, J., SCHLOSSMAN, S. F. & COLTEN, H. R. (1983). Inhibition of phagocytosis of complement C3- or immunoglobulin G-coated particles and of C3bi binding by monoclonal antibodies to a monocyte-granulocyte membrane glycoprotein (Mol). *J. clin. Invest.* **72**, 171–179.

BEATTY, P. G., LEDBETTER, J. A., MARTIN, P. J., PRICE, T. H. & HANSEN, J. A. (1983). Definition of a common leukocyte cell-surface antigen (Lp95–150) associated with diverse cell-mediated immune functions. *J. Immun.* **131**, 2913–2918.

BELLER, D. I., SPRINGER, T. A. & SCHREIBER, R. D. (1982). Anti-Mac-1 selectively inhibits the mouse and human type three complement receptor. *J. exp. Med.* **156**, 1000–1009.

BERGER, M., O'SHEA, J., CROSS, A. S., FOLKS, T. M., CHUSED, T. M., BROWN, E. J. & FRANK, M. M. (1984). Human neutrophils increase expression of C3bi as well as C3b receptors upon activation. *J. clin. Invest.* **74**, 1566–1571.

BEUTLER, B., MAHONEY, J., LETRANG, N., PEKALA, P. & CERAMI, A. (1985). Purification of cachectin, a lipoprotein lipase-supressing hormone secreted by endotoxin-treated RAW 264.7 cells. *J. exp. Med.* **161**, 984–995.

BLACKWELL, J. M., EZEKOWITZ, R. A. B., ROBERTS, M. B., CHANNON, J. Y., SIM, R. B. & GORDON, S. (1985). Macrophage complement and lectin-like receptors bind Leishmania in the absence of serum. *J. exp. Med.* **162**, 324–331.

BOHNSACK, J. F., KLEINMAN, H. K., TAKAHASHI, T., O'SHEA, J. J. & BROWN, E. J. (1985). Connective tissue proteins and phagocytic cell function. Laminin enhances complement and Fc-mediated phagocytosis by cultured human phagocytes. *J. exp. Med.* **161**, 912–923.

BORREGAARD, N., MILLER, L. J. & SPRINGER, T. A. (1987). Chemoattractant-regulated mobilization of a novel intracellular compartment in human neutrophils. *Science* **237**, 1204–1206.

BOUCAUT, J. C., DARRIBERE, T., POOLE, T. J., AOYAMA, H., YAMADA, K. M. & THIERY, J. P. (1984). Biologically active synthetic peptides as probes of embryonic development: a competitive peptide inhibitor of fibronectin function inhibits gastrulation in amphibian embryos and neural crest cell migration in avian embryos. *J. Cell Biol.* **99**, 1822–1830.

BULLOCK, W. E. & WRIGHT, S. D. (1987). The role of adherence-promoting receptors, CR3, LFA-1, and p150,95 in binding of *Histoplasma capsulatum* by human macrophages. *J. exp. Med.* **165**, 195–210.

CARLO, J. R., RUDDY, S., STUDER, E. J. & CONRAD, D. H. (1979). Complement receptor binding of C3b-coated cells treated with C3b inactivator, beta1H globulin and trypsin. *J. Immun.* **123**, 523–528.

CASTAGNA, M., TAKAI, Y., KAIBUCHI, K., SANO, K., KIKKAWA, U. & NISHIZUKA, Y. (1982). Direct activation of calcium-activated, phospholipid-dependent protein kinase by tumor-promoting phorbol esters. *J. biol. Chem.* **257**, 7847–7851.

CHEN, W.-T., WANG, J., HASEGAWA, T., YAMADA, S. S. & YAMADA, K. M. (1986). Regulation of fibronectin receptor distribution by transformation, exogenous fibronectin, and synthetic peptides. *J. Cell Biol.* **103**, 1649–1661.

CHERESH, D. A., PYTELA, R., PIERSCHBACHER, M. D., KLIER, F. G., RUOSLAHTI, E. & REISFELD, R. A. (1987). An Arg-Gly-Asp-directed receptor on the surface of human melanoma cells exists in a divalent cation-dependent functional complex with disialoganglioside GD2. *J. Cell Biol.* **105**, 1163–1173.

DANA, N., STYRT, B., GRIFFIN, J. D., TODD, R. F. III, KLEMPNER, M. S. & ARNAOUT, M. A. (1986). Two functional domains in the phagocyte membrane glycoprotein Mo1 identified with monoclonal antibodies. *J. Immun.* **137**, 3259–3263.

DETMERS, P. A., WRIGHT, S. D., OLSEN, E., KIMBALL, B. & COHN, Z. A. (1987). Aggregation of complement receptors on human neutrophils in the absence of ligand. *J. Cell Biol.* **105**, 1137–1145.

DING, A., WRIGHT, S. D. & NATHAN, C. F. (1987). Activation of mouse peritoneal macrophages by monoclonal antibodies to Mac-1 (complement receptor type 3). *J. exp. Med.* **165**, 733–749.

DURUM, S. K., SCHMIDT, J. A. & OPPENHEIM, J. J. (1985). Interleukin-1: An immunological perspective. *A. Rev. Immun.* **3**, 263–287.

DUSTIN, M. L., ROTHLEIN, R., BHAN, A. K., DINARELLO, C. A. & SPRINGER, T. A. (1986). Induction by IL-1 and interferon-gamma: Tissue distribution, biochemistry, and function of a natural adherence molecule (ICAM-1). *J. Immun.* **137**, 245–254.

EZEKOWITZ, R. A. B., SIM, R. B., HILL, M. & GORDON, S. (1984). Local opsonization by secreted macrophage complement components. Role of receptors for complement in uptake of zymosan. *J. exp. Med.* **159**, 244–260.

GRIFFIN, F. M. JR & GRIFFIN, J. A. (1980). Augmentation of macrophage complement receptor function in vitro. II. Characterization of the effects of a unique lymphokine upon the phagocytic capabilities of macrophages. *J. Immun.* **125**, 844–849.

GRIFFIN, J. A. & GRIFFIN, F. M. JR (1979). Augmentation of macrophage complement receptor function in vitro. I. Characterization of the cellular interactions required for the generation of a T-lymphocyte product that enhances macrophage complement receptor function. *J. exp. Med.* **150**, 653–675.

GUYRE, P. M., MORGANELLI, P. M. & MILLER, R. (1983). Recombinant immune interferon increases immunoglobulin G Fc receptors on cultured human mononuclear phagocytes. *J. clin. Invest.* **72**, 393–397.

HARLAN, J. M., KILLEN, P. D., SENECAL, F. M., SCHWARTZ, B. R., YEE, E. K., TAYLOR, F. R., BEATTY, P. G., PRICE, T. H. & OCHS, H. (1985). The role of neutrophil membrane protein GP-150 in neutrophil adhesion to endothelia in vitro. *Blood* **66**, 167–178.

HEMLER, M. E., HUANG, C. & SCHWARTZ, L. (1987). The VLA protein family: characterization of five distinct cell surface heterodimers each with a common 130,000 Mr beta subunit. *J. biol. Chem.* **262**, 3300–3309.

HIRST, R., HORWITZ, A., BUCK, C. & ROHRSCHNEIDER, L. (1986). Phosphorylation of the fibronectin receptor complex in cells transformed by oncogenes that encode tyrosine kinases. *Proc. natn. Acad. Sci. U.S.A.* **83**, 6470–6474.

HOGG, N., TAKACS, L., PALMER, D. G., SELVENDRAN, Y. & ALLEN, C. (1986). The p150,95 molecule is a marker of human mononuclear phagocytes: comparison with expression of class II molecules. *Eur. J. Immun.* **16**, 240–248.

HYNES, R. O. (1987). Integrins: a family of cell surface receptors. *Cell* **48**, 549–554.

INABA, K. & STEINMAN, R. M. (1987). Monoclonal antibodies to LFA-1 and to CD4 inhibit the mixed leukocyte reaction after the antigen-dependent clustering of dendritic cells and T lymphocytes. *J. exp. Med.* **165**, 1403–1417.

KEIZER, G. D., BORST, J., VISSER, W., SCHWARTING, R., DEVRIES, J. E. & FIGDOR, C. G. (1987). Membrane glycoprotein p150,95 of human cytotoxic T cell clones is involved in conjugate formation with target cells. *J. Immun.* **138**, 3130–3136.

KOHL, S., SPRINGER, T. A., SCHMALSTEIG, F. C., LOO, L. S. & ANDERSON, D. C. (1984). Defective natural killer cytotoxicity and polymorphonuclear leukocyte antibody-dependent cellular cytotoxicity in patients with LFA-1/OKM-1 deficiency. *J. Immun.* **133**, 2972–2978.

LANIER, L. L., ARNAOUT, M. A., SCHWARTING, R., WARNER, N. L. & ROSS, G. D. (1985). p150/95, Third member of the LFA-/CR3 polypeptide family identified by anti-Leu M5 monoclonal antibody. *Eur. J. Immun.* **15**, 713–718.

LAW, S. K. A. (1988). C3-receptors on macrophages. *J. Cell Sci.* **Suppl. 9**, 67–97.

LEBIEN, T. W. & KERSEY, J. H. (1980). A monoclonal antibody (TA-1) reactive with human T lymphocytes and monocytes. *J. Immun.* **125**, 2208–2214.

LORING, J., BLIMELIUS, B. & WESTON, J. A. (1982). Extracellular matrix materials influence quail neural cell differentiation in vitro. *Devl Biol.* **90**, 165–174.

MARLIN, S. D., MORTON, C. G., ANDERSON, D. C. & SPRINGER, T. A. (1986). LFA-1 immunodeficiency disease. Definition of the genetic defect and chromosomal mapping of alpha and beta subunits of the lymphocyte function-associated antigen 1 (LFA-1) by complementation in hybrid cells. *J. exp. Med.* **164**, 855–867.

MARTZ, E. (1986). LFA-1 and other accessory molecules functioning in adhesions of T and B lymphocytes. *Hum. Immun.* **18**, 3–37.

MENTZER, S. J., BIERER, B. E., ANDERSON, D. C., SPRINGER, T. A. & BURAKOFF, S. J. (1986b). Abnormal cytolytic activity of lymphocyte function-associated antigen-1-deficient cytolytic T lymphocyte clones. *J. clin. Invest.* **78**, 1387–1391.

MENTZER, S. J., GROMKOWSKI, S. H., KRENSKY, A. M., BURAKOFF, S. J. & MARTZ, E. (1985). LFA-1 membrane molecule in the regulation of homotypic adhesions of human B lymphocytes. *J. Immun.* **135**, 9–11.

MENTZER, S. J., KRENSKY, A. M. & BURAKOFF, S. J. (1986a). Mapping functional epitopes of the LFA-1 glycoprotein: monoclonal antibody inhibition of NK and CTL effectors. *Hum. Immun.* **17**, 288–296.

MIEDEMA, F., TETTEROO, P. A. T., HESSELINK, G. W., SPITS, H. & MELIEF, C. J. M. (1984). Both Fc receptors and lymphocyte-function-associated antigen 1 on T gamma lymphocytes are required for antibody-dependent cytotoxicity (killer cell activity). *Eur. J. Immun.* **14**, 518–523.

MORRISON, D. C. & ULEVITCH, R. J. (1978). The effects of bacterial endotoxins on host mediating systems. *Am. J. Path.* **93**, 527–617.

MOSSER, D. M. & EDELSON, P. J. (1985). The mouse macrophage receptor for C3bi (CR3) is a major mechanism in the phagocytosis of leishmania promastigotes. *J. exp. Med.* **135**, 2785.

NAIDET, C., SEMERIVA, M., YAMADA, K. M. & THIERY, J. P. (1987). Peptides containing the cell-attachment recognition signal Arg-Gly-Asp prevent gastrulation in Drosophila embryos. *Nature, Lond.* **325**, 348–350.

NATHAN, C. F. (1987). Neutrophil activation on biological surfaces: massive secretion of hydrogen peroxide in response to products of macrophages and lymphocytes. *J. clin. Invest.* **80**, 1550–1560.

O'SHEA, J., BROWN, E. J., SELIGMANN, B. E., METCALF, J. A., FRANK, M. M. & GALLIN, J. I. (1985). Evidence for distinct intracellular pools of receptors for C3b and C3bi in human neutrophils. *J. Immun.* **134**, 2580–2587.

PETREQUIN, P. R., TODD, R. F. III, DEVALL, L. J., BOXER, L. A. & CURNUTTE, J. T. III (1987). Association between gelatinase release and increased plasma membrane expression of the Mol glycoprotein. *Blood* **69**, 605–610.

POMMIER, C. G., INADA, S., FRIES, L. F., TAKAHASHI, T., FRANK, M. M. & BROWN, E. J. (1983). Plasma fibronectin enhances phagocytosis of opsonized particles by human peripheral blood monocytes. *J. exp. Med.* **157**, 1844–1854.

ROSEN, H. & GORDON, S. (1987). Monoclonal antibody to the murine type 3 complement receptor inhibits adhesion of myelomonocytic cells in vitro and inflammatory cell recruitment in vivo. *J. exp. Med.* **166**, 1685–1701.

ROSS, G. D., CAIN, J. A. & LACHMAN, P. J. (1985a). Membrane complement receptor type three (CR3) has lectin-like properties analogous to bovine conglutinin and functions as a receptor for zymosan and rabbit erythrocytes as well as a receptor for iC3b. *J. Immun.* **134**, 3307–3315.

ROSS, G. D. & LAMBRIS, J. D. (1982). Identification of a C3bi-specific membrane complement receptor that is expressed on lymphocytes, monocytes, neutrophils, and erythrocytes. *J. exp. Med.* **155**, 96–110.

ROSS, G. D., THOMPSON, R. A., WALPORT, M. J., SPRINGER, T. A., WATSON, J. V., WARD, R. H. R., LIDA, J., NEWMAN, S. L., HARRISON, R. A. & LACHMAN, P. J. (1985b). Characterization of patients with an increased susceptibility to bacterial infections and a genetic deficiency of leukocyte membrane complement receptor type 3 and the related membrane antigen LFA-1. *Blood* **66**, 882–890.

ROTHLEIN, R., DUSTIN, M. L., MARLIN, S. D. & SPRINGER, T. A. (1986). A human intercellular adhesion molecule (ICAM-1) distinct from LFA-1. *J. Immun.* **137**, 1270–1274.

ROTHLEIN, R. & SPRINGER, T. A. (1986). The requirement for lymphocyte function-associated antigen 1 in homotypic leukocyte adhesion stimulated by phorbol esters. *J. exp. Med.* **163**, 1132–1149.

ROVASIO, R. A., DELOUVEE, A., YAMADA, K. M., TIMPL, R. & THIERY, J. P. (1983). Neural crest cell migration: Requirements for exogenous fibronectin and high cell density. *J. Cell Biol.* **96**, 462–473.

RUOSLAHTI, E. & PIERSCHBACHER, M. D. (1986). Arg-Gly-Asp: a versatile cell recognition signal. *Cell* **44**, 517–518.

SANCHEZ-MADRID, F., KRENSKY, A. M., WARE, C. F., ROBBINS, E., STROMINGER, J. L., BURAKOFF, S. J. & SPRINGER, T. A. (1982). Three distinct antigens associated with human T-lymphocyte-mediated cytolysis: LFA-1, LFA-2, and LFA-3. *Proc. natn. Acad. Sci. U.S.A.* **79**, 7489–7493.

SANCHEZ-MADRID, F., NAGY, J. A., ROBBINS, E., SIMON, P. & SPRINGER, T. A. (1983). Characterization of a human leukocyte differentiation antigen family with distinct α subunits and a common β subunit: The lymphocyte-function associated antigen (LFA-1), the C3bi complement receptor (OKM1/Mac1), and the p150,95 molecule. *J. exp. Med.* **158**, 1785–1803.

SANDERSON, C. J. (1976). The mechanism of T cell mediated cytotoxicity. II. Morphological studies of cell death by time-lapse microcinematography. *Proc. R. Soc. Lond. B.* **92**, 241–255.

SCHLEIMER, R. P. & RUTLEDGE, B. K. (1986). Cultured human vascular endothelial cells acquire adhesiveness for neutrophils after stimulation with interleukin 1, endotoxin, and tumor-promoting phorbol diesters. *J. Immun.* **136**, 649–654.

SCHWARTING, R., STEIN, H. & WANG, C. Y. (1985). The monoclonal antibodies S-HCLl (Leu-14) and S-HCL3 (Leu-M5) allow the diagnosis of hairy cell leukemia. *Blood* **65**, 974–983.

SIEBER-BLUM, M., SIEBER, F. & YAMADA, K. M. (1981). Cellular fibronectin promotes adrenergic differentiation of quail neural crest cells in vitro. *Expl Cell Res.* **133**, 285–292.

SPRINGER, T. A., THOMPSON, W. S., MILLER, L. J., SCHMALSTIEG, F. C. & ANDERSON, D. C. (1984). Inherited deficiency of the Mac-1, LFA-1, p150,95 glycoprotein family and its molecular basis. *J. exp. Med.* **160**, 1901–1918.

STEINMAN, R. M., INABA, K., SCHULER, G. & WITMER, M. (1986). Stimulation of the immune response: contribution of dendritic cells. In *Mechanism of host resistance to infectious agents, tumors and allografts* (ed. R. M. Steinman and R. J. North), pp. 71–97. New York: Rockefeller University Press.

STRASSMAN, G., SPRINGER, T. A., SOMERS, S. D. & ADAMS, D. O. (1986). Mechanisms of tumor cell capture by activated macrophages: evidence for involvement of lymphocyte function-associated (LFA)-1 antigen. *J. Immun.* **136**, 4329–4333.

TODD, R. F. III & FREYER, D. R. (1988). The CD11/CD18 leukocyte glycoprotein deficiency. In *Phagocytic Defects* (ed. J. T. Curnutte), pp. 13–31. New York: W. B. Saunders.

TODD, R. F. III, ARNAOUT, M. A., ROSIN, R. E., CROWLEY, C. A., PETERS, W. A. & BABIOR, B. M. (1984). Subcellular localization of the large subunit of Mo1 (Mo1: formerly gp 110), a surface glycoprotein associated with neutrophil adhesion. *J. clin. Invest.* **74**, 1280–1290.

WALLIS, W. J., HICKSTEIN, D. D., SCHWARTZ, B. R., JUNE, C. H., OCHS, H. D., BEATTY, P. G., KLEBANOFF, S. J. & HARLAN, J. M. (1986). Monoclonal antibody-defined functional epitopes on the adhesion-promoting glycoprotein complex (CDw18) of human neutrophils. *Blood* **67**, 1007–1013.

WEST, C. M., LANZA, R., ROSENBLOOM, J., LOWE, M., HOLTZER, H. & AVDALOVIC, N. (1979). Fibronectin alters the phenotypic properties of cultured chick embryo chondroblasts. *Cell* **17**, 491–501.

WILCOX, M. & LEPTIN, M. (1985). Tissue-specific modulation of a set of related cell surface antigens in *Drosophila. Nature, Lond.* **316**, 351–354.

WRIGHT, S. D., CRAIGMYLE, L. S. & SILVERSTEIN, S. C. (1983*b*). Fibronectin and serum amyloid P component stimulate C3b- and C3bi-mediated phagocytosis in cultured human monocytes. *J. exp. Med.* **158**, 1338–1343.

WRIGHT, S. D., DETMERS, P. A., JONG, M. T. C. & MEYER, B. C. (1986). Interferon-gamma depresses binding of ligand by C3b and C3bi receptors on cultured human monocytes, an effect reversed by fibronectin. *J. exp. Med.* **163**, 1245–1259.

WRIGHT, S. D. & JONG, M. T. C. (1986). Adhesion-promoting receptors on human macrophages recognize *E. coli* by binding to lipopolysaccharide. *J. exp. Med.* **164**, 1876–1888.

WRIGHT, S. D., LICHT, M. R., CRAIGMYLE, L. S. & SILVERSTEIN, S. C. (1984). Communication between receptors for different ligands on a single cell. Ligation of fibronectin receptors induces a reversible alteration in the function of C3 receptors in cultured human monocytes. *J. Cell Biol.* **99**, 336–339.

WRIGHT, S. D. & MEYER, B. C. (1985). The fibronectin receptor of human macrophages recognizes the amino acid sequence, Arg-Gly-Asp-Ser. *J. exp. Med.* **162**, 762–767.

WRIGHT, S. D. & MEYER, B. C. (1986). Phorbol esters cause sequential activation and deactivation of complement receptors on polymorphonuclear leukocytes. *J. Immun.* **136**, 1759–1764.

WRIGHT, S. D., RAO, P. E., VAN VOORHIS, W. C., CRAIGMYLE, L. S., IIDA, K., TALLE, M. A., GOLDSTEIN, G. & SILVERSTEIN, S. C. (1983*a*). Identification of the C3bi receptor on human monocytes and macrophages by using monoclonal antibodies. *Proc. natn. Acad. Sci. U.S.A.* **80**, 5699–5703.

WRIGHT, S. D., REDDY, P. A., JONG, M. T. C. & ERICKSON, B. W. (1987). The C3bi receptor (CR3) recognizes a region of complement protein C3 containing the sequence Arg-Gly-Asp. *Proc. natn. Acad. Sci. U.S.A.* **84**, 1965–1968.

WRIGHT, S. D. & SILVERSTEIN, S. C. (1982). Tumor-promoting phorbol esters stimulate C3b and C3b′ receptor-mediated phagocytosis in cultured human monocytes. *J. exp. Med.* **156**, 1149–1164.

WRIGHT, S. D. & SILVERSTEIN, S. C. (1983). Receptors for C3b and C3bi promote phagocytosis but not the release of toxic oxygen from human phagocytes. *J. exp. Med.* **158**, 2016–2023.

YAMAMOTO, K. & JOHNSTON, R. B. JR (1984). Dissociation of phagocytosis from stimulation of the oxidative metabolic burst in macrophages. *J. exp. Med.* **159**, 405–416.

J. Cell Sci. Suppl. 9, 121–133 (1988)
Printed in Great Britain © The Company of Biologists Limited 1988

The structure and function of vertebrate mannose lectin-like proteins

R. A. B. EZEKOWITZ[1] AND P. D. STAHL[2]

[1]*Children's Hospital Medical Center, Enders 7, 320 Longwood Avenue, Boston, MA 02115, USA*
[2]*Department of Cell Biology and Physiology, Washington University School of Medicine, 660 S. Euclid Avenue, St Louis, MO 63110, USA*

Summary

Sugar-specific recognition is now well established as an important determinant of cell–cell interactions and host defence mechanisms. Macrophages, in particular, are known to express a variety of lectin-like proteins that are specific for oligosaccharides terminating in mannose, fucose, galactose and sialic acid. This review focuses on mannose recognition systems. Terminal mannose is rarely found on mammalian cell surfaces whereas it is ubiquitous on the surfaces of lower organisms. Mammals have evolved at least two mechanisms to recognize terminal mannose residues. These are, first, a mannose receptor located on the surface of macrophages and second, a mannose-binding protein found in blood plasma and secreted by hepatocytes. The mannose receptor is a 175K ($K = 10^3 M_r$) membrane glycoprotein. The receptor binds glycoproteins bearing high-mannose chains avidly at neutral pH but poorly at pH 5–6. The receptor recycles rapidly between the cell surface, where ligand binding occurs, and various acid intracellular compartments, where the ligand is discharged. The pH dependency of binding and the rapid recycling of receptor allow cells to accumulate many ligand molecules over an extended time. Endocytosis via this pathway appears to be regulated since mannose receptor expression is closely regulated. For example, the receptor is absent from monocytes but strongly expressed on 3- to 4-day-old monocyte-derived macrophages. Receptor expression can be up- and down-regulated by anti-inflammatory steroids and γ interferon, respectively. The mechanisms are poorly understood as is the physiological basis for modulation.

    The mannose-binding protein is a large oligomeric plasma protein secreted by liver and present in significant amounts in serum. The basic subunit of the mannose-binding protein is a 32K protein, which shows homology with other lectin-like proteins, notably certain surfactant proteins of the lung. The structure of the mannose-binding protein has been deduced from sequence information and DNA cloning experiments. The elaboration of the mannose-binding protein by the liver is regulated; it appears to be an acute phase reactant. Recent evidence suggests that the mannose-binding protein may play some opsonic role in the recognition and killing of organisms. In this review, it is suggested that the mannose receptor and the mannose-binding protein operate 'hand in glove' to deal with infectious agents that express mannose on their surfaces.

Introduction

Mannose is a ubiquitous component of bacterial pathogens, parasites, yeasts and the envelope glycoprotein of certain viruses. While most mammalian cell surface and secreted glycoproteins have complex oligosaccharide chains terminating in sialic acid, an occasional secretory protein and most lysosomal hydrolases do contain high-mannose chains. This stems from the fact that intracellular targeting of lysosomal hydrolases involves mannose phosphate residues (Kornfeld & Kornfeld, 1985). Several years ago, it became clear that mammals possess a macrophage-specific cell surface receptor that recognizes oligosaccharides terminating in mannose or fucose (Stahl *et al.* 1976, 1978; Schlesinger *et al.* 1978). Parallel work indicated that rabbit liver (Kawasaki *et al.* 1978; Townsend & Stahl, 1981; Maynard & Baenziger, 1982) and plasma (Kawasaki *et al.* 1983) contain a soluble protein that binds mannose oligosaccharides and whose specificity is similar to the mannose receptor. Hepato-cyte-derived mannose-binding proteins have now been isolated from the serum of man and rodents (Maynard & Baenziger, 1982; Summerfield & Taylor, 1986). In this review we will discuss two major areas. First, the macrophage mannose receptor, its role in endocytosis, its characterization and purification from macrophage mem-branes and the regulation of its surface expression. Second, the hepatocyte-derived human serum mannose-binding protein will be reviewed including its structure–function relationships, its homology to other vertebrate lectins and its up-regulation as an acute phase reactant. Finally we will discuss the relationship between these two mannose-specific lectin-like proteins and propose a model for their physiological function in host defence.

The mannose receptor: structure and function

Plasma clearance experiments (Stahl *et al.* 1976) pointed to the existence of a receptor that bound glycoproteins bearing high-mannose chains. Receptor activity was especially rich in liver and spleen, but other tissues were positive as well. Most eukaryotic glycoproteins bear complex chains terminating in sialic acid but there are several notable exceptions, in particular most lysosomal hydrolases. Others include thyroglobulin, the third component of complement and immunoglobulin M (IgM) (Kornfeld & Kornfeld, 1985). It is now known that the mannose receptor is expressed by a wide variety of macrophages and that it mediates the uptake into macrophages of an assortment of mannose glycoproteins and artificial glyconconju-gates. Glycoconjugates (Lee *et al.* 1976), prepared by derivatizing bovine serum albumin with mannose, have proven to be invaluable as high-affinity ligands for a variety of receptors, including the mannose receptor, particularly when the molar ratio of sugar to protein is >20:1 (Hoppe & Lee, 1983). L-Fucose was as effective as mannose when bound to proteins and this has given rise to the term mannose/fucose receptor (Shepherd *et al.* 1981). L-Fucose, when appropriately viewed in three dimensions, has an orientation about C2, C3 and C4 that gives it properties similar to D-mannose. The only naturally occurring fucosylated glycoprotein ligand identified thus far is salivary amylase (Niesen *et al.* 1984). Glycoconjugates have been used to quantify receptor distribution. Binding studies indicate that alveolar macrophages possess about 100 000 cell surface receptors ($K_d = 20$ nM) (Stahl *et al.* 1980). However, cells whose membranes have been permeabilized with detergents contain 500 000 receptor sites (Wileman *et al.* 1984), consistent with the conclusion that macrophages contain a large intracellular pool of receptors. The existence of an intracellular pool of receptors is supported by proteolysis experiments. About 20 % of the total cellular receptor pool is available to proteases when cells are incubated at

4°C whereas all of the receptors can be inactivated with protease at 37°C (Stahl *et al.* 1980). Given the observation that an alveolar macrophage can take up 2×10^6 molecules h^{-1}, these data lead to the conclusion that receptors rapidly recycle and that each receptor must traverse a complete cycle every 10–15 min. Correlative morphological studies at the electron-microscope level have shown that mannosylated ligands are taken up into coated vesicles, which, after losing their coats, fuse with each other (Harding *et al.* 1985). Larger translucent vesicles become tubular within 8–10 min, a process apparently required for receptor–ligand sorting. The intracellular life-time of the receptor in cultured macrophages is likely to be several days, which indicates that a given receptor may recycle hundreds of times before it is degraded or inactivated.

The major function of the mannose receptor in macrophages is presumed to be the transfer of internalized proteins to lysosomes. However, kinetic experiments have suggested that alternative pathways may exist. For example, a small, but significant, fraction of receptor molecules traverse a pathway following internalization that does not include passage through an acid environment (Tietze *et al.* 1982). This minor pathway has been referred to as receptor–ligand cycling. Other receptor–ligand systems that follow a similar pathway in other cell types include the low-density lipoprotein (LDL) receptor (Aulinskas *et al.* 1985) and the asialoglycoprotein receptor (Townsend *et al.* 1984; Simmons & Schwartz, 1984). These processes have been variously referred to as retro-endocytosis and diacytosis, respectively. Another example of this may be illustrated by the pathway followed by internalized high-density lipoprotein (HDL) in macrophages. Recent studies suggest that HDL can enter cells by receptor-mediated endocytosis and that, within the vacuolar compartment, cholesterol can be absorbed by exchange from cytoplasmic stores (Schmitz *et al.* 1985). This is thought to be followed by the exocytotic release of HDL resulting in the net discharge of cholesterol from the cells. Whether these are independently regulated endocytic pathways in macrophages remains to be determined.

In addition to its role in receptor-mediated endocytosis, the mannose receptor also mediates phagocytosis, independently of Fc and C3 receptors (Sung *et al.* 1983). The participation of the mannose receptor in phagocytosis raises several interesting questions about receptor structure–function relationships. Receptor-mediated pinocytosis requires clustering in coated pits followed by internalization and recycling, whereas receptor-mediated phagocytosis, according to the 'zipper' hypothesis, requires mobility in the membrane (Griffin *et al.* 1975). Whether different populations of receptor molecules mediate these two physiological functions, remains to be determined.

Recent progress on the biochemistry of the mannose receptor has revealed that the receptor is a 175K (K $= 10^3 M_r$) membrane glycoprotein (Wileman *et al.* 1986). The rabbit (Lennartz *et al.* 1987*a*), human (Lennartz *et al.* 1987*b*), rat (Haltiwanger & Hill, 1986) and mouse (R. Fiani & P. D. Stahl, unpublished results) receptors have been isolated. Isolation has been achieved by affinity chromatography on mannose–Sepharose. Elution from the affinity column is achieved by mannose, EDTA or low pH. These three conditions relate to known properties of the receptor. First, the receptor recognizes glycopeptides bearing more than one terminal mannose residue (Maynard & Baenziger, 1981). The monosaccharide, mannose, is a poor inhibitor but, as expected, it is effective at high concentrations in blocking receptor binding. Second, the receptor requires Ca^{2+} for full binding activity. Removal of Ca^{2+} with EGTA impairs binding and allows receptor elution from the column. Third, the receptor binds ligands avidly at neutral pH but poorly at pH 5 (Lennartz *et al.* 1987*a,b*). The pH dependency of binding accounts for the separation of receptor and ligand within acidified endosomes.

Based on digestion experiments with endoglycosidase F, the receptor is known to be a glycoprotein bearing complex oligosaccharide chains. Biosynthetic studies using anti-receptor antibodies to immunoprecipitate solubilized receptor molecules have shown that newly synthesized receptor is endoglycosidase H sensitive (M. R. Lennartz *et al.* unpublished results). An interesting question has emerged from these findings. Does the mannose receptor, which is a high-mannose chain bearing glycoprotein, bind to itself or to its neighbours in the endoplasmic reticulum immediately following its synthesis, or is the receptor synthesized as an inactive precursor? Pulse–chase studies show that exit of newly synthesized receptor from the endoplasmic reticulum is not unusually slow, suggesting that the receptor is not retained by virtue of its mannose-binding property. However, treatment of macro-phages with the drug swainsonine (Chung *et al.* 1984), which blocks processing of high-mannose chains, results in a complete inactivation of mannose receptor activity within hours. This observation suggests that the environment in which the mannose receptor normally operates is deficient in high-mannose oligosaccharides.

Expression of the mannose receptor appears to be closely regulated. The receptor is not expressed by circulating monocytes nor by most macrophage-like cell lines (e.g. J774, P338D1, U937). Macrophage-like cell lines treated with 5-azacytidine do express the receptor (Diment *et al.* 1987). Cells treated with the drug and cloned in soft agar continue to express the receptor after extended periods in culture. When monocytes are allowed to differentiate in culture, expression of the receptor commences (Shepherd *et al.* 1982). Expression of the receptor in cultured monocyte-derived macrophages results in an increased accumulation of uptake activity over several days. Whereas monocytes are receptor-negative, resident and thioglycollate-elicited macrophages express intermediate levels of mannose receptor (Stahl & Gordon, 1982; Ezekowitz *et al.* 1981). Alveolar macrophages express high levels. The reasons for variable expression of the receptor among tissue macrophage populations remains uncertain. Activated macrophages, either prepared from animals infected with BCG or following treatment *in vitro* with γ interferon, express low to intermediate levels of receptor (Ezekowitz *et al.* 1981, 1986). The nature of the down-regulation produced by macrophage activation (i.e. decreased receptor num-ber, decreased ligand affinity or decreased recycling time) remains to be determined. Interestingly, the level of expression appears to be normal in macrophages infected with organisms that live and grow within intracellular vacuoles, for example, *Leishmania* (Shepherd *et al.* 1983). In fact, the evidence suggests that certain organisms may use the mannose receptor to gain access to the vacuolar compartment of macrophages. Yet another finding, which reveals fine control of mannose receptor expression, is the modulation observed when macrophages are treated with anti-inflammatory steroids. Incubation of rat or human macrophages with dexamethasone leads to an enhancement of mannose receptor expression (Shepherd *et al.* 1985; Mokoena & Gordon, 1985). Receptor levels and uptake can be elevated by several-fold following 24 h incubation with low levels of steroid. The effect can be blocked by addition of inhibitors of protein synthesis. These data suggest that regulation of receptor levels may be achieved, in part, by regulation of receptor synthesis.

It is likely that the mannose plays a role in host defense for reasons outlined above. Whether the receptor plays some role in the transport or shuttling of lysosomal hydrolases in macrophages remains to be determined. Suggestive evidence supporting a role has been published. Shepherd *et al.* (1985) have shown that, under certain circumstances, mannan can stimulate lysosomal enzyme secretion and Diment *et al.* (1987) have shown an increased correlation between lysosomal enzyme secretion and mannose receptor expression. Lee and colleagues have shown that neoglycoproteins can elicit secretion of hydrolases when such glycoconjugates contain mannose but not galactose. Moreover, secretion was stimulated in the presence of cycloheximide, suggesting that the secretory load was derived from pre-existing lysosomes.

Mannose-binding proteins

Mannose-binding proteins (MBP) have been isolated from the livers of rats (Kawasaki & Ashwell, 1977; Mizuno *et al.* 1981; Maynard & Baenziger, 1982; Townsend & Stahl, 1981) and man (Wild *et al.* 1983; Summerfield & Taylor, 1986) and subsequently found in the serum of rats (Kawasaki & Ashwell, 1977; Mizuno *et al.* 1981), rabbits (Kawasaki *et al.* 1978) and man (Kawasaki *et al.* 1983; Summerfield & Taylor, 1986). Much more is known about the structure of mannose-binding proteins than is known about their function. Drickamer *et al.* (1986) characterized two homologous rat MBPs, the so-called rat MBP-A and rat MBP-C. They form at least trimers of a basic 32K subunit and form part of a family of lectin-like proteins, which include five membrane-bound hepatic receptors (Drickamer, 1987).

While the rat seems to possess distinct liver and serum MBPs, the presence of similar distinct forms in the human has not been clearly documented. Mannose-binding proteins isolated from human liver and serum have identical apparent molecular weights, binding characteristics and share immunological cross-reactivity (Wild *et al.* 1983; Summerfield & Taylor, 1986; Kawasaki *et al.* 1983). The isolation of cDNA clones that encode two homologous human mannose-binding proteins has extended our knowledge of the structure and function of human MBP (Ezekowitz *et al.* 1988). In this section we will review the structure of the human MBP, its relationships to other vertebrate lectins and discuss the regulation of its synthesis, which might provide insight into its role as an opsonin.

Common structural features of human MBP-C, rat MBP-C and rat MBP-A

The sequence of the human MBP is strikingly homologous to the rat MBPs, in particular rat MBP-C. As shown in Fig. 1 the human MBP and the rat MBP-C can be aligned with only three gaps. In this alignment, the sequences of these two mature proteins are 51% homologous. An alignment between human MBP and the rat MBP-A with seven gaps allows a homology of 48% between these two native proteins. The overall organization of these proteins appears identical. Human MBP-C consists of a N-terminal signal sequence followed by a short segment (21 amino acid residues) rich in cysteine residues, then a collagen-like domain of 56 residues, and finally a C-terminal non-collagen-like domain of 148 amino acids.

Signal sequences

Since MBPs are found in the circulation, the presence of a typical hydrophobic signal sequence is an expected feature of these molecules. The human MBP-C signal

```
Met-Ser-Leu-Phe-     Thr-Ser-Phe-Leu-Leu-Leu-Cys-Val-Leu-Thr-Ala-Val-Tyr-Ala-                     Glu-Thr-Leu-Thr-   R-MBP-C
Met-Ser-Cys-Phe-Ile-Thr-Pro-Ser-Leu-Leu-Leu-Ser-Met-Val-Ala-Ala-Ser-Tyr-Ser-                       Glu-Thr-Val-Thr-Cys- H-MPB-C
Met-Leu-Leu-Leu-     Pro-Leu-Leu-Val-Leu-Leu-Cys-Val-Val-Val-Val-Ser-Ser-Ser-Gly-Ser-Gln-Thr-Cys-Glu-Glu-Thr-Leu-Lys- R-MBP-A

Glu-Gly-Ala-Gln-Ser-Ser-Cys-Pro-      Val-Ile-Ala-Cys-Ser-Ser-Pro-Gly-Leu-Asn-Gly-Phe-Pro-Gly-Lys-Asp-Gly-His-Asp-Gly-Ala- R-MBP-C
Glu-Asp-Ala-Gln-Lys-Thr-Cys-Pro-Ala-Val-Ile-Ala-Cys-Ser-Ser-Pro-Gly-Ile-Asn-Gly-Phe-Pro-Gly-Lys-Asp-Gly-Arg-Asp-Gly-Thr- H-MBP-C
                    Thr-Cys-Ser-      Val-Ile-Ala-Cys-                                    Gly-Arg-Asp-Gly-Arg-Asp-Gly-Pro- R-MBP-A

Lys-Gly-Glu-Lys-Gly-Glu-Pro-Gly-Gln-Gly-Leu-Arg-Gly-Leu-Gln-Gly-Pro-Pro-Gly-Lys-Val-Gly-Pro-Ala-Gly-Pro-Pro-Gly-Asn-Pro- R-MBP-C
Lys-Gly-Arg-Lys-Gly-Gly-Thr-Gly-Gln-Gly-Leu-Arg-Gly-Leu-Gln-Gly-Pro-Pro-Gly-Lys-Leu-Gly-Pro-Pro-Gly-Asn-Pro-Gly-Pro-Ser- H-MBP-C
Lys-Gly-Glu-Lys-Gly-Glu-Pro-Gly-Gln-Gly-Leu-Arg-Gly-Leu-Gln-Gly-Pro-Pro-Gly-Lys-Leu-Gly-Pro-Pro-Gly-Ser-Val-Gly-Ala-Pro- R-MBP-A

Gly-Ser-Lys-Gly-Ala-The-Gly-Pro-Lys-Gly-Asp-Arg-Gly-                 Glu-Ser-Val-Glu-Phe-Asp-Thr-Thr-Asn-Ile-Asp-Leu-Glu-Ile-Ala- R-MBP-C
Gly-Ser-Pro-Gly-Pro-Lys-Gly-Gln-Gly-Gly-Asp-Pro-Gly-                 Lys-Ser-Pro-Asp-Gly-Asp-Ser-Ser-Pro-Gly-Cys-Leu-Arg-Lys-Lys- H-MBP-C
Gly-Ser-Gln-Gly-Pro-Lys-Gly-Gln-Lys-Gly-Asp-Arg-Gly-Asp-Ser-Arg-Ala-Ile-Glu-Val-Lys-Leu-Ala-Asn-Met-Glu-Ala-Glu-Ile-Asn- R-MBP-A

Ala-Leu-Arg-Ser-Glu-Leu-Arg-Ala-Met-Arg-Lys-Trp-Val-Leu-Leu-Ser-Met-Ser-Glu-Asn-Val-Gly-Lys-Lys-Tyr-Phe-Met-Ser-Ser-Val- R-MBP-C
Ser-Ser-Ala-Asn-Arg-Asn-Gly-Thr-Tyr-Gln-Lys-Cys-Leu-Thr-Phe-Ser-Leu-Gly-Lys-Gln-Val-Gly-Lys-Lys-Phe-Phe-Leu-Thr-Asn-Gly- H-MBP-C
Thr-Leu-Lys-Ser-Lys-Leu-Glu-Leu-Thr-Asn-Lys-Leu-His-Ala-Phe-Ser-Met-Gly-Lys-Lys-Ser-Gly-Lys-Lys-Phe-Phe-Val-Thr-Asn-His- R-MBP-A
                                                          Gly                    Gly-Lys-Lys-Phe-Phe-Val-Thr-Asn-His- INVARIANT

Arg-Arg-Met-Pro-Leu-Asn-Arg-Ala-Lys-Ala-Leu-Cys-Ser-Glu-Leu-Gln-Gly-Thr-Val-Ala-Thr-Pro-Arg-Asn-Ala-Glu-Glu-Asn-Arg-Ala- R-MBP-C
Glu-Ile-Met-Thr-Phe-Glu-Lys-Val-Lys-Ala-Leu-Cys-Val-Lys-Phe-Gln-Pro-Leu-Trp-Pro-Pro-Pro-Gly-Met-Ala-Ala-Glu-Asn-Gly-Ala- H-MBP-C
Glu-Arg-Met-Pro-Phe-Ser-Lys-Val-Lys-Ala-Leu-Cys-Ser-Glu-Leu-Arg-Gly-Thr-Val-Ala-Ile-Pro-Arg-Asn-Ala-Glu-Glu-Asn-Lys-Ala- R-MBP-A
                                         Cys                         Pro                          Asn        INVARIANT

Ile-Gln-Asn-Val-Ala-Lys-Asp-Val-Ala-Phe-Leu-Gly-Ile-Thr-Asp-Gln-Arg-Thr-Glu-Asn-Val-Phe-Glu-Asp-Leu-Thr-Gly-Asn-Arg-Val- R-MBP-C
Ile-Gln-Asn-Leu-Ile-Lys-Glu-Glu-Ala-Phe-Leu-Gly-Met-Pro-Asp-Glu-Lys-Thr-Glu-Gly-Gln-Phe-Val-Asp-Leu-Thr-Gly-Asn-Arg-Leu- H-MBP-C
Ile-Gln-Glu-Val-Ala-Lys-Thr-Ser-Ala-Phe-Leu-Gly-Ile-Thr-Asp-Glu-Val-Thr-Glu-Gly-Gln-Phe-Met-Tyr-Val-Thr-Gly-Gly-Arg-Leu- R-MBP-A
                                   Gly    Thr Asp                      Phe                    Thr        INVARIANT

Arg-Tyr-Thr-Asn-Trp-Asn-Glu-Gly-Glu-Pro-Asn-Asn-Val-Gly-Ser-Gly-Glu-Asn-Cys-Val-Val-Leu-Leu-Thr-Asn-Gly-Lys-Trp-Asn-Asp- R-MBP-C
Thr-Tyr-Thr-Asn-Trp-Asn-Glu-Gly-Glu-Pro-Asn-Asn-Ala-Gly-Ser-Asp-Glu-His-Cys-Ala-Glu-Leu-Gln-Gly-Gln-Trp-Asn-Asp- H-MBP-H
Thr-Tyr-Ser-Asn-Trp-Lys-Lys-Asp-Glu-Pro-Asn-Asp-His-Gly-Ser-Gly-Glu-Asp-Cys-Val-Thr-Ile-Val-Asp-Asn-Gly-Leu-Trp-Asn-Asp- H-MBP-A
              Trp                  Pro              Gly          Glu    Cys                  Gly    Trp Asn Asp  INVARIANT

Val-Pro-Cys-Ser-Asp-Ser-Phe-Leu-Val-Val-Cys-Glu-Phe-Ser-Asp            R-MBP-C
Ser-Pro-Cys-Phe-His-Leu-Pro-Ser-Ala-Val-Cys-Glu-Phe-Pro-Ile            H-MBP-H
Ile-Ser-Cys-Gln-Ala-Ser-His-Thr-Ala-Val-Cys-Glu-Phe-Pro-Ala           R-MBP-A
        Cys                    Cys Glu                      INVARIANT
```

Fig. 1. Comparison of animal lectin sequences. The sequences of the two rat MBPs, R-MBP-A and -C are compared with the human MBP-C(H-MBP-C). The invariant residues represent sequences invariant in 12 lectin-like proteins including the human and rat hepatic asialoglycoprotein receptors, the avian hepatic receptor, the apoprotein of dog and human surfactant, the N-terminal portion of a galactose-specific lectin isolated from the haemolymph of *Sarcophaga perigrina*, a lectin isolated from the coelomic fluid of a sea urchin *Anthocidaris crassispina*, a chicken cartilage core proteoglycan protein and the IgE Fc receptor. Residues that are identical between the MBPs, human and rat are boxed to emphasize homology.

sequence has the features of N-terminal signal sequences found on almost all eukaryotic secretory proteins (Von Heijne, 1983). The N terminus of the mature human and rat proteins is glutamic acid. This is preceded by a serine or alanine which would conform to the general rule that the amino acid in the position preceding cleavage by the signal peptidase tends to be a residue with a small side chain like serine or alanine. The lack of specific conservation of residues within the signal or at the cleavage boundary is similar to comparisons made between signal sequences in otherwise highly homologous proteins (Von Heijne, 1983).

Interchain disulphide bonds

The presence of a number of cysteine residues in the short N-terminal non-collagen-like segment are found in both human and rat MBPs (Fig. 1). In the rat protein these interchain disulphide bonds are removed when MBPs are digested with collagenase (Drickamer *et al.* 1986). When MBP purified from human sera is analysed by polyacrylamide gel electrophoresis under non-reducing conditions it occurs as multimers, composed of an aggregate of 30K subunits. Strong reduction and alkylation are required to reduce this multimeric form to the basic subunit suggesting that the cysteines in the N-terminal domain of human MBP-C are probably involved in disulphide bond formation.

Collagen-like domains

This region is highly conserved and there are sequences of near identity between the human MBP-C and both rat MBPs. A point of note is that there is a single identical interruption in the Gly–X–Y repeat structure, the sequence Gly–Gln–Gly (residues 297–303), in a highly conserved portion of both collagenous domains. This aberration in the regular Gly–X–Y–Gly repeat is also found in some other proteins that contain collagen-like regions, like the apoproteins of pulmonary surfactant (White *et al.* 1985), and the A and C chains of C1q (Reid, 1983). It is known that the interruption is the site of an intron in human MBP (S. Herman *et al.*, unpublished results), rat MBP (Drickamer & McCleary, 1987) and in the human surfactant apoprotein gene (White *et al.* 1985). The collagen sequence is more closely related to that found in non-fibrillar collagen molecules than fibrillar collagen, in that the distortions in the triple helical structure are found in non-fibrillar collagen (for a review see Martin *et al.* 1985). All of this suggests that the collagen portion of these molecules evolved from a common ancestral gene. Other portions of the collagen-like domain resemble the triple-helix-forming segments of collagen in that a large number of the X and Y positions are occupied by prolines. The detailed analysis of the human (J. Baenziger, personal communication) and rat proteins reveals that a high proportion of the prolines in the Y position are hydroxyproline. Of some interest is the finding that the sequence Arg–Gly–Asp–Ser (RGDS), which is recognized by a family of cell surface receptors known as integrins (Hynes, 1987), is not found in the human MBP-C or the rat MBP-C whereas it is present in the rat MBP-A. Although the human protein does contain the sequence Asp–Gly–Asp–Ser, the functional significance of this motif is not known.

Comparison of human MBP with other mammalian carbohydrate-binding proteins

Several recent reports have drawn attention to striking homologies between mammalian lectin-like proteins (for a review see Drickamer, 1987). The primary structures of several animal lectins have been reported (Takahashi *et al.* 1985; Giga *et al.* 1987; Shigaku *et al.* 1986). Fig. 1 illustrates the invariant residues of 12 proteins that bear homology with the human MBP (these are listed in the legend). The homologies are greatest in the C termini of the mammalian lectin-like proteins, which are the putative carbohydrate-binding domains. Although strong sequence homology exists, each protein has a distinct pattern of carbohydrate-binding specificity; the MBPs recognize mannose, the rat and human hepatic lectins are specific for galactose and *N*-acetylgalactosamine, and the chicken hepatic lectin recognizes *N*-acetylglucosamine. The binding specificity of the sea urchin lectin is not well characterized, and the inclusion of the IgE lymphocyte Fc receptor in this family suggests that it may have lectin-like properties, which may or may not relate to IgE binding. The cartilage proteoglycans and the apoproteins, SP28-36, of pulmonary surfactant are most homologous to the galactose-binding proteins and, on the basis of these predictions, these proteins do in fact interact with galactose (Benson *et al.* 1985; Haagsman *et al.* 1987).

Regulation of MBP synthesis

Variability of MBP levels isolated from different sera (from $100 \, \text{ng ml}^{-1}$ to $50 \, \mu\text{g ml}^{-1}$ as determined by a radioimmunoassay (R. A. B. Ezekowitz, unpublished results)) led us to investigate whether the hepatic synthesis of MBP may be regulated. Northern analyses were carried out on RNA isolated from normal liver derived from a liver biopsy sample for a staging laporotomy for Hodgkins disease and RNA isolated from a patient who had suffered major trauma 48 h prior to death. The latter RNA was greatly enriched for acute phase reactants. Radiolabelled human MBP cDNA hybridized only to the acute phase RNA. A major species of RNA of about 3·5 kb represents the human MBP-C. A larger mRNA of about 5·5 kb is a consistent finding. This larger species may represent (1) additional 5′ or 3′ untranslated sequence, (2) a larger mRNA that codes for a homologous mannose-binding protein or (3) a splicing intermediate. Further analysis revealed that the expression of MBP was restricted to liver and certain liver cell lines. Unlike some other acute phase proteins, the synthesis of MBP is not up-regulated *in vitro* by interleukin-1 and/or tumour necrosis factor (R. A. B. Ezekowitz, unpublished results). However, mRNA levels are greatly induced by γ interferon. This appears to be a rapid event, which is observed after 30 min of exposure to the lymphokine. The presence of a heat-shock element (described by Pelham, 1982) in the 5′ region of the human MBP gene (G. Herman *et al.*, unpublished results), led us to investigate whether MBP mRNA was induced by heat shock. Preliminary studies show that raising the temperature of HepG2 cells to 45 °C for 60 min greatly induces MBP RNA (R. A. B.

Ezekowitz *et al.*, unpublished results). This study supports the idea that this element is active and that the MBP is indeed a heat-shock protein.

Function of human MBP

The circumstances under which MBP synthesis is induced as part of the acute phase response, its up-regulation in response to heat shock and γ interferon suggest a role for MBP in natural immunity. Human MBP could have a primary role in the engagement of mannose-rich pathogens in the circulation. For this to occur MBP would be expected to distinguish mannose on pathogens from cell surface glyco-proteins. Specificity at this level is feasible when one considers that most glyco-proteins contain less than six oligosaccharide chains. Organisms coated with high-mannose chains, on the other hand, would be highly multivalent. Thus, it would be reasonable to expect the mannose-containing surface of an infectious agent to become coated with MBP, even if many of the sugar–lectin interactions were of a low affinity type.

MBP opsonizes *Salmonella*

Human MBP is able to enhance uptake of mannose-rich *Salmonella* by polymorpho-nuclear leukocytes in the absence of serum. In the absence of MBP or serum no specific uptake of these strains of bacteria is observed. All the MBP-dependent and 50 % of the serum-related uptake can be specifically abrogated by yeast mannan, a mannose-rich glycoprotein (M. Kulhman & R. A. B. Ezekowitz, unpublished results).

MBP inhibits *in vitro* infectivity of HIV

The presence of high-mannose oligosaccharide chains on the external domain of the envelope glycoprotein of HIV, the human immunodeficiency virus, (Montagnier *et al.* 1985; T. Gregory & M. Spellman, personal communication) suggested to us that this MBP may interfere with the life cycle of this pathogenic retrovirus. The importance of glycosylation in the biology of the virus has been inferred from studies that showed that certain plant lectins, which recognize particular configurations of high-mannose, inhibit HIV infection *in vitro* (Lifson *et al.* 1986). These obser-vations are supported by studies that show that deglycosylated forms of gp 120 fail to interact with CD4 (Matthews *et al.* 1987). We have shown that MBP was able to inhibit *in vitro* infection of susceptible cells by the human immunodeficiency virus (R. A. B. Ezekowitz *et al.*, unpublished results). The precise molecular basis for MBP-mediated inhibition of HIV infection *in vitro* is not clear. It is possible that, through its interaction with the exposed mannose chains on the envelope glyco-protein, MBP interferes with the topology of the virus, either by masking those epitopes required for adhesion to a cell surface receptor, or perhaps, less likely, by inducing some conformational change in the virus.

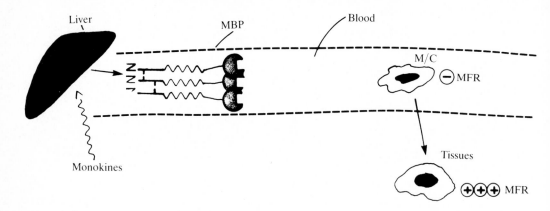

Fig. 2. A model of mannose lectin-like recognition. Monokines released in response to infection cause augmented release of MBP from the liver. These MBPs serve to recognize mannose-containing pathogens in the blood. In tissue, macrophages, which express high levels of MFR, serve to recognize mannose-rich pathogens in the absence of serum and hence circulating MBP.

The implication of these recent studies is that MBP may provide a natural *in vivo* mechanism for preventing either HIV infection or limiting viral spread. This prospect is supported by studies that show the ability of MBP to distinguish HIV-infected H9 cells from uninfected H9 cells. This may apply to other viruses and virally infected cells, which may express high-mannose oligosaccharides as part of their viral envelope or on the external surface of infected cells. Therefore MBP may be part of an early response to infection.

Conclusion

It now appears that vertebrate lectin-like proteins, which recognize certain configurations of mannose oligosaccharides, have a key role in host defence (Fig. 2). The macrophage mannose receptor is expressed at high levels on tissue macrophages. These cells are positioned along the portals of maximum antigen entry forming a lattice beneath epithelial surfaces in the skin, gut, kidney and lung. At these sites, they are able to bind and ingest mannose-rich pathogens directly. This results in the release of a wide range of macrophage products like reactive oxygen intermediates, neutral proteinases, arachidonic acid metabolites and monokines (for a review see Ezekowitz, 1988).

The macrophage mannose receptor is not expressed on circulating monocytes. However, plasma contains a MBP, which appears to serve as the mannose recognition protein in the circulation. The proposed functional relationship between these lectin-like proteins is shown in Fig. 2. Present studies indicate that the similarity in binding characteristics between these proteins is based on structural homology (R. A. B. Ezekowitz & P. D. Stahl, unpublished observations). It is hoped that future studies will allow better definition of the structural and functional relationship between these lectin-like proteins.

References

AULINSKAS, T. H., ORAM, J. F., BIERMAN, E. L., COETZEE, G. A., JEVERS, W. & VANDER WESTHUYZEN, D. R. (1985). Retro-endocytosis of low density lipoprotein by cultured human skin fibroblast. *Arterioscelerosis* **5**, 45–54.

BENSON, B., HAWGWOOD, S., SCHILLING, J., CLEMENTS, J., DANIM, P., CORDELL, B. & WHITE, R. T. (1985). Structure of canine pulmonary surfactant apoprotein: cDNA and complete amino acid sequence. *Proc. natn. Acad. Sci. U.S.A.* **82**, 6379–6383.

CHUNG, K. N., SHEPHERD, V. L. & STAHL, P. D. (1984). Swainsonine and castanospermine blockade of mannose glycoprotein uptake by macrophages: Apparent inhibition of receptor-mediated endocytosis by endogenous ligands. *J. biol. Chem.* **259**, 14637–14641.

DIMENT, S., LEECH, M. & STAHL, P. D. (1987). Generation of macrophage variants with 5-azacytidine: Selection for mannose receptor expression. *J. Leukocyte Biol.* **42**, 485–590.

DRICKAMER, K. (1987). Structure and biosynthesis of membrance receptors which mediate endocytosis of glycoproteins. *Kidney International* **32 (Suppl 23)**, 67–81.

DRICKAMER, K., DORSAL, M. S. & REYNOLDS, L. (1986). Mannose-binding proteins isolated from rat liver contain carbohydrate-recognition domains linked to collagenous tail. *J. biol. Chem.* **261**, 6578–6588.

DRICKAMER, K. & MCCREARY, V. (1987). Exon structure of a mannose-binding protein gene reflects its evolutionary relationship to the asialoglycoprotein receptor and non fibrillar collagens. *J. biol. Chem.* **262**, 2582–2593.

EZEKOWITZ, R. A. B. (1988). The macrophage. In *Biological Aspects in Natural Immunity* (ed. D. Nelson), New York: Academic Press (in press).

EZEKOWITZ, R. A. B., AUSTYN, J., STAHL, P. & GORDON, S. (1981). Surface properties of activated mouse macrophages – BCG infection reduces expression of antigen F4/80 and Fc and mannose-specific receptors for endocytosis whilst enhancing IA antigens. *J. exp. Med.* **154**, 60–76.

EZEKOWITZ, R. A. B., DAY, L. & HERMAN, G. (1988). A human mannose-binding protein in an acute phase reactant that shares sequence homology with other vertebrate lectins. *J. exp. Med.* **167**, 1034–1046.

EZEKOWITZ, R. A. B., HILL, M. & GORDON, S. (1986). Interferon alpha/beta selectively antagonizes down-regulation of mannosyl fucosyl receptors on macrophages activated by interferon gamma. *Biochem. biophys. Res. Commun.* **136**, 737–744.

GIGA, Y., ATUSUSHI, I. & TAKAHASHI, K. (1987). The complete amino acid sequence of echinoiden, a lectin from the coelomic fluid of the sea urchin *Anthocidaris crassispina. J. biol. Chem.* **262**, 6197–6209.

GRIFFIN, F., GRIFFIN, J., LEIDER, J. & SILVERSTEIN, S. (1975). Studies on the mechanism of phagocytosis. I. Requirements for circumferential attachment of particle bound ligands to specific receptors on the macrophage plasma membrane. *J. exp. Med.* **142**, 1263–1275.

HAAGSMAN, H. P., HAGWOOD, S., SEARGENT, T., BUCKLEY, D., WHITE, R. T., DRICKAMER, K. & BENSON, B. J. (1987). The major lung surface protein, SP 28-36 is a calcium-dependent carbohydrate-binding protein. *J. biol. Chem.* **262**, 13877–13886.

HALTIWANGER, R. S. & HILL, R. C. (1986). The isolation of a rat alveolar macrophage lectin. *J. biol. Chem.* **261**, 7440–7449.

HARDING, C., LEVY, M. & STAHL, P. (1985). Morphological analysis of ligand uptake and processing: The role of multivesicular endosomes and CURL in receptor ligand processing. *Eur. J. Cell Biol.* **36**, 230–238.

HOPPE, C. & LEE, Y. C. (1983). The binding and processing of mannose-bovine serum albumin derivatives by rabbit alveolar macrophages. *J. biol. Chem.* **258**, 14193–14202.

HYNES, R. D. (1987). Integrins. A family of cell surface receptors. *Cell* **48**, 549–551.

KAWASAKI, T. & ASHWELL, G. (1977). Isolation and characterization of an avian hepatic binding protein specific for N-acetylglucosamine-terminated glycoproteins. *J. biol. Chem.* **252**, 6536–6544.

KAWASAKI, T., ETON, R. & YAMASHURA, I. (1978). Isolation and characterization of a mannose-binding protein from rabbit liver. *Biochem. biophys. Res. Commun.* **81**, 1018–1026.

KAWASAKI, N., KAWASAKI, T. & YAMASHURA, I. (1983). Isolation and characterization of a mannose-binding protein from human serum. *J. Biochem.* **94**, 937–952.

KORNFELD, R. & KORNFELD, S. (1985). Assembly of asparagine linked oligosaccharides. *A. Rev. Biochem.* **54**, 631–653.

LEE, Y. C., STOWELL, C. P. & KRANTZ, M. J. (1976). 2-Imino-2-methoxyethyl-1-thioglycosides: New reagents for attaching sugars to proteins. *Biochemistry* **15**, 3956–3965.

LENNARTZ, M. R., COLE, F. S., SHEPHERD, V., WILEMAN, T. E. & STAHL, P. D. (1987*b*). Isolation and characterization of a mannose-specific endocytosis receptor from human placenta. *J. biol. Chem.* **262**, 9942–9944.

LENNARTZ, M. R., WILEMAN, T. E. & STAHL, P. D. (1987*a*). Isolation and characterization of a mannose-specific endoytosis receptor from rabbit alveolar macrophages. *Biochem. J.* **245**, 705–711.

LIFSON, J., COUTRE, S., HAUNG, E. & ENGELMAN, E. (1986). Role of envelope glycoprotein carbohydrate in human immunodeficiency virus (HIV) infectivity and virus-induced cell fusion. *J. exp. Med.* **164**, 2101–2106.

MARTIN, G. R., TIMPL, R., MULLER, P. K. & KUHN, K. (1985). The genetically distinct collagens. *Trends Biochem. Sci.* **10**, 285–287.

MATTHEWS, T. J., WEINHOLD, K. J., LYERLY, H. K., LANGLOIS, A. J., WIGZELL, H. & BOLOGNESI, D. (1987). Interaction between the human T-cell lymphotropic virus type III$_B$ envelope glycoprotein GP 120 and the surface antigen CD4: Role of carbohydrate in binding and cell fusion. *Proc. natn. Acad. Sci. U.S.A.* **84**, 5424–5428.

MAYNARD, Y. & BAENZIGER, J. U. (1981). Oligosaccharide specific endocytosis by isolated rat hepatic reticuloendothelial cells. *J. biol. Chem.* **256**, 8063–8072.

MAYNARD, Y. & BAENZIGER, J. U. (1982). Characterization of a mannose and *N*-acetylglucosamine-specific lectin present in rat hepatocytes. *J. biol. Chem.* **257**, 3708–3716.

MIZUNO, Y., KOZUTSUMI, Y., KAWASAKI, T. & YAMASHINA, I. (1981). Isolation and characterization of a mannose-binding protein from rat liver. *J. biol. Chem.* **256**, 4247–4256.

MOKENA, T. & GORDON, S. (1985). Human macrophage activation modulation of mannosyl, fucosyl receptor *in vitro* by lymphokines, gamma and alpha interferons and dexamethasone. *J. clin. Invest.* **75**, 624–635.

MONTAGNIER, L., CLAVEL, F., KRUST, B., CHAMMARET, S., REY, F., BARRE-SINOUSSI, F. & CHERMANN, J. C. (1985). Identification and antigenicity of the major envelope glycoprotein of lymphadenopathy-associated virus. *Virology* **114**, 283–289.

NIESEN, T. E., ALPERS, D. H., STAHL, P. D. & ROSENBLUM, J. L. (1984). Metabolism of glycosylated human salivary amylase: *in vivo* plasma clearance by rat hepatic endothelial cells and *in vitro* receptor mediated pinocytosis by rat macrophages. *J. Leukocyte Biol.* **36**, 307–320.

PELHAM, H. R. B. (1982). A regulatory upstream promoter element in the *Drosophila* Hsp 70 heat-shock gene. *Cell* **30**, 517–528.

REID, K. B. M. (1983). Proteins involved in the activation and control of the two pathways of human complement. *Biochem. Soc. Trans.* **11**, 1–11.

SCHLESINGER, P., MANDELL, B., MILLER, J., RODMAN, J., WHITE, R., DOEBBER, T. & STAHL, P. (1978). Liver Kupffer cell mediated plasma clearance of glycoproteins and lysosomal glycosidases, *β*-glucuronidase and *N*-acetyl-*β*-D-glycosaminidase. *Biochem. J.* **176**, 103–109.

SCHMITZ, G., ROBENER, H., LOHMANN, U. & ASSMANN, G. (1985). Interaction of high density lipoproteins with cholesteryl ester-laden macrophages: Biochemical and morphological characterization of cell surface receptor binding, endocytosis and resecretion of high density lipoproteins by macrophages. *EMBO J.* **4**, 613–622.

SHEPHERD, V., CAMPBELL, E., SENIOR, R. & STAHL, P. (1982). Characterization of the mannose/fucose receptor on human mononuclear phagocytes. *J. Reticuloendothelial Soc.* **32**, 423–431.

SHEPHERD, V. L., KONISH, M. & STAHL, P. (1985). Dexamethasone increases expression of mannose receptors and decreases extracellular accumulation of lysosomal enzymes in macrophages. *J. biol. Chem.* **260**, 160–164.

SHEPHERD, V., LEE, Y. C., SCHLESINGER, P. H. & STAHL, P. D. (1981). L-Fucose terminated glycoconjugates are recognized by pinocytosis receptors on macrophages. *Proc. natn. Acad. Sci. U.S.A.* **78**, 1019–1022.

SHEPHERD, V. L., STAHL, P., BERN, T. P. & RABINOVITCH, M. (1983). Receptor-mediated entry of *β*-glucuronidase into the parisitophorous vacuoles of macrophages infected with *Leishmania mexicana amazonensis*. *J. exp. Med.* **157**, 1471–1482.

SHIGAKU, S., TAKAAKI, T., KOSHER, R. A. & TANSIER, M. L. (1986). Cloning and sequence analysis of a partial cDNA for chicken cartilage proteoglycan core protein. *Proc. natn. Acad. Sci. U.S.A.* **83**, 5081–5090.

SIMMONS, C. F. & SCHWARTZ, A. L. (1984). Cellular pathways of galactose-terminal ligand movement in a cloned human hepatoma cell line. *Mol. Pharmacol.* **26**, 509–519.

STAHL, P. & GORDON, S. (1982). Expression of a mannosyl-fucosyl receptor for endocytosis on cultured primary macrophage and their hybrids. *J. Cell Biol.* **93**, 49–56.

STAHL, P., RODMAN, J. S., MILLER, J. & SCHLESINGER, P. (1978). Evidence for receptor-mediated binding of glycoproteins, glycoconjugates and lysosomal glycosidases by alveolar macrophages. *Proc. natn. Acad. Sci. U.S.A.* **75**, 1399–1403.

STAHL, P., RODMAN, J. S., SCHLESINGER, P. & DOEBBER, T. (1976). Clearance of lysosomal glycosidases from plasma: inhibition with agalacto-orosomucoid. *Nature, Lond.* **264**, 86–88.

STAHL, P., SCHLESINGER, P. H., SIGARDSON, E., RODMAN, J. S. & LEE, Y. C. (1980). Receptor mediated pinocytosis of mannose-glycoconjugates by macrophages: characterization and evidence for receptor recycling. *Cell* **19**, 207–215.

SUMMERFIELD, J. A. & TAYLOR, M. E. (1986). Mannose-binding proteins in human serum: identification of mannose-specific immunoglobulins and a calcium-dependent lectin of broader carbohydrate specificity, secreted by hepatocytes. *Biochim. biophys. Acta* **883**, 197–206.

SUNG, S.-S. J., NELSON, R. S. & SILVERSTEIN, S. C. (1983). Yeast mannans inhibit binding and phagocytosis of zymosan by mouse peritoneal macrophages. *J. Cell Biol.* **96**, 160–166.

TAKAHASHI, H., KOMANO, H., KAWAGUCHI, N., KITAMURA, N., NAKANISHI, S. & NATON, S. (1985). Cloning and sequencing of a cDNA of *Sarcophaga perigrina* humoral lectin induced by injury of the body wall. *J. biol. Chem.* **260**, 12228–12236.

TIETZE, C., SCHLESINGER, P. & STAHL, P. (1982). The mannose-specific endocytosis receptor of alveolar macrophages: Demonstration of two functionally distinct intracellular pools of receptors and their roles in receptor recycling. *J. Cell Biol.* **92**, 417–424.

TOWNSEND, R. & STAHL, P. (1981). Isolation and characterization of a mannose/N-acetylglucosamine/fucose binding protein from rat liver. *Biochem. J.* **194**, 209–214.

TOWNSEND, R. R., WALL, D. A., HUBBARD, A. L. & LEE, Y. C. (1984). Rapid release of galactose-terminated ligands after endocytosis by hepatic parenchymal cells: Evidence for a role of carbohydrate structure in the release of internalized ligand from receptor. *Proc. natn. Acad. Sci. U.S.A.* **81**, 466–470.

VON HEIJNE, G. (1983). Patterns of amino acids near signal-sequence cleavage sites. *Eur. J. Biochem.* **133**, 17–26.

WHITE, R. T., DANOM, D., MILLER, J., SPRATL, K., SCHILLING, J., HAGWOOD, S., BENSON, B. & CORDELL, B. (1985). Isolation and characterization of the human pulmonary surfactant apoprotein gene. *Nature, Lond.* **317**, 361–368.

WILD, J., ROBINSON, D. & WINCHESTER, B. (1983). Isolation of mannose-binding proteins from human liver. *Biochem. J.* **210**, 167–177.

WILEMAN, T., BOSHANS, R., SCHLESINGER, P. & STAHL, P. (1984). Monensin inhibits recycling of macrophage mannoseglycoprotein receptor and ligand delivery to lysosomes. *Biochem. J.* **220**, 665–675.

WILEMAN, T., LENNARTZ, M. & STAHL, P. (1986). Identification of the macrophage mannose receptor as a 175 KD membrane protein. *Proc. natn. Acad. Sci. U.S.A.* **83**, 2501–2505.

J. Cell Sci. Suppl. 9, 135–149 (1988)
Printed in Great Britain © The Company of Biologists Limited 1988

Macrophage lipoprotein receptors

ALAN M. FOGELMAN[1], BRIAN J. VAN LENTEN[1], CRAIG WARDEN[1],
MARGARET E. HABERLAND[1] AND PETER A. EDWARDS[1,2]

*Division of Cardiology, [1]Departments of Medicine and [2]Biological Chemistry, School of Medicine,
University of California, Los Angeles, CA 90024-1679, USA*

Summary

Macrophages possess a number of surface receptors that are capable of mediating the internaliz-ation of lipoproteins. The low-density lipoprotein (LDL) receptor of human monocyte macro-phages recognizes apolipoprotein B-100 and apolipoprotein E and is rapidly regulated in response to changes in intracellular cholesterol levels. In contrast, in J774 macrophages LDL receptor regulation is defective and LDL can cause massive cholesterol accumulation. The β migrating very low density lipoprotein (β-VLDL) receptor is poorly regulated by cellular cholesterol concen-trations, readily recognizes apolipoprotein E, poorly recognizes apolipoprotein B-100, and is immunologically related to the LDL receptor. The scavenger receptor (acetyl-LDL receptor) appears to have a molecular weight of 250 000 and is not regulated by cellular cholesterol levels. This receptor recognizes LDL that has been chemically or biologically altered. LDL complexes can also enter macrophages and cause cholesterol accumulation. Examples of such complexes are LDL–dextran sulphate complexes, LDL–proteoglycan aggregates, LDL–mast cell granule complexes, LDL–heparin–fibronectin–denatured collagen complexes, and LDL–antibody com-plexes. The entry of lipoprotein into macrophages by a pathway that is poorly regulated or is not regulated by cellular cholesterol concentrations appears to be a prerequisite for the formation of arterial foam cells.

Introduction

Atherosclerosis is a disease of arteries, which is both episodic and focal in nature. The earliest morphological event in the development of the atherosclerotic lesion is the diapedesis of blood monocytes into the subendothelial space. Within days to weeks these monocytes convert into lipid-laden macrophages. As a result of the foamy appearance of these cells in histological sections they are often referred to as foam cells. The predominant lipids in these lesions are cholesteryl esters. The accumulation of cholesteryl esters within the macrophage probably results from the receptor-mediated endocytosis of plasma-derived lipoproteins, some of which may have been modified in the artery wall. Several receptors on macrophages capable of mediating these events have been the subject of extensive research in recent years.

The low-density lipoprotein (LDL) receptor pathway

On the basis of studies of mouse peritoneal macrophages Brown and Goldstein initially concluded that macrophages lacked LDL receptors (Goldstein *et al.* 1979). However, several laboratories (Fogelman *et al.* 1980; Shechter *et al.* 1981; Traber & Kayden, 1980; Soutar & Knight, 1982) have since demonstrated that human monocyte-macrophages express an active LDL receptor pathway. Despite the presence of normal LDL receptors on these cells exposure to high levels of LDL *in vitro* did not lead to cholesteryl ester accumulation of the type seen in atherosclerotic lesions (Shechter *et al.* 1981). Since the LDL receptor pathway is highly regulated to preserve cellular cholesterol homeostasis (Brown & Goldstein, 1986) it was not surprising that normal LDL did not cause cholesteryl ester accumulation in cultured macrophages (Shechter *et al.* 1981). In an apparent paradox, it has been observed that macrophages in the artery walls of patients that lacked LDL receptors were filled with cholesteryl esters (Buja *et al.* 1979). Additionally, after injection of radiolabelled LDL into mutant rabbits (Watanabe hereditable hyperlipidemic, WHHL) that are genetically deficient in LDL receptors, the radiolabel rapidly appeared in macrophages in the subendothelial space (Steinberg *et al.* 1985). These observations suggest that alternative mechanisms account for the accumulation of lipoprotein-derived cholesteryl esters in foam cells.

The search for alternative pathways

It has been demonstrated that LDL recovered from human artery walls (Hoff *et al.* 1979) or from inflammatory fluid in rabbits (Raymond *et al.* 1985) is more electronegative than circulating LDL. These findings suggest that plasma LDL may be modified in the artery wall. LDL is but one source from which macrophage cholesteryl esters might be derived. Whereas LDL is rich in apolipoprotein B-100, after cholesterol feeding most animals accumulate a cholesteryl-ester-rich particle in their plasma, which is rich in apolipoprotein E. These E-rich lipoproteins float in the ultracentrifuge in the very low density lipoprotein (VLDL) fraction. These particles contain apolipoprotein B as well as apolipoprotein E and migrate in an electrophoretic field with characteristics intermediate between LDL and VLDL. Hence these particles are called beta migrating VLDL or β-VLDL. These particles also accumulate in the plasma of patients with familial type III hyperlipoproteinemia (Hui *et al.* 1984).

The β-VLDL receptor

While LDL was recognized poorly by mouse peritoneal macrophages Goldstein *et al.* (1980) found that β-VLDL was taken up by a high-affinity receptor on these cells. This receptor was poorly down-regulated compared to the LDL receptor on fibroblasts and consequently it was named the β-VLDL receptor. In other experiments these investigators found that β-VLDL also stimulated cholesteryl ester synthesis in human monocyte-macrophages while LDL did not (Mahley *et al.* 1980). In 1982 Gianturco *et al.* showed that β-VLDL, but not LDL, effectively competed for the uptake of hypertriglyceridemic VLDL (VLDL taken from hypertriglyceridemic subjects) by mouse peritoneal macrophages: these results suggested that the hypertriglyceridemic VLDL was also recognized by the β-VLDL receptor. In the following year Van Lenten *et al.* (1983) demonstrated that postprandial lipoproteins from normal fat-fed volunteers, but not their fasting lipoproteins, effectively competed for the uptake of β-VLDL by human monocyte-macrophages. Van Lenten *et al.* (1983) also showed that monocytes from a child with 5 % of the normal number of LDL receptors poorly recognized LDL, but recognized β-VLDL normally, suggesting that the LDL and β-VLDL receptors were genetically distinct. In 1984 Baker *et al.* reported that the uptake of LDL by aortic endothelial cells was dependent upon cellular density, but that the uptake of β-VLDL was not. Baker *et al.* (1984) also demonstrated that aortic endothelial cells from the mutant WHHL rabbits, which are deficient in LDL receptors, took up LDL poorly but internalized β-VLDL normally, providing what was thought to be further evidence that the LDL and β-VLDL receptors are genetically distinct.

Reasoning that if excess cholesterol enters into macrophages in the artery wall by receptor-mediated processes, Van Lenten *et al.* (1985*a*) studied the receptor-mediated uptake of lipoproteins in sterol-loaded human monocyte-macrophages. These investigators found that under these conditions of cholesterol loading there was no evidence for receptor-mediated uptake of chylomicrons (the large triglycer-ide-rich lipoproteins formed in the intestine after a meal) or LDL. These data were consistent with the Brown and Goldstein model, which predicts down-regulation of LDL receptors with cellular cholesterol loading. However, the sterol-loaded human monocyte-macrophages internalized β-VLDL and chylomicron remnants (postpran-dial particles produced by the metabolism of circulating chylomicrons that are acted upon by lipoprotein lipase: this enzyme removes triglyceride and results in the production of remnants, which are relatively enriched in cholesteryl esters and apolipoprotein E) by a lower affinity, but specific and saturable, process that was dependent on apolipoprotein E (Van Lenten *et al.* 1985*a*). Van Lenten *et al.* (1985*a*) also demonstrated that macrophages from WHHL rabbits recognized LDL poorly, but recognized β-VLDL normally, providing what was thought to be even further evidence that the LDL receptor and the β-VLDL receptor were genetically distinct. Subsequently, Ishii *et al.* (1986) also reported that β-VLDL, but not LDL, stimulated cholesteryl ester synthesis in WHHL macrophages.

All of the evidence up to this point indicated that the LDL receptor and the β-VLDL receptor were distinct. However, in, 1986 Koo *et al.* found that ligand blots of Triton X-100 extracts of mouse peritoneal macrophages identified a single protein when probed with ^{125}I-β-VLDL. The protein cross-reacted with antibodies against the bovine LDL receptor. The molecular weight of this receptor was approximately 5000 less than that of the human fibroblast LDL receptor. These investigators also demonstrated that pre-incubation of the mouse macrophages with LDL receptor antibody inhibited the binding of both β-VLDL and LDL to the cells and also inhibited lipoprotein-induced enhancement of cholesteryl ester synthesis. Moreover, the binding of ^{125}I-β-VLDL to the mouse macrophages correlated directly with the amount of protein recognized on immunoblots with antibody to the bovine LDL receptor. They concluded that the β-VLDL receptor on mouse peritoneal macro-phages was an unusual LDL receptor that binds LDL poorly, but binds apolipopro-tein E-containing lipoproteins with very high affinity, and this receptor is resistant to down-regulation by intracellular cholesterol (Koo *et al.* 1986).

The following year Ellsworth *et al.* (1987) reported that the uptake of ^{125}I-β-VLDL and ^{125}I-chylomicron remnants in murine macrophage cell lines was competitively inhibited by specific polyclonal antiserum directed against the LDL receptor of rat liver. The anti-LDL receptor immunoglobulin G (IgG), ^{125}I-β-VLDL, and ^{125}I-chylomicron remnants bound to two protein components, of apparent molecular weights of 125 000 and 111 000, on nitrocellulose blots of detergent-solubilized macrophage membranes. Between 70 % and 90 % of ^{125}I-lipoprotein binding was confined to the 125K (K = $10^3 M_r$) peptide. Binding of ^{125}I-β-VLDL and ^{125}I-chylomicron remnants to these proteins was competitively inhibited by anti-LDL receptor antibodies. The authors concluded that β-VLDL and chylomicron remnants were recognized by murine macrophages by an LDL receptor that is immunologically related to the LDL receptor of rat liver (Ellsworth *et al.* 1987).

The experiments in Fig. 1 show that when human monocyte-macrophages were cholesterol-loaded there was no detectable specific uptake of LDL. Under the same conditions of cholesterol loading, β-VLDL uptake was decreased by approximately 50 %, but even under these conditions β-VLDL uptake exceeded LDL uptake in the absence of cholesterol loading. However, the uptake of both β-VLDL and LDL was inhibited under both control and cholesterol loading conditions when anti-bovine LDL receptor IgG was present. Pre-immune IgG had no effect. These experiments indicate that the β-VLDL receptor of human monocyte-macrophages is immunologically related to the LDL receptor.

All of the above studies are consistent with the recognition of β-VLDL, hypertriglyceridemic VLDL, postprandial VLDL, and chylomicron remnants by a receptor on macrophages that poorly recognizes apolipoprotein B-100 (the apolipoprotein of LDL), but which recognizes apolipoprotein E with high affinity.

Hobbs *et al.* (1986) recently reported a mutation in a family with familial hypercholesterolemia in which the deletion of an exon encoding for a cysteine-rich repeat in the LDL receptor resulted in a receptor that failed to recognize apolipoprotein B-100, but which recognized apolipoprotein E with high affinity. These authors proposed that the ability to bind the single copy of apolipoprotein B-100 in LDL may require a precise arrangement of multiple binding sites, an arrangement that is not possible when one of the sites is deleted. They hypothesized that the binding of β-VLDL, on the other hand, may be more flexible since each β-VLDL particle contains multiple copies of apolipoprotein E, which might be able to rearrange themselves on the surface of the particles so as to conform to an altered receptor. Another possibility was also mentioned, that the binding of LDL might require some type of oligomerization of the LDL receptor, whereas binding of β-VLDL might not require such complex formation. Deletion of a cysteine-rich repeat might prevent oligomerization and thus prevent LDL binding without affecting β-VLDL binding (Hobbs *et al.* 1986).

Yamamoto *et al.* (1986) have shown that the defect in the LDL receptor of the WHHL rabbit is a deletion in the cysteine-rich ligand-binding domain of the receptor, which impedes transport of the receptor to the cell surface. A similar defect

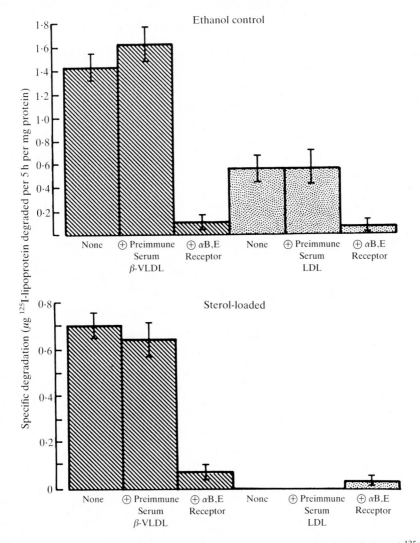

Fig. 1. The effect of anti-bovine adrenal LDL receptor IgG on the degradation of ^{125}I-rabbit β-VLDL and ^{125}I-human LDL in human monocyte-macrophages pre-incubated in the presence or absence of sterols in the medium. Normal human monocytes were cultured in 30% autologous serum as previously described (Van Lenten *et al.* 1985*a*). After 4 days the medium was removed and the cells were transferred to 0·1% human serum albumin in 0·5 ml of serum-free medium supplemented with $1\,\mu g\,ml^{-1}$ 25-hydroxycholesterol and $16\,\mu g\,ml^{-1}$ cholesterol in ethanol (bottom panel, sterol-loaded) or with ethanol alone (top panel, ethanol control) as described previously (Van Lenten *et al.* 1985*a*). On day 7, the medium was removed and the cells were washed three times. The cells were then incubated with 0·5 ml of medium containing $4\,\mu g\,ml^{-1}$ ^{125}I-rabbit β-VLDL (cross hatched bars) or $4\,\mu g\,ml^{-1}$ ^{125}I-human LDL (stippled bars) in the presence or absence of a 100-fold excess of non-radioactive lipoprotein and in the absence (None) or presence of $200\,\mu g\,ml^{-1}$ preimmune IgG (+Preimmune Serum) or in the presence of $200\,\mu g\,ml^{-1}$ anti-bovine adrenal LDL receptor IgG (+αB, E Receptor). After 5 h at 37 °C the medium was removed and the ^{125}I-labelled acid-soluble content determined as previously described (Van Lenten *et al.* 1985*a*). The values shown are the mean ± 1 s.d. of quadruplicate wells.

has been seen in a human (Yamamoto *et al.* 1986). These defects allow approximately 5 % of the receptors to reach the cell surface. If the deletion of the cysteine-rich region of the WHHL rabbit and some familial hypercholesterolemia homozygotes (e.g. the child in the studies of Van Lenten *et al.* (1983)) are similar to that described by Hobbs *et al.* (1986) one might have sufficient receptor to bind the apolipoprotein E in β-VLDL without binding apolipoprotein B-100 (LDL). If this were indeed the case many of the apparent contradictions in the studies reported above would be resolved. These issues await further research. However, regardless of the mechanism by which β-VLDL and chylomicron remnants are internalized by macrophages, these lipoproteins may be important in producing cholesteryl ester accumulation in arterial macrophages.

The scavenger receptor

In 1976 Goldstein and Brown observed that treatment of LDL with acetic anhydride caused the acetylation of the ϵ-amino groups of the lysine residues in LDL. This chemical modification rendered the LDL more electronegative and prevented the lipoprotein from being recognized by the LDL receptor (Basu *et al.* 1976). Consequently, LDL treated with acetic anhydride (acetyl-LDL) was poorly taken up by fibroblasts. However, in, 1979 Goldstein *et al.* found that acetyl-LDL was avidly taken up by mouse peritoneal macrophages, while native LDL was poorly recognized and internalized. As a consequence of the marked internalization and degradation of the acetyl-LDL, the mouse peritoneal macrophages became massively enriched in cholesteryl esters (Goldstein *et al.* 1979). Unfortunately, extensive studies failed to identify an *in vivo* process that could produce such acetylation. In, 1980 Fogelman *et al.* found that malondialdehyde (which is produced *in vivo* by the metabolism of arachidonic acid and by lipid peroxidation) reacted with LDL *in vitro* to produce a more electronegative particle. This malondialdehyde-treated LDL (MDA-LDL) was not recognized by the LDL receptor of human monocyte-macrophages and appeared to be recognized by a different receptor on the human monocyte-macrophages (Fogelman *et al.* 1980). This receptor was shown to be the same receptor that recognized acetyl-LDL and it was also found to produce massive cholesteryl ester accumulation in human monocyte-macrophages (Shechter *et al.* 1981). This receptor became known as the scavenger receptor as it seemed to recognize a number of negatively charged proteins and compounds (Brown *et al.* 1980).

The activity of this scavenger receptor was found to be independent of cellular cholesterol concentrations (Fogelman *et al.* 1981). Scavenger receptor activity was low in freshly isolated human monocytes but increased 10-fold as the monocytes converted into macrophages in culture (Fogelman *et al.* 1981). Experiments indicated that the scavenger receptor and the LDL receptor were on the same cell (Fogelman *et al.* 1981). However, LDL receptor activity declined with increasing cell density while scavenger receptor activity increased with increasing cell density (Fogelman *et al.* 1981; Mazzone & Chait, 1982). Lymphokines prevented the expression of the scavenger receptor as did endotoxin (Fogelman *et al.* 1982, 1983;

Van Lenten *et al.* 1985*b*, 1986). Diphosphoryl Lipid A was found to be the active principal in preventing the expression of this receptor on human monocyte-macrophages (Van Lenten *et al.* 1985*b*). The entry of endotoxin into human monocytes and the subsequent suppression of scavenger receptor activity appeared to depend on formation of an endotoxin–LDL complex followed by the receptor-mediated endocytosis of this complex *via* the LDL receptor pathway (Van Lenten *et al.* 1986). The only agent thus far identified that increases scavenger receptor activity in cultured human monocyte-macrophages is dexamethasone (Hirsch & Mazzone, 1986).

The scavenger receptor has only been found on monocyte-macrophages, Kupffer cells and on endothelial cells (Baker *et al.* 1984; Stein & Stein, 1980; Dresel *et al.* 1985; Pitas *et al.* 1985; Netland *et al.* 1985; Nagelkerke *et al.* 1983; Horiuchi *et al.* 1985*a*), particularly hepatic sinusoidal cells (Pitas *et al.* 1985; Netland *et al.* 1985; Nagelkerke *et al.* 1983; Horiuchi *et al.* 1985*a*).

Goldstein and Brown had suggested that scavenger receptor recognition resulted primarily from protein modification by reagents that produced a more electronegative protein (Goldstein *et al.* 1980; Brown *et al.* 1980). Such modifications included acetylation with acetic anhydride, aceto-acetylation, Schiff's base formation with malondialdehyde, maleylation with maleic anhydride or succinylation with succinic anhydride. Subsequently, Haberland *et al.* (1982, 1984) and Haberland & Fogelman (1985) demonstrated that negative charge was involved in receptor recognition, but that negative charge alone was not sufficient for receptor recognition. Indeed, the reagents employed appeared to alter the protein so that clusters of negative charges appeared due to conformational shifts in the protein. Moreover, at least in the case of one ligand, maleyl-albumin, removal of the reagent (i.e. de-maleylation) left a conformationally altered protein, which was still recognized by the scavenger receptor even though the de-maleylated protein had lost its electronegativity (Haberland & Fogelman, 1985). This suggested that the primary sequence of albumin could be induced, by a conformational change, to expose clusters of negative charge that were recognized by the scavenger receptor, even though the overall charge of the protein was not different from native albumin, which is not recognized by the scavenger receptor (Haberland & Fogelman, 1985). In support of this hypothesis was the finding that changing the conformation of the de-maleylated protein by exposure to guanidine HCl resulted in a loss of receptor recognition (Haberland & Fogelman, 1985).

Haberland *et al.* also demonstrated that some reagents that modify lysine residues are more efficient than others in producing molecules that are recognized by the scavenger receptor. The modification of only 16 % of the lysine residues in LDL by malondialdehyde produces scavenger receptor recognition (Haberland *et al.* 1982) while approximately two thirds of the lysine residues need to be modified by acetylation with acetic anhydride in order to achieve a similar degree of scavenger receptor recognition (Haberland *et al.* 1984).

Oxidation of LDL to a form recognized by the scavenger receptor *via* a metal-ion-dependent process and/or by cell-dependent processes have also been demonstrated in several laboratories (Morel *et al.* 1984; Henrickson *et al.* 1981; Parthasarathy *et al.* 1985; Heinecke *et al.* 1986). Cultured endothelial cells (Morel *et al.* 1984; Henrickson *et al.* 1981; Parthasarathy *et al.* 1985), and arterial smooth muscle cells (Heinecke *et al.* 1986), have been shown to be capable of oxidizing LDL to a form recognized by the scavenger receptor. Steinbrecher (1987) has recently shown that products of LDL lipid oxidation are capable of modifying the lysine residues of LDL and hence may induce a conformational change that leads to recognition of the modified lipoprotein by the scavenger receptor. Products of lipid oxidation that might mediate such lysine modification include 4-hydroxynonenal (Jurgens *et al.* 1985) and malondialdehyde (Fogelman *et al.* 1980). To date, only malondialdehyde has been shown to be present *in vivo* where it co-localized with apolipoprotein B in the atherosclerotic lesions of the WHHL rabbit (Haberland *et al.* 1988). Kita *et al.* (1987) recently demonstrated that probucol, an antioxidant, prevented the progression of atherosclerosis in WHHL rabbits. They hypothesized that this agent limited oxidative LDL modification and hence prevented foam cell formation (Kita *et al.* 1987).

The scavenger receptor has neither been purified to homogeneity nor has its normal function been established. Phillips *et al.* (1985) have demonstrated that thrombin-activated platelets secrete products that prevent the uptake and hydrolysis of modified LDL by macrophages. However, the natural ligand(s) of the scavenger receptor is unknown and probably will remain unknown until the receptor is purified. Partial purifications of the scavenger receptor have indicated that this protein has a molecular weight of approximately 250 000 (Via *et al.* 1985; Kodama & Krieger, 1986; Dresel *et al.* 1987). Figs 2, 3 demonstrate that binding activity can be recovered from human monocyte-macrophages in an HPLC fraction, which contains a 250K protein that is seen on a ligand blot in the absence but not in the presence of a competitive inhibitor of the scavenger receptor. While this 250K protein may well be the scavenger receptor, it should be noted that at least two other macrophage proteins have been identified that can also bind ligands of the scavenger receptor (Horiuchi *et al.* 1985*a,b,c*; Vlassara *et al.* 1986). These receptors have been presumed to be different from the scavenger receptor based on cross-competition experiments. However, both the receptor for formaldehyde-treated serum albumin (Horiuchi *et al.* 1985*a,b,c*) and the receptor for glucose-modified proteins (Vlassara *et al.* 1986) bind acetyl-LDL. Thus, it is possible that these receptors *in vivo* could also mediate the uptake of scavenger receptor ligands.

Maleyl-albumin was one of the original ligands of the scavenger receptor described by Goldstein *et al.* (1979). Recently, Haberland *et al.* (1986*a,b*) demonstrated in freshly isolated human monocytes that this ligand was also recognized by a different receptor, which mediates monocyte chemotaxis.

Other receptor-mediated processes for the unregulated uptake of cholesteryl-ester-rich ligands by macrophages

Yet another mechanism for the unregulated uptake of cholesteryl-ester-rich particles by macrophages was described by Basu *et al.* in 1979, the dextran sulphate pathway.

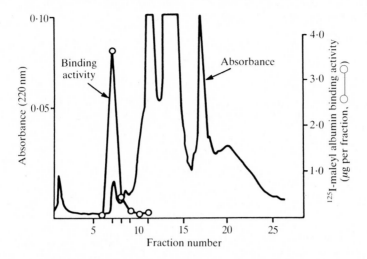

Fig. 2. Partial purification of the human monocyte-macrophage scavenger receptor. Human monocyte-macrophages were cultured in 30% autologous serum as described previously (Van Lenten *et al*. 1985a). After 7 days the medium was removed and the cells were washed three times with phosphate buffered saline (PBS) and then lysed with 15 ml of buffer containing 1% NP-40, 0·5% sodium deoxycholate, 150 mM-NaCl, 50 mM-Tris pH 8·3, 10 mM-EDTA, and protease inhibitors (30 μg ml^{-1} aprotinin, 20 μg ml^{-1} pepstatin, and 0·5 mM-phenylmethylsulphonylfluoride). All subsequent buffers contained these protease inhibitors. The lysate was applied to an ion exchange (PEI) column and eluted essentially as described by Via *et al*. (1985). The eluate was then subjected to gel permeation chromatography on a TSK 400 HPLC column essentially as described by Dresel *et al*. (1987). The phosphatidylcholine liposome filter assay to measure ^{125}I-maleyl-albumin binding to HPLC fractions was performed essentially as described by Via *et al*. (1985). Absorbance is indicated on the left ordinate and the binding of ^{125}I-maleyl-albumin is shown on the right ordinate (open circles).

They found that the uptake and degradation of ^{125}I-LDL by mouse peritoneal macrophages was increased markedly by the addition of high-molecular-weight dextran sulphate. The dextran sulphate and ^{125}I-LDL formed a complex, which was taken up and degraded with saturation kinetics suggesting a specific cell-surface high-affinity binding site. Competition studies indicated that this was neither the LDL receptor nor the scavenger receptor. These experiments indicated that macrophages have the capacity to ingest large amounts of LDL in association with high-molecular-weight sulphated polysaccharides and that this ingestion can lead to cholesteryl ester deposition in these cells.

Vijayagopal *et al*. (1985) later demonstrated that proteoglycan aggregates extracted from bovine aorta, when complexed to LDL *in vitro* in the presence of Ca^{2+}, were taken up and degraded by mouse peritoneal macrophages by a high-affinity saturable process. The uptake of these complexes was inhibited by unlabelled acetyl-LDL, but not LDL or polyinosinic acid or fucoidin, leaving open the question of which receptor mediated the uptake of these complexes. Exposure of the mouse peritoneal macrophages to the proteoglycan aggregate–LDL complex produced increased cholesteryl ester synthesis and massive cholesteryl ester accumulation.

Kokkonen & Kovanen (1987) recently demonstrated that stimulation of mast cells can lead to the formation of LDL–granule complexes which can be phagocytosed by macrophages and cause cholesterol accumulation.

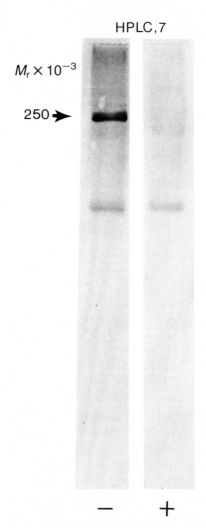

Fig. 3. Binding of malondialdehyde-altered LDL (MDA-LDL) by partially purified human monocyte-macrophage scavenger receptor. Proteins from fraction 7 of the experiment described in Fig. 2 were separated on a 6% polyacrylamide gel under non-denaturing conditions essentially as described by Via *et al.* (1985). They were then electrophoretically transferred to nitrocellulose. Non-specific protein binding sites on the nitrocellulose strips were blocked with non-fat dry milk. The nitrocellulose strips were incubated with $100 \mu g \, ml^{-1}$ MDA-LDL in the absence (−) or presence (+) of $500 \mu g \, ml^{-1}$ polystyrene sulphonate. Bound MDA-LDL was detected by exposing the strips to an affinity-purified rabbit antibody to MDA-LDL. This was followed by exposing the strips to biotin-labelled goat anti-rabbit IgG. After washing, the strips were exposed to avidin complexed with biotinylated alkaline phosphatase. Finally, the strips were washed and developed for colour with the alkaline phosphatase reagents 5-bromo-4-chloro-3-indolylphosphate ρ toluidine salt and nitroblue tetrazolium chloride.

Falcone *et al.* (1984) prepared insoluble complexes of LDL, heparin, fibronectin and dentured collagen (gelatin) and found that this complex was taken up by mouse peritoneal macrophages at a slower rate than LDL or acetyl-LDL and was degraded less effectively, resulting in an accumulation of undegraded cholesteryl esters within the cell. The cell cytoplasm was filled with phagosomes containing material similar in appearance to the LDL–matrix complexes rather than the lipid droplets character-istic of foam cells.

Another pathway that might mediate cholesteryl ester accumulation in macro-phages is the Fc receptor pathway. Witztum *et al.* (1984) demonstrated the presence of auto-antibodies to glycosylated proteins in the plasma of patients with diabetes. Glycosylated LDL–antibody complexes could be cleared by the Fc receptor. Since the Fc receptor is not regulated by cellular cholesterol levels this could lead to macrophage cholesteryl ester accumulation (Brown & Goldstein, 1983; Klimov *et al.* 1985).

The LDL receptor of the J774 cell appears to be poorly regulated as shown by Tabas *et al.* (1985) who found that unmodified LDL caused cholesteryl ester accumulation in J774 macrophages. They reported that LDL was internalized by the LDL receptor but in comparison with fibroblasts, the LDL receptor and HMG-CoA reductase activity in J774 cells were relatively resistant to down regulation by LDL or 25-hydroxycholesterol. Consequently the cells continued to take up LDL *via* the receptor and to accumulate cholesteryl esters. In addition, J774 cells appeared to accumulate cholesteryl esters from LDL internalized by non-specific processes. Subsequently, Tabas *et al.* (1986) found that inhibition of the enzyme acyl coenzyme A:cholesterol acyl transferase (ACAT) in J774 macrophages enhanced down-regulation of the LDL receptor and HMG-CoA reductase in these cells, and consequently prevented LDL-induced cholesterol accumulation. In contrast to the findings with J774 macrophages, down-regulation of the human fibroblast LDL receptor was not enhanced by their ACAT inhibitor. They concluded that in J774 macrophages, but not in fibroblasts, ACAT competes for a regulatory pool of intracellular cholesterol, and results in diminished receptor and reductase down-regulation, which in turn results in cellular LDL-cholesterol accumulation, and foam cell formation (Tabas *et al.* 1986).

Non-receptor-mediated processes

Wolfbauer *et al.* (1986) and Minor *et al.* (1986) have demonstrated that non-receptor-mediated uptake may also lead to massive cholesteryl ester accumulation. They exposed smooth muscle cells to cholesteryl-ester-rich lipid droplets extracted from macrophages. After repeated failure to transfer the cholesteryl esters in the medium to the smooth muscle cells, they cultured the smooth muscle cells on coverslips and then inverted these on the medium containing the lipid droplets. The result was massive cholesteryl ester accumulation. Apparently the buoyant lipid droplets floated to the surface under standard culture conditions and, consequently, they did not come in contact with the smooth muscle cells. In the artery wall the lipid droplets released from dying macrophages would probably be trapped in the collagen network and could come into contact with the smooth muscle cells. Such a scenario would explain the observed early appearance of cholesterol-laden macrophage cells and the later appearance of cholesterol-loaded smooth muscle cells.

Conclusion

Both receptor-mediated and non-receptor-mediated processes can deliver cholesteryl-ester-rich molecules into macrophages. A better understanding of these processes will advance our understanding of macrophage biology and may lead to more rationale therapies for atherosclerosis.

We thank Fara Elahi and Ken Ho for excellent technical assistance in preparing human monocytes and Susan C. Murphy for the preparation of this manuscript. We thank Dr Tom Innerarity of the Gladstone Foundation (San Francisco, CA) for the gift of the anti-bovine adrenal LDL receptor IgG. This work was supported in part by United States Public Health Service Grants HL 30568, IT32 HL 07412, and RR 865, the Laubisch Fund, and the M. K. Grey Fund.

References

BAKER, D. P., VAN LENTEN, B. J., FOGELMAN, A. M., EDWARDS, P. A., KEAN, C. & BERLINER, J. A. (1984). LDL, scavenger and β-VLDL receptors on aortic endothelial cells. *Arteriosclerosis* **4**, 248–255.

BASU, S. K., BROWN, M. S., HO, Y. K. & GOLDSTEIN, J. L. (1979). Degradation of low density lipoprotein dextran sulfate complexes associated with deposition of cholesteryl esters in mouse macrophages. *J. biol. Chem.* **254**, 7141–7146.

BASU, S. K., GOLDSTEIN, J. L., ANDERSON, R. G. W. & BROWN, M. S. (1976). Degradation of cationized low density lipoprotein and regulation of cholesterol metabolism in homozygous familial hypercholesterolemia fibroblasts. *Proc. natn. Acad. Sci. U.S.A.* **73**, 3178–3182.

BROWN, M. S., BASU, S. K., FALCK, J. R., HO, Y. K. & GOLDSTEIN, J. L. (1980). The scavenger cell pathway for lipoprotein degradation: specificity of the binding site that mediates the uptake of negatively-charged LDL by macrophages. *J. supramolec. Struct.* **13**, 67–81.

BROWN, M. S. & GOLDSTEIN, J. L. (1983). Lipoprotein metabolism in the macrophage: implications for cholesterol deposition in atherosclerosis. *A. Rev. Biochem.* **52**, 233–261.

BROWN, M. S. & GOLDSTEIN, J. L. (1986). A receptor mediated pathway for cholesterol homeostasis. *Science* **232**, 34–47.

BUJA, M. L., KOVANEN, P. T. & BILHEIMER, D. W. (1979). Cellular pathology of homozygous familial hypercholesterolemia. *Am. J. Path.* **97**, 327–358.

DRESEL, H. A., FRIEDRICH, E., VIA, D. P., SCHETTLER, G. & SINN, H. (1985). Characterization of binding sites for acetylated low density lipoprotein in the rat liver *in vivo* and *in vitro*. *EMBO J.* **4**, 1157–1162.

DRESEL, H. A., FRIEDRICH, E., VIA, D. P., SINN, H., ZIEGLER, R. & SCHETTLER, G. (1987). Binding of acetylated low density lipoprotein and maleylated bovine serum albumin to the rat liver: one or two receptors? *EMBO J.* **6**, 319–326.

ELLSWORTH, J. L., KRAEMER, F. B. & COOPER, A. D. (1987). Transport of β-very low density lipoproteins and chylomicron remnants is mediated by the low density lipoprotein receptor pathway. *J. biol. Chem.* **262**, 2316–2325.

FALCONE, D. J., MATED, N., SHIO, H., MINICK, C. R. & FOWLER, S. D. (1984). Lipoprotein-heparin-fibronectin-denatured collagen complexes enhance cholesteryl ester accumulation in macrophages. *J. Cell Biol.* **99**, 1266–1274.

FOGELMAN, A. M., HABERLAND, M. E., SEAGER, J., HOKOM, M. & EDWARDS, P. A. (1981). Factors regulating the activities of the low density lipoprotein receptor and the scavenger receptor on human monocyte-macrophages. *J. Lipid Res.* **22**, 1131–1141.

FOGELMAN, A. M., SEAGER, J., HABERLAND, M. E., HOKOM, M., TANAKA, R. & EDWARDS, P. A. (1982). Lymphocyte-conditioned medium protects human monocyte-macrophages from cholesteryl ester accumulation. *Proc. natn. Acad. Sci. U.S.A.* **79**, 922–926.

FOGELMAN, A. M., SEAGER, J., GROOPMAN, J. E., BERLINER, J. A., HABERLAND, M. E., EDWARDS, P. A. & GOLDE, D. W. (1983). Lymphokines secreted by an established lymphocyte line modulate receptor-mediated endocytosis in macrophages derived from human monocytes. *J. Immun.* **131**, 2368–2373.

FOGELMAN, A. M., SCHECHTER, I., SEAGER, J., HOKOM, M., CHILD, J. S. & EDWARDS, P. A. (1980). Malondialdehyde alteration of low density lipoprotein leads to cholesteryl ester accumulation in human monocyte-macrophages. *Proc. natn. Acad. Sci. U.S.A.* **77**, 2214–2218.

GIANTURCO, S. H., BRADLEY, W. A., GOTTO, A. M. F., JR, MORRISETT, J. D. & PEAVY, D. L. (1982). Hypertriglyceridemic very low density lipoproteins induce triglyceride synthesis and accumulation in mouse peritoneal macrophages. *J. clin. Invest.* **70**, 168–178.

GOLDSTEIN, J. L., HO, Y. K., BASU, S. K. & BROWN, M. S. (1979). Binding site on macrophages that mediates uptake and degradation of acetylated low density lipoprotein producing massive cholesterol deposition. *Proc. natn. Acad. Sci. U.S.A.* **76**, 333–337.

GOLDSTEIN, J. L., HO, Y. K., BROWN, M. S., INNERARITY, T. L. & MAHLEY, R. (1980). Cholesteryl ester accumulation in macrophages resulting from receptor-mediated uptake and degradation of hypercholesterolemic canine β-VLDL. *J. biol. Chem.* **255**, 1839–1848.

HABERLAND, M. E. & FOGELMAN, A. M. (1985). Scavenger receptor-mediated recognition of maleyl-bovine albumin and the demaleylated protein in human monocyte-macrophages. *Proc. natn. Acad. Sci. U.S.A.* **82**, 2693–2697.

HABERLAND, M. E., FOGELMAN, A. M. & EDWARDS, P. A. (1982). Specificity of receptor-mediated recognition of malondialdehyde-modified low density lipoproteins. *Proc. natn. Acad. Sci. U.S.A.* **79**, 1712–1716.

HABERLAND, M. E., FONG, D. & CHENG, L. (1988). Malondialdehyde-altered protein occurs in artheroma of Watanabe hereditable hyperlipidemic (WHHL) rabbits. *Science* (in press).

HABERLAND, M. E., OLCH, C. L. & FOGELMAN, A. M. (1984). Role of lysines in mediating interaction of modified low density lipoproteins with the scavenger receptor of human monocyte-macrophages. *J. biol. Chem.* **259**, 11 305–11 311.

HABERLAND, M. E., RASMUSSEN, R. R. & FOGELMAN, A. M. (1986*b*). Receptor recognition of maleyl-albumin induces chemotaxis in human monocytes. *J. clin. Invest.* **78**, 827–831.

HABERLAND, M. E., RASMUSSEN, R. R., OLCH, C. L. & FOGELMAN, A. M. (1986*a*). Two distinct receptors account for recognition of maleyl-albumin in human monocytes during differentiation *in vitro*. *J. clin. Invest.* **77**, 631–639.

HEINECKE, J. W., BAKER, L., ROSEN, H. & CHAIT, A. (1986). Superoxide-mediated modification of low density lipoprotein by arterial smooth muscle cells. *J. clin. Invest.* **77**, 757–761.

HENRICKSON, T., MAHONEY, E. M. & STEINBERG, D. (1981). Enhanced macrophage degradation of low density lipoprotein previously incubated with cultured endothelial cells: recognition by receptors for acetylated low density lipoproteins. *Proc. natn. Acad. Sci. U.S.A.* **78**, 6499–6503.

HIRSCH, I. J. & MAZZONE, T. (1986). Dexamethasone modulates lipoprotein metabolism in cultured human monocyte-derived macrophages. *J. clin. Invest.* **77**, 485–490.

HOBBS, H. H., BROWN, M. S., GOLDSTEIN, J. L. & RUSSELL, D. W. (1986). Deletion of exon encoding cysteine-rich repeat of low density lipoprotein receptor alters its binding specificity in a subject with familial hypercholesterolemia. *J. biol. Chem.* **261**, 13 114–13 120.

HOFF, H. F., BRADLEY, W. A., HEIDERMAN, C. L., GAUBATZ, J. W., KARAGAS, M. D. & GOTTO, A. M. JR (1979). Characterization of low density lipoprotein-like particles in the human aorta from grossly normal and atherosclerotic regions. *Biochim. biophys. Acta* **573**, 361–374.

HORIUCHI, S., TAKATA, K., MAEDA, H. & MORINO, Y. (1985*a*). Scavenger function of sinusoidal liver cells. *J. biol. Chem.* **259**, 53–56.

HORIUCHI, S., TAKATA, K. & MORINO, Y. (1985*b*). Characterization of a membrane-associated receptor from rat sinusoidal liver cells that binds formaldehyde-treated serum albumin. *J. biol. Chem.* **260**, 475–481.

HORIUCHI, S., TAKATA, K. & MORINO, Y. (1985c). Purification of a receptor for formaldehyde-treated albumin from rat liver. *J. biol. Chem.* **260**, 482–488.

HUI, D. Y., INNERARITY, T. L. & MAHLEY, R. W. (1984). Defective hepatic lipoprotein receptor binding of β-very low density lipoprotein from type III hyperlipoproteinemic patients. *J. biol. Chem.* **259**, 860–869.

ISHII, K., KITA, T., KUME, N. & YOKODE, M. (1986). Study of lipoprotein receptor of macrophages from normal and WHHL rabbits: an animal model of familial hypercholesterolemia. *Arteriosclerosis* **6**, 541a.

JURGENS, G., LANG, J. & ESTERBAUER, H. (1985). Modification of human low-density lipoprotein by the lipid peroxidation product 4-hydroxynonenal. *Biochim. biophys. Acta* **875**, 103–114.

KITA, T., NAGANO, Y., YOKODE, M., ISHII, K., KUME, N., OOSHIMA, A., YOSHIDA, H. & KAWAI, C. (1987). Probucol prevents the progression of atherosclerosis in Watanabe heritable hyperlipidemic rabbit, an animal model for familial hypercholesterolemia. *Proc. natn. Acad. Sci. U.S.A.* **84**, 5928–5931.

KLIMOV, A. N., DENISENKO, A. D., POPOV, A. V., NAGORNEV, V. A., PLESKOV, V. M., VINOGRADOV, A. G., DENSIENKO, T. V., MAGRACHEVA, E. Y., KHEIFES, G. M. & KUZNETZOV, A. S. (1985). Lipoprotein-antibody immune complexes, their catabolism and role in foam cell formation. *Atherosclerosis* **58**, 1–15.

KODAMA, T. & KRIEGER, M. (1986). Purification of a bovine liver acetyl-LDL binding protein. *Arteriosclerosis* **6**, 527a.

KOKKOKEN, J. O. & KOVANEN, P. T. (1987). Stimulation of mast cells leads to cholesterol accumulation in macrophages *in vitro* by a mast cell granule-mediated uptake of low density lipoprotein. *Proc. natn. Acad. Sci. U.S.A.* **84**, 2287–2291.

KOO, C., WERNETTE-HAMMOND, M. E. & INNERARITY, T. L. (1986). Uptake of canine β-very low density lipoproteins by mouse peritoneal macrophages is mediated by a low density lipoprotein receptor. *J. biol. Chem.* **261**, 11 194–11 201.

MAHLEY, R. W., INNERARITY, T. L., BROWN, M. S., HO, Y. K. & GOLDSTEIN, J. L. (1980). Cholesteryl ester synthesis in macrophages: Stimulation by β- very low density lipoproteins from cholesterol-fed animals of several species. *J. Lipid Res.* **21**, 970–980.

MAZZONE, T. & CHAIT, A. (1982). Autoregulation of the modified low density lipoprotein receptor in human monocyte-derived macrophages. *Arteriosclerosis* **2**, 487–492.

MINOR, L. K., GLICK, J. M. & ROTHBLAT, G. H. (1986). Smooth muscle foam cells in culture: uptake of artificial lipid inclusions. *Arteriosclerosis* **6**, 523a.

MOREL, D. W., DiCORLETO, P. E. & CHISOLM, G. (1984). Endothelial and smooth muscle cells after low density lipoprotein *in vitro* by free radical oxidation. *Arteriosclerosis* **4**, 357–364.

NAGELKERKE, J. F., BARTO, K. P. & VAN BERKEL, T. J. C. (1983). In vivo and in vitro uptake and degradation of acetylated low density lipoprotein by rat liver endothelial, Kupffer, and parenchymal cells. *J. biol. Chem.* **258**, 12 221–12 227.

NETLAND, P. A., ZETTER, B. R., VIA, D. P. & VOYTA, J. C. (1985). *In situ* labelling of vascular endothelium with fluorescent acetylated low density lipoprotein. *Histochem. J.* **17**, 1309–1320.

PARTHASARATHY, S., STEINBRECHER, U. P., BARNETT, J., WITZTUM, J. L. & STEINBERG, D. (1985). Essential role of phospholipase A_2 activity in endothelial cell-induced modification of low density lipoprotein. *Proc. natn. Acad. Sci. U.S.A.* **82**, 3000–3004.

PHILLIPS, D. R., ARNOLD, K. & INNERARITY, T. (1985). Platelet secretory products inhibit lipoprotein metabolism in macrophages. *Nature, Lond.* **316**, 746–748.

PITAS, R. E., BOYLES, J., MAHLEY, R. W. & BISSELL, D. M. (1985). Uptake of chemically modified low density lipoproteins *in vivo* is mediated by specific endothelial cells. *J. Cell Biol.* **100**, 103–117.

RAYMOND, T. L., REYNOLDS, S. A. & SWANSON, J. A. (1985). Lipoproteins of the extravascular space: enhanced macrophage degradation of low density lipoproteins from interstitial inflammatory fluid. *J. Lipid Res.* **26**, 1356–1362.

SHECHTER, I., FOGELMAN, A. M., HABERLAND, M. E., SEAGER, J., HOKOM, M. & EDWARDS, P. A. (1981). The metabolism of native and malondialdehyde-altered low density lipoproteins by human monocyte-macrophages. *J. Lipid Res.* **22**, 63–71.

SOUTER, A. K. & KNIGHT, B. L. (1982). Degradation by cultured monocyte-derived macrophages from normal and familial hypercholesterolemic subjects of modified and unmodified low-density lipoproteins. *Biochemic. J.* **204**, 549–556.

STEIN, O. & STEIN, Y. (1980). Bovine aortic endothelial cells display macrophage-like properties towards acetylated ^{125}I-labelled low density lipoprotein. *Biochim. biophys. Acta* **620**, 631–635.

STEINBERG, D., PITTMAN, R. C. & CAREW, T. E. (1985). Mechanisms involved in the uptake and degradation of low density lipoprotein by the artery wall in vivo. *Ann. N.Y. Acad. Sci.* **454**, 195–206.

STEINBRECHER, U. P. (1987). Oxidation of human low density lipoprotein results in derivatization of lysine residues of apolipoprotein B by lipid peroxide decomposition products. *J. biol. Chem.* **262**, 3603–3608.

TABAS, I., WEILAND, D. A. & TALL, A. R. (1985). Unmodified low density lipoprotein causes cholesteryl ester accumulation in J774 macrophages. *Proc. natn. Acad. Sci. U.S.A.* **82**, 416–420.

TABAS, I., WEILAND, D. A. & TALL, A. R. (1986). Inhibition of Acyl coenzyme A: Cholesterol acyl transferase in J774 macrophages enhances down regulation of the low density lipoprotein receptor and 3-hydroxy-3-methylglutaryl-Coenzyme A reductase and prevents low density lipoprotein-induced cholesterol accumulation. *J. biol. Chem.* **261**, 3147–3155.

TRABER, M. G. & KAYDEN, H. J. (1980). Low density lipoprotein receptor activity in human monocyte-derived macrophages and its relation to atheromatous lesions. *Proc. natn. Acad. Sci. U.S.A.* **77**, 5466–5470.

VAN LENTEN, B. J., FOGELMAN, A. M., HABERLAND, M. E. & EDWARDS, P. A. (1986). The role of lipoproteins and receptor-mediated endocytosis in the transport of bacterial lipopolysaccharide. *Proc. natn. Acad. Sci. U.S.A.* **83**, 2704–2708.

VAN LENTEN, B. J., FOGELMAN, A. M., HOKOM, M. M., BENSON, L., HABERLAND, M. E. & EDWARDS, P. A. (1983). Regulation of the uptake and degradation of β-VLDL in human monocyte-macrophages. *J. biol. Chem.* **258**, 5151–5157.

VAN LENTEN, B. J., FOGELMAN, A. M., JACKSON, R. L., SHAPIRO, S., HABERLAND, M. E. & EDWARDS, P. A. (1985*a*). Receptor-mediated uptake of remnant lipoproteins by cholesterol-loaded human monocyte-macrophages. *J. biol. Chem.* **260**, 8783–8788.

VAN LENTEN, B. J., FOGELMAN, A. M., SEAGER, J., RIBI, E., HABERLAND, M. E. & EDWARDS, P. A. (1985*b*). Bacterial endotoxin selectively prevents the expression of scavenger-receptor activity on human monocyte-macrophages. *J. Immun.* **134**, 3718–3721.

VIA, D. P., DRESEL, H. A., CHENG, S.-L. & GOTTO, A. M. (1985). Murine macrophage tumors are a source of a 260,000-Dalton acetyl-low density lipoprotein receptor. *J. biol. Chem.* **260**, 7379–7386.

VIJAYAGOPAL, P., SRINIVASAN, S. R., JONES, K. M., RADHAKRISHNAMURTHY, B. & BERENSON, G. S. (1985). Complexes of low-density lipoproteins and arterial proteoglycan aggregates promote cholesteryl ester accumulation in mouse macrophages. *Biochem. biophys. Acta* **837**, 251–261.

VLASSARA, H., BROWNLEE, M. & CERAMI, A. (1986). Novel macrophage receptor for glucose-modified proteins is distinct from previously described scavenger receptors. *J. exp. Med.* **164**, 1301–1309.

WITZTUM, J. L., STEINBRECHER, U. P., KESANIEMI, Y. A. & FISHER, M. (1984). Autoantibodies to glucosylated proteins in the plasma of patients with diabetes mellitus. *Proc. natn. Acad. Sci. U.S.A.* **81**, 3204–3208.

WOLFBAUER, G., GLICK, J. M., MINOR, L. K. & ROTHBLAT, G. H. (1986). Development of the smooth muscle foam cell: uptake of macrophage lipid inclusions. *Proc. natn. Acad. Sci. U.S.A.* **83**, 7760–7764.

YAMAMOTO, T., BISHOP, R. W., BROWN, M. S., GOLDSTEIN, J. L. & RUSSELL, D. W. (1986). Deletion in cysteine-rich region of LDL receptor impedes transport to cell surface in WHHL rabbit. *Science* **232**, 1230–1237.

J. Cell Sci. Suppl. 9, 151–167 (1988)
Printed in Great Britain © The Company of Biologists Limited 1988

Protein myristoylation as an intermediate step during signal transduction in macrophages: its role in arachidonic acid metabolism and in responses to interferon γ

ALAN A. ADEREM

The Rockefeller University, 1230 York Avenue, New York, NY 10021, USA

Summary

The role of macrophages in the regulation of inflamation and immunity is, in part, due to their secretory repertoire. Among the important mediators released by macrophages are the products of both the cyclooxygenase and lipoxygenase pathways of arachidonic acid (20:4) metabolism. The principal focus of this paper is the mechanism by which bacterial lipopolysaccharides (LPS) regulate 20:4 metabolism in macrophages. LPS has the capacity to *prime* macrophages for greatly enhanced 20:4 metabolism when the cells are subsequently challenged with a spectrum of triggers. Concomitant with priming, LPS also promotes the covalent attachment of myristic acid to a set of macrophage proteins. The time and concentration dependence of LPS-induced protein myristoylation is consistent with a role for myristoylation in LPS priming of the 20:4 cascade. One of the myristoylated proteins is a 68K ($K = 10^3 M_r$) protein kinase C substrate which associates with membranes upon myristoylation. LPS-primed macrophages show greatly increased phosphorylation of the 68K protein when the cells are subsequently treated with protein kinase C activating phorbol esters. It is proposed that the myristoylation of the 68K protein promotes its attachment to the membrane where it is more closely associated with activated protein kinase C (PKC), an association which would ensure more efficient catalysis during the mobilization and oxygenation of 20:4.

This paper also examines protein myristoylation during T-cell-mediated activation of macrophages. Immune-activated macrophages have an enhanced capacity to kill several infectious agents by oxidative mechanisms. The lymphokine γ-interferon (IFNγ) rapidly induces the myristoylation of a 48K protein. This 48K protein is also myristoylated in murine macrophages that have been activated *in vivo* by intraperitoneal injection of *Corynebacterium parvum*, suggesting that it may be an important intermediate in the activation of macrophages for enhanced microbicidal capacity.

Introduction

During the course of our investigation into the molecular mechanism by which bacterial lipopolysaccharide (LPS) primes macrophages for enhanced arachidonic acid (20:4) metabolism we discovered that LPS also promotes the covalent attachment of the 14-carbon fatty acid, myristic acid, to a select group of macrophage proteins, including a major, specific substrate of protein kinase C. While the focus of this paper is on stimulus-dependent protein myristoylation in the murine peritoneal macrophage, I have also included information to situate these acylation reactions within a broader context. The chapter therefore begins with a discussion of 20:4 metabolism in macrophages and its modulation by LPS. An account of protein myristoylation in macrophages and its effects on protein kinase C dependent phosphorylation follows. Protein myristoylation during immune activation of macrophages is considered and finally, the function and enzymology of myristoylation in other cells are briefly discussed.

Arachidonic acid metabolism in macrophages

Macrophages are a major source of arachidonic acid (20:4) metabolites, which are important mediators of inflammation (Davies et al. 1984). When macrophage phagocytic receptors interact with particulate ligands such as immune complexes or bacteria, phospholipases are activated and 20:4 is released from membrane phospholipids. The free 20:4 is then oxygenated via the cyclooxygenase pathway to prostaglandin E_2 (PGE_2) and prostacyclin (PGI_2), or along the lipoxygenase pathway to leukotriene C (LTC) and hydroxyeicosatetranoic acids (HETEs) (Scott et al. 1980; Bonney et al. 1978, 1979; Rouzer et al. 1980).

The cyclooxygenase products (prostaglandins, prostacyclin and thromboxane) have been shown to influence smooth muscle tone, platelet aggregation, lymphocyte function, myelopoiesis, vascular permeability as well as pain and fever. The lipoxygenase product leukotriene B (LTB) mediates neutrophil aggregation, secretion and adhesion to vascular endothelium, as well as chemotactic activity for a variety of white blood cells: LTC mediates smooth muscle contraction and increased vascular permeability (reviewed in Davies et al. 1984).

Regulation of 20:4 metabolism in macrophages

Regulation of the lipoxygenase and cyclooxygenase pathways in macrophages is exerted at a number of levels. Briefly, the amount and types of 20:4 metabolites vary with the stimulus, the activation state of the cell, the tissue of origin and the species. For example:

(1) The ratio of cyclooxygenase to lipoxygenase metabolites secreted by macrophages depends on the agonist. Thus the soluble agonist, phorbol myristate acetate (PMA), stimulates the release of only cyclooxygenase products, while particulate stimuli such as zymosan and immune complexes trigger the release of both cyclooxygenase and lipoxygenase metabolites (Humes et al. 1982; Tripp et al. 1985; Aderem et al. 1986a). The profile of 20:4 metabolites produced appears to be related to the capacity of the stimulus to trigger Ca^{2+} transients (Tripp et al. 1985; Aderem & Cohn, 1986, 1988) and will be discussed in detail below.

(2) Murine resident peritoneal macrophages have low microbicidal and tumoricidal activity and secrete large quantities of 20:4 metabolites, while BCG-activated peritoneal macrophages have high microbicidal and tumoricidal capacity and secrete small amounts of 20:4 metabolites (Scott et al. 1982). Resident cells secrete predominantly PGI_2, PGE_2 and LTC while BCG-activated macrophages only release small quantities of thromboxane B_2 (TxB_2) and PGE_2 (Scott et al. 1982).

(3) The profile of 20:4 metabolites also varies with tissue of origin. While both murine resident peritoneal macrophages and pulmonary tissue macrophages secrete LTC, only peritoneal macrophages secrete significant quantities of PGE_2 and PGI_2 (Rouzer et al. 1982).

(4) There are differences in 20:4 metabolites secreted by macrophages of different species. For example, in contrast to the mouse, the major products secreted by human monocytes are TxB, LTB, LTC and HETEs while PGE_2 is produced in very low concentration and prostacyclin is completely absent (Pawlowski *et al.* 1983).

(5) Bacterial lipopolysaccharide has the capacity to prime macrophages for enhanced 20:4 metabolism when the cells are subsequently stimulated (Aderem *et al.* 1986a). While the amount of 20:4 metabolites released to the medium is greatly increased, LPS treatment does not alter the proportion of cyclooxygenase and lipoxygenase products (see below).

The effect of LPS on phagocyte function

LPS induces the secretion of a large number of macrophage products including plasminogen activator, tumour necrosis factor, interleukin-1 and granulocyte macrophage colony stimulating factor (GM-CSF) (for reviews see Morrison & Ulevitch, 1978; Homma *et al.* 1984). Furthermore, LPS primes macrophages (Pabst & Johnston, 1980) and neutrophils (Guthrie *et al.* 1984) for enhanced release of reactive oxygen intermediates on subsequent challenge with a variety of triggers.

Little is known about the mechanisms by which LPS stimulates these complex responses in macrophages. Early cellular responses to LPS treatment include inositol lipid turnover (Ogmundsdottir & Weir, 1979), protein phosphorylation (Weiel *et al.* 1986) and the synthesis of specific proteins (Hamilton *et al.* 1986). We have recently reported that LPS promotes the myristoylation of three macrophage proteins (Aderem *et al.* 1986b), including a major protein kinase C substrate. We describe data below that suggest that these novel transacylation reactions might constitute a major transduction pathway for LPS-induced response.

LPS modulates 20:4 metabolism in macrophages

LPS is by itself a poor trigger of the 20:4 cascade (Fig. 1); (Aderem *et al.* 1986a). However, pre-incubation of cells for 30–60 min with LPS ($10\,\text{ng ml}^{-1}$) enhances both the amount and the rate of 20:4 secretion in response to a second stimulus. For example, PMA-induced 20:4 secretion is increased 3- to 15-fold in cells pretreated with LPS (Fig. 1). Similarly, LPS also synergizes with zymosan (yeast cell wall), immune complexes and the Ca^{2+} ionophore, A23187 (Aderem *et al.* 1986a). When unprimed cells are stimulated, secretion of 20:4 commences only after a lag phase. This lag phase is significantly shortened in LPS-treated cells (Fig. 1, inset). Treatment with LPS thus speeds and potentiates 20:4 release presumably by establishing one or more preconditions necessary for activation of the phospholipase.

Further support for this hypothesis is provided by the ability of LPS to render macrophages responsive to latex particles. Latex particles are ingested by macrophages, but without the release and metabolism of 20:4. However, when cells are primed with LPS for at least 45 min before ingestion of the latex beads, large amounts of PGI_2 and PGE_2 are secreted (Fig. 2).

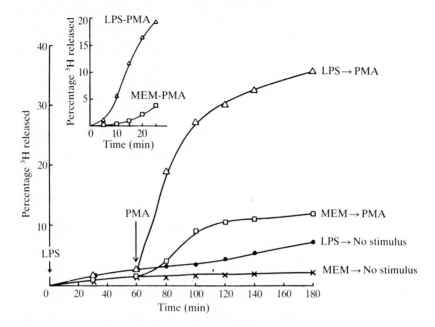

Fig. 1. LPS priming potentiates PMA-induced 20:4 metabolism in macrophages. Murine resident peritoneal macrophages were isolated and labelled to equilibrium with [^{3}H]20:4. The cells were then pre-incubated for 60 min in medium plus or minus LPS (100 ng ml^{-1}). PMA (50 nM) was then added (arrow) and 20:4 metabolite secretion was determined at the times indicated. The data are expressed as the percentages of radiolabel released. (Reprinted, with permission, from Aderem *et al.* 1986*a*.)

These and other data led us to postulate that activation of 20:4 metabolism in macrophages requires two distinct steps; a *priming* step followed by a *triggering* step (Aderem *et al.* 1986*a*). Receptor-mediated particulate stimulation of the 20:4 cascade is capable of both priming and triggering, LPS is capable of priming and latex particles can only generate the triggering step. We suggest below that the second, or triggering step, is an increase in intracellular Ca^{2+}, and that the first, or priming step, is related to stimulus-dependent myristoylation of proteins involved in signal response coupling.

Calcium regulates the triggering step

Since the phagocytosis of latex is accompanied by an increase in intracellular calcium, and latex is only capable of generating the triggering signal, we tested the possibility that an increase in intracellular calcium constituted the triggering signal (Aderem & Cohn, 1988). Low concentrations (0·1 µM) of the calcium ionophore, A23187, do not trigger the 20:4 cascade in macrophages. However, when the cells are first primed with LPS (10 ng ml^{-1}) for 60 min and then challenged with A23187, a rapid release of a large amount of 20:4 metabolites ensues. The order in which stimuli are added is critical. If the cells are first challenged with A23187 and subsequently treated with LPS, no release of 20:4 metabolites is observed.

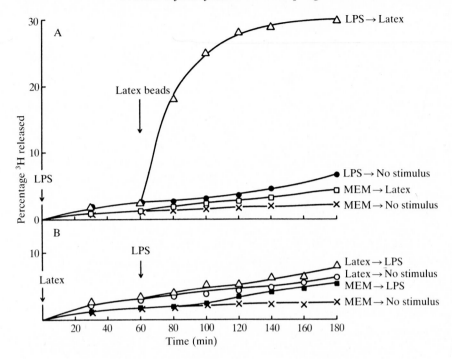

Fig. 2. A. Macrophages primed with LPS secrete 20:4 metabolites in response to latex beads. Murine resident peritoneal macrophages were isolated and labelled with [^{3}H]20:4. The cells were then pre-incubated for 60 min in medium plus or minus LPS (100 ng ml^{-1}). Latex particles were then added and 20:4 metabolite secretion was determined at the specified times. The data are expressed as the percentage of radiolabel released. 20:4 metabolites were secreted only when the cells were treated sequentially with LPS and latex (△). Latex alone (□) and LPS alone (●) do not promote the release of 20:4 metabolites. B. The latex particles were added first and LPS was added second. (Reprinted, with permission, from Aderem *et al.* 1986*a*.)

To be sure that the calcium, and not A23187, was critical for the triggering step, cells were cultured in Ca^{2+}-free medium and exposed sequentially to LPS and A23187. In the absence of external Ca^{2+} very little 20:4 was secreted into the medium. After the addition of Ca^{2+} to the external medium a rapid release of 20:4 metabolites occurs, confirming that an increase in intracellular Ca^{2+} triggers 20:4 metabolite secretion in the LPS-primed cell.

A second role for calcium in the control of macrophage 20:4 metabolism has been found. It is to increase the activity of the lipoxygenase pathway. Low concentrations of LPS (10 ng ml^{-1}) or A23187 (0·1 μM) do not promote the secretion of any 20:4 metabolites. High concentrations of LPS (1 μg ml^{-1}) cause the release of cyclooxygenase products only. However, when macrophages are treated sequentially with LPS and A23187 both cyclooxygenase and lipoxygenase pathways are activated, LTC production being increased 150-fold (Aderem & Cohn, 1988).

A similar shift in profile of 20:4 metabolite secretion has been reported for macrophages treated with PMA and A23187 (Tripp *et al.* 1985; Aderem & Cohn,

1986). While PMA alone stimulates macrophages to secrete cyclooxygenase pro-
ducts, a combination of PMA and A23187 promotes the release of large amounts of
LTC as well. Therefore, increasing the Ca^{2+} concentration within macrophages with
A23187 results in the activation of the lipoxygenase pathway.

These data imply that the cyclooxygenase and lipoxygenase pathways have
different Ca^{2+} requirements. We have shown this to be true by using LPS-primed
macrophages that have been treated with A23187 in the absence of external Ca^{2+} as a
model system in which to titrate the Ca^{2+} concentration dependence of each
pathway. Neither cyclooxygenase nor lipoxygenase metabolites are secreted in the
absence of Ca^{2+} in the medium. This is consistent both with our previous finding
that 20:4 metabolite secretion in macrophages is completely dependent on extracellular Ca^{2+} regardless of the nature of the stimulus (Aderem *et al.* 1986*c*), and with
the requirements of macrophage phospholipases for Ca^{2+} (Wightman *et al.*
1981*a*,*b*). When Ca^{2+} is titrated into the system, cyclooxygenase products are
detected at one order of magnitude lower Ca^{2+} concentration in the medium than are
lipoxygenase metabolites.

The data also suggest that Ca^{2+} regulates macrophage 20:4 metabolism at two
distinct steps. First, Ca^{2+} is required for the activation of the phospholipases that
promote the release of 20:4 from the membrane phospholipid. Second, relatively
higher concentrations of Ca^{2+} are required both to activate the 5-lipoxygenase
enzyme and to promote its reversible association with the membrane fraction
(Rouzer & Samuelsson, 1987). Thus agonists such as PMA, which mobilize
relatively small amounts of intracellular Ca^{2+} (Di Virgilio *et al.* 1984), promote the
secretion of only cyclooxygenase products, whereas particulate agonists such as
immune complexes, which stimulate rather larger increases in intracellular Ca^{2+}
(Young *et al.* 1984), cause the secretion of both cyclooxygenase and lipoxygenase
products.

Stimulus-induced myristoylation of macrophage proteins

While investigating the biochemical mechanism of LPS priming of macrophages for
enhanced 20:4 metabolism, we discovered that LPS stimulates the selective
myristoylation of proteins with molecular mass of 68K ($K = 10^3 M_r$) and a doublet of
36–42K (Aderem *et al.* 1986*b*) (Fig. 3) The myristate is linked to the proteins
through amide bonds, since it is not released by treatment with hydroxylamine. The
reaction appears to be specific for myristic acid, as palmitate and arachidonate are not
incorporated into these proteins.

The temporal response and LPS concentration dependence of the myristoylation
reaction is compatible with it having a role in LPS-dependent priming of macrophages for enhanced 20:4 metabolism (Aderem *et al.* 1986*a*,*b*).

We postulated above that agonists, such as zymosan, that promote 20:4 secretion
from macrophages must be capable of generating both the priming and triggering
signals. It is of interest, therefore, that zymosan also promotes the myristoylation of

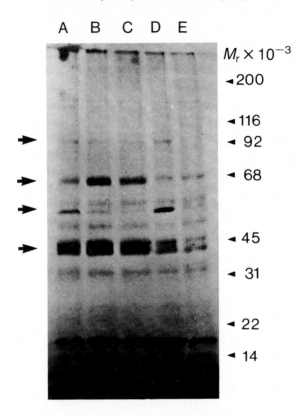

Fig. 3. Fluorograph after SDS–polyacrylamide gel electrophoresis of murine macrophage cell lysates labelled with [^{3}H]myristic acid. Cells were incubated for 2 h in the presence of [^{3}H]myristic acid and the following stimuli: zymosan (lane A); LPS (lane B); an active LPS derivative (lane C); PMA (lane D); no stimulus (lane E). The cells were then extracted in lysis buffer containing protease inhibitors. Following the removal of nuclei, the lysates were boiled with SDS and dithiothreitol and electrophoresed. Arrows indicate specific protein bands whose acylation has been induced by treatment with the various stimuli. (Reprinted, with permission, from Aderem *et al.* 1986*b*.)

three proteins with molecular masses identical to those acylated in response to LPS (Aderem *et al.* 1986*b*).

We have examined the effect of protein synthesis inhibitors on the myristoylation of macrophage proteins and on 20:4 secretion. A combination of cycloheximide (5 μg ml^{-1}) and emetine (5 μg ml^{-1}), which inhibits macrophage protein synthesis by 97 % (Aderem *et al.* 1986*c*), inhibits protein myristoylation at the earliest time point measurable (<5 min). This suggests either that myristoylation is coupled to translation or that the myristoyl transferase is turning over very rapidly. Regardless of which of these two possibilities is correct, it is of interest that 20:4 secretion is also inhibited by protein synthesis inhibitors on the same time scale (Aderem *et al.* 1986*c*; Bonney *et al.* 1980). The exquisite sensitivity of 20:4 metabolism to protein synthesis inhibitors could be explained if protein myristoylation is an intermediate in the activation of 20:4 metabolism.

LPS promotes the myristoylation of a protein kinase C substrate

The 68K protein whose myristoylation is induced by LPS is similar or identical to the 80/87K protein, a major specific substrate for protein kinase C found in brain and fibroblasts (Wu *et al.* 1982; Albert *et al.* 1986; Blackshear *et al.* 1986; Rozengurt *et al.* 1983; for reviews see Neidel & Blackshear, 1986; Woodgett *et al.* 1987). The macrophage 68K protein can be immune precipitated with a polyclonal rabbit antiserum raised against the "87 kD" major specific protein kinase C substrate of bovine brain (Aderem *et al.* 1988a). Further evidence that the 68K macrophage protein is a protein kinase C substrate is provided by the observation that PMA triggers its phosphorylation. The *Staphylococcus aureus* V8 protease map of the phosphorylated 68K murine protein is identical to that of the bovine 87K phosphoprotein. The two-dimensional phosphopeptide maps following thermolysin digestion of the murine macrophage and bovine brain proteins are also identical. When subjected to isoelectric focusing, the phosphorylated and myristoylated protein from murine macrophages and the phosphorylated proteins from murine, rat and bovine brain were found to be acidic with a pI of approximately 4·5.

The apparent molecular mass of the brain and fibroblast 80/87K protein has been reported to vary with the species and with the analytical gel system used (Albert *et al.* 1986, 1987; Blackshear *et al.* 1986; Neidel & Blackshear, 1986; Woodgett *et al.* 1987). To monitor the electrophoretic behaviour of the PKC substrate protein from a variety of cells and tissues, the mouse macrophage, mouse brain, rat brain and bovine brain proteins were electrophoresed together in two gel systems. On a 6%–12% linear gradient SDS–polyacrylamide gel (Neville's buffer), the apparent molecular mass values obtained were 68K, 69K, 70K and 76K, respectively. On an 8% SDS–polyacrylamide gel (Laemmli buffer) the molecular mass values were 79K, 80K, 83K and 87K respectively. The variability in apparent molecular mass observed with different gel systems may be explained by the results of hydrodynamic studies of the bovine brain 87K protein which show a calculated molecular mass of 68K, and suggest that the protein is an asymmetric, highly elongated monomer (Albert *et al.* 1987).

Subcellular localization of the 68K protein kinase C substrate

We have compared the distribution, between the membrane and cytosolic fractions, of the myristoylated and phosphorylated 68K PKC substrate. The major portion (>90%) of the myristolated 68K protein was found in the membrane fraction, whereas the major portion (>75%) of the phosphorylated 68K protein was observed in the cytosolic fraction. As a working hypothesis we propose the following sequence of events to explain the observed distributions of the myristoylated and phosphorylated forms of the 68K protein (Fig. 4). (1) LPS promotes the myristoylation of the 68K protein. (2) The myristoylated protein moves to the membrane where it is more closely associated with PKC, which is known to be active at the membrane

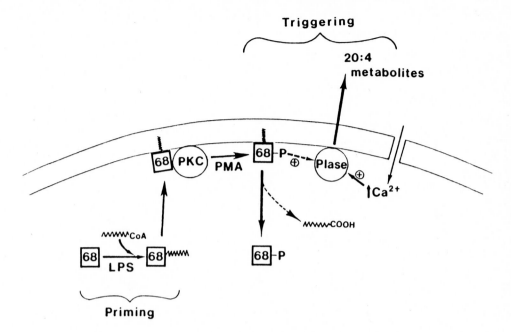

Fig. 4. LPS-dependent myristoylation of the 68K PKC substrate might be an intermediate in LPS priming of macrophages for enhanced 20:4 metabolism. This hypothetical model stems from data that LPS promotes the myristoylation of the 68K protein. The myristic acid moiety then targets the protein to the membrane where it associates with PKC. These two steps represent priming. Triggering commences when PMA activates PKC or when a particle interacts with a receptor and provides signals that activate PKC. This leads to the enhanced phosphorylation of the membrane-bound 68K protein. PKC-dependent phosphorylation(s) is followed by the activation of phospholipase(s) leading to the secretion of 20:4 metabolites. An increase in intracellular calcium could function to activate the phospholipase or PKC. Since most of the 68K phosphorylated protein is found in the cytoplasm it is possible that phosphorylation promotes the dissociation of this protein from the membrane. This might be accompanied by de-myristoylation since myristoylated 68K protein is not observed in the cytoplasm. The continuous arrows represent pathways for which evidence exists. The broken arrows represent speculative pathways.

(Nishizuka, 1986). (3) PKC phosphorylates the 68K protein. (4) The phosphorylated 68K protein is then de-myristoylated and released to the cytoplasm. This hypothetical sequence of events is supported by several lines of evidence. First, in all systems described thus far myristoylation appears to occur co-translationally or very soon after translation (Wilcox *et al.* 1987; for a review see Sefton & Buss, 1987). This also appears to be the case in macrophages, since LPS-induced myristoylation of the 68K protein is rapidly blocked by protein synthesis inhibitors as described above. Second, in at least two instances protein-bound myristic acid has been shown to have a role in targeting proteins to the membrane. Myristoylation of p60[src] and Moloney murine leukemia virus p65[gag] protein is necessary for plasma membrane association, transforming potential and viral budding (Pellman *et al.* 1985; Cross *et al.* 1984; Kamps *et al.* 1985; Rein *et al.* 1986). Third, LPS pre-treatment of macrophages results in greatly increased PMA-dependent phosphorylation of the 68K protein and also results in a shift in the PMA dose-response curve such that half-maximal phosphorylation of p68 in LPS-treated cells is obtained with concentrations of PMA 10-fold less than those required in macrophages not treated with LPS (A. Rosen & A. Aderem, unpublished results). Fourth, pulse-chase experiments with [^{3}H]myristic acid, ^{32}P$_i$ and [^{35}S]methionine suggest that PMA induces both the phosphorylation and de-myristoylation of the 68K protein (A. Rosen & A. A. Aderem, preliminary results).

The myristic acid moiety of a protein could facilitate protein association with membranes by simple insertion into the membrane. However, myristic acid-dependent targeting of the protein to the membrane appears more selective. Thus myristoylated p60^{src} associates only with the plasma membrane, suggesting that a receptor for myristoylated proteins might exist (Pellman *et al.* 1985). Protein–protein interaction also appears to be important since myristoylated p60^{src} preferentially associates with a detergent-resistant cellular fraction in fibroblasts (Hamaguchi & Hanafusa, 1987) and the myristoylated 68K protein is associated with a detergent-resistant fraction in macrophages (A. Rosen & A. Aderem, unpublished results). Phosphorylation of the myristoylated 68K protein might interrupt its association with the membrane without necessarily promoting its de-myristoylation. Mechanisms by which this might be affected include the introduction of a phosphate group near the site of interaction or a conformational transition of the protein.

LPS enhances the phosphorylation of the 68K protein

Two lines of evidence suggest that LPS is capable of influencing PKC-dependent pathways within macrophages. First, treatment of macrophages with LPS results in increased phosphorylation of the 68K PKC substrate. However, LPS-dependent phosphorylation of the 68K protein occurs more slowly than does PMA-dependent phosphorylation (half-maximal phosphorylation with LPS in 60 min; half maximal phosphorylation with PMA in 7 min). Furthermore, the maximal level of phosphorylation obtained with LPS is approximately 50% of that obtained with PMA. Second, the synergy between LPS and A23187 in activating the lipoxygenase pathway can be mimicked by PMA, a known activator of PKC. LPS could either activate PKC directly or *potentiate* its activity in an alternative way.

It has been reported that LPS does activate partially purified PKC *in vitro* (Wightman & Raetz, 1984). In this system, it is possible that LPS is substituting for phosphatidyl serine, a necessary cofactor of PKC. The structure of lipid A resembles this phospholipid, and the classic inhibitor of LPS action (Morrison & Ulevitch, 1978), polymyxin B, is known to inhibit PKC activity by neutralizing phosphatidyl serine (Mazzei *et al.* 1982). However, we have shown that LPS does not activate highly purified PKC (A. Aderem & K. Albert, unpublished observation).

Since LPS does not activate purified PKC directly, we favour the hypothesis that LPS treatment *potentiates* PKC activity in response to other signals. Stimulation of protein kinase C activity in intact cells causes a shift in the subcellular location of the enzyme from the cytosol to the membrane (Nishizuka, 1986). In macrophages, as mentioned above, LPS-induced myristoylation of the 68K PKC substrate promotes its association with the membrane. LPS might therefore potentiate PKC activity by promoting subcellular association of PKC and its substrates. This hypothesis is supported by the observation that LPS-primed cells show greatly increased phosphorylation of the 68K protein when the cells are subsequently challenged with PMA. The observation that LPS-dependent activation of the PKC pathway is much slower than the PMA response also supports the 'potentiation' hypothesis.

20:4 metabolism in PKC down-regulated macrophages

Prolonged exposure to PMA results in many cell types becoming partially or completely deficient in specific phorbol ester binding sites, immunoreactive PKC and PKC activity (for a review see Neidel & Blackshear, 1986). This down-regulation has been exploited to assess the role of PKC in a variety of cellular events. We found that macrophages that had been treated with 250 nM-PMA for 24 h showed a 95 % decrease in [^{3}H]phorbol dibutyrate binding, no detectable immunoreactive PKC, and no PMA-dependent phosphorylation of the 68K specific PKC substrate. PMA-dependent activation of 20:4 metabolism was completely inhibited, suggesting that PMA stimulates 20:4 metabolism via a PKC-dependent pathway.

A model for LPS priming of macrophage 20:4 metabolism

Treatment of macrophages with LPS for 20–40 min results in the cells becoming primed for greatly enhanced 20:4 metabolism when subsequently challenged with a variety of stimuli. Coincident with the establishment of the primed state, LPS also promotes the myristoylation of three proteins. One of these proteins (68K) is a major substrate for PKC. Myristoylation of this protein directs it to the membrane where it is more closely associated with activated PKC (Fig. 4). This multimolecular assembly at the membrane results in greater catalytic efficiency and potentiated 20:4 metabolism.

Protein myristoylation in other systems

It is becoming evident that a number of cellular and retroviral proteins have the capacity to become myristoylated. Most of these proteins have a role in cellular regulation, and they include the catalytic subunit of cAMP-dependent protein kinase (Carr *et al.* 1982), calcineurin B, a component of a calmodulin-binding phosphatase (Aitken *et al.* 1982), NADH–cytochrome b_5 reductase (Ozols *et al.* 1984), a M_r 56 000 tyrosine protein kinase expressed in the murine lymphoma cell line LSTRA (Marchildon *et al.* 1984) and p60[src], the tyrosine kinase encoded by the Rous sarcoma virus (Schultz *et al.* 1985; Buss & Sefton, 1985).

The function of protein myristoylation is only beginning to be understood. Acylation of p60[src] is essential for association of the protein with the plasma membrane and for expression of this kinase's transforming potential (Cross *et al.*

1984; Kamps *et al.* 1985). Since non-myristoylated p60[v-src] retains its tyrosine kinase activity (Cross *et al.* 1984), it is probable that myristoylation functions to *target* the enzyme to the plasma membrane where it exerts its biological effects. The myristoylated retroviral gag proteins may exploit this cellular targeting mechanism to localize viral budding since the myristoylation of the Moloney murine leukemia virus Pr65[gag] protein is essential for membrane association and virus particle formation (Rein *et al.* 1986). However, some myristoylated proteins appear to be soluble (Carr *et al.* 1982; Olson *et al.* 1985), suggesting that protein acylation may serve functions other than facilitating protein association with membranes.

Myristoyl transferase

We have not yet characterized the myristoyl transferase(s), the enzyme(s) that covalently attach myristic acid to macrophage proteins. However, Towler and colleagues have recently purified an *N*-myristoyl transferase (NMT) from *Saccharomyces cerevisiae*, which catalyses the covalent attachment of myristic acid to synthetic peptides whose sequences were derived from those of known *N*-myristoyl proteins (Towler *et al.* 1987*a,b*; Towler & Glaser, 1986). The native NMT is a 55K monomer, which has a strict specificity for myristoyl CoA as the acyl donor. The enzyme activity is present in both crude membrane and soluble fractions prepared from yeast, as well as BC_3Hl murine muscle cells (D. A. Towler, personal communication), and has a slightly alkaline pH optimum which suggests that it is not lysosomal. The purified NMT does not exhibit intrinsic methionase activity, suggesting that another enzyme must first remove the initiator methionine from the nascent apo-myristoyl proteins before myristoylation can occur.

NMT exhibits a high degree of selectivity for the sequence of its substrate peptide and a consensus sequence required for effective myristoylation has been elucidated (Towler *et al.* 1987*a*). The following rules apply: (1) NMT has an absolute requirement for amino-terminal Gly in its peptide substrates. (2) Neutral amino acids (Asn, Ser, Gln, Ala, Val) are allowed at position two while charged residues and Pro are not. Peptides with aromatic or bulky hydrophobic residues at position two bind to the enzyme but are poor substrates. (3) A wider spectrum of amino acids can be accommodated at positions three and four in NMT substrates, although peptides with uncharged residues at position three are bound with greater affinity. (4) Position five is critical in NMT–ligand interactions, with Ser^5 being a highly favoured residue. A charged residue such as Asp^5 renders a peptide totally inactive as a substrate. Peptides with Pro at positions five or six do not function as NMT substrates. (5) Residues beyond the first six amino acids play a role in substrate recognition by NMT but the precise structural requirement in this region of NMT ligands remain to be elucidated.

The consensus data described above are supported by the sequences of known myristoylated proteins. Since the substrate specificity of the NMT is phylogenically conserved, it is possible to identify potential *N*-myristoyl proteins by examining eukaryotic sequences. For example, it was shown that synthetic peptides derived from the N termini of the HTLV-III gag protein and from the guanine nucleotide-binding proteins (G proteins), $G_{\alpha i}$, could be myristoylated *in vitro* by NMT. Later it was noted that the gag and $G_{\alpha i}$ proteins were myristoylated *in situ* (Buss *et al.* 1987; Paul *et al.* 1987). It is also possible that some myristoyl proteins may be acylated at a cryptic site exposed by proteolytic cleavage.

It should be borne in mind that the NMT from yeast was isolated using a peptide substrate derived from the sequence of known myristoylated proteins. The method is therefore likely to select for an enzyme whose specificity approximates the sequence of this peptide and it raises the possibility that other myristoyl transferase enzymes may exist which have different substrate specificities. However, the observation that all the known myristoylated proteins contain the consensus sequence seems to argue against the existence of multiple myristoyl transferases.

The elucidation of a consensus sequence required for myristoylation allows one to predict whether a protein is a candidate for myristoylation or not. Thus, the prediction by Towler *et al.* that the G proteins and the gag protein of HIV would be myristoylated has been borne out (Buss *et al.* 1987; Paul *et al.* 1987). However, certain proteins that contain the myristoylation sequence have been found to be non-myristoylated. For example, a subset of G proteins, $G_{\alpha 45}$ and $G_{\alpha 52}$, contain the N-terminal glycine but are not myristoylated (Buss *et al.* 1987). This is a very interesting observation since it suggests either that myristoylation of a consensus site does not occur obligatorily or that de-myristoylation can occur.

De-myristoylation

The palmitic acid attached to the transferrin receptor has been shown to turnover more rapidly than the receptor protein (Omary & Trowbridge, 1981). Whether myristic acid is removed enzymatically from acylated proteins prior to the degradation of the protein has yet to be addressed. In the case of p60[src], the half-life of the myristoyl group is the same as that of the polypeptide, suggesting that this protein is not de-acylated (Buss *et al.* 1984). However, we have observed that PMA-dependent phosphorylation of the 68K protein alters its subcellular location from the membrane to the cytosol, and preliminary data suggest that PMA-dependent de-acylation might accompany this change in subcellular distribution (A. Rosen & A. Aderem, unpublished results).

Protein myristoylation as an early signal in T-cell-mediated activation of macrophages

The intracellular events leading to the activation of macrophages by antigen-specific T cells are largely unknown. During cell-mediated immunity, macrophages acquire an increased capacity to secrete reactive oxygen intermediates and to kill microbes and tumour cells. Treatment of macrophages with γ interferon (IFNγ), and with other cytokines like interleukin-4 and GM-CSF, induces properties that are similar to those of macrophages activated *in situ* (Nathan *et al.* 1983; Schreiber *et al.* 1983).

We have investigated the effect of IFNγ on macrophage protein myristoylation (Aderem *et al.* 1986*b*). Treatment of murine resident peritoneal macrophages with recombinant IFNγ ($10\,U\,ml^{-1}$) greatly enhances the myristoylation of a 48K protein. This effect is observed within 1 h and is maximal by 3 h. Neither IFNα nor IFNβ induce the myristoylation of the 48K protein, suggesting that this event is related to the macrophage activating capacity of IFNγ, and not to its antiviral activity. IFNγ-induced myristoylation of the 48K protein appears to be specific for macrophages since it does not occur in human umbilical vein endothelial cells or murine 3T3 fibroblasts.

Consistent with it having a role in macrophage activation, the 48K protein is constitutively myristoylated in macrophages activated *in vivo* by intraperitoneal injection of heat-killed *C. parvum*. The identity of the 48K protein is not yet known. A number of workers have described a 47K protein that is phosphorylated in normal neutrophils upon exposure to a variety of activators of the respiratory burst. This 47K protein remains unphosphorylated in neutrophils from patients with autosomal recessive chronic granulamatous disease, which are incapable of generating reactive oxygen intermediates (Heyworth & Segal, 1986). Since activated macrophages have a greatly increased capacity to generate reactive oxygen metabolites, it is important to investigate the possible relationship between the myristoylated 48K macrophage protein and the phosphorylated 47K neutrophil protein.

The LPS-primed macrophage has proved an excellent model system in which to study the convergence of three distinct signal transduction systems, namely those mediated by protein myristoylation, protein phosphorylation and calcium. The biological read-outs, such as 20:4 metabolism and the release of reactive oxygen intermediates, are clear and distinct, and since the cells are terminally differentiated the signals are not obscured by those involved in the regulation of the cell cycle. A number of proteins that are likely to have a role in signal transduction have been identified. They include the 68K PKC substrate and the 48K protein whose myristoylation is induced by IFNγ. Future studies will concentrate on the identity and function of these proteins.

I thank Dr Zanvil A. Cohn for support and guidance, Drs Paul Greengard and Antony Rosen for many stimulating discussions, Doug Marratta and Matthew Keum for excellent technical assistance, and Drs Kathy Barker and Ralph Steinman for critically reading the manuscript. The work on the 68K protein was done in collaboration with K. A. Albert, J. K.-T. Wang and Paul Greengard. This work was supported by National Institutes of Health Grant AI 25032 and AI 07012 and by a grant-in-aid from the Squibb Institute for Medical Research. A. A. Aderem is a Pew Scholar in the Biomedical Sciences.

References

Aderem, A. A., Albert, K. A., Keum, M. M., Wang, J. K. T., Greengard, P. & Cohn, Z. A. (1988*a*). Stimulus-dependent myristoylation of major substrate for protein kinase C. *Nature, Lond.* **332**, 362–364.

Aderem, A. A., Cohen, D. S., Wright, S. D. & Cohn, Z. A. (1986*a*). Bacterial lipopolysaccharides prime macrophages for enhanced release of arachidonic acid metabolites. *J. exp. Med.* **164**, 165–179.

ADEREM, A. A., KEUM, M. M., PURE, E. & COHN, Z. A. (1986*b*). Bacterial lipopolysaccharides, phorbol myristate acetate, and zymosan induce the myristoylation of specific macrophage proteins. *Proc. natn. Acad. Sci. U.S.A.* **83**, 5817–5821.

ADEREM, A. A. & COHN, Z. A. (1986). Bacterial lipopolysaccharides modify signal transduction in the arachidonic acid cascade in macrophages. In *Biochemistry of macrophages, Ciba Foundation Symposium 118* (ed. M. O'Conner), pp. 196–210. London: Pitman.

ADEREM, A. A. & COHN, Z. A. (1988). Calcium ionophore synergizes with bacterial lipopolysaccharides in activating macrophage arachidonic acid metabolism. *J. exp. Med.* **167**, 623–631.

ADEREM, A. A., MARRATTA, D. E. & COHN, Z. A. (1988*b*). Interferon-gamma induces the myristoylation of a 48K protein in macrophages. *Proc. natn. Acad. Sci. U.S.A.* (in press).

ADEREM, A. A., SCOTT, W. A. & COHN, Z. A. (1986*c*). Evidence for sequential signals in the induction of the archidonic acid cascade in macrophages. *J. exp. Med.* **163**, 139–154.

AITKEN, A., COHEN, P., SANTIKARN, S., WILLIAMS, D. H., CALDER, A. G., SMITH, A. & KLEE, C. B. (1982). Identification of the NH_2-terminal blocking group of calcineurin B as myristic acid. *FEBS. Lett.* **150**, 314–318.

ALBERT, K. A., WALAAS, S. I., WANG, J. K.-T. & GREENGARD, P. (1986). Widespread occurrence of "87 kDa", a major specific substrate for protein kinase C. *Proc. natn. Acad. Sci. U.S.A.* **83**, 2822–2826.

ALBERT, K. A., NAIRN, A. C. & GREENGARD, P. (1987). The 87K protein, a major specific substrate for protein kinase C: Purification from bovine brain and characterization. *Proc. natn. Acad. Sci. U.S.A.* **84**, 7046–7050.

BLACKSHEAR, P. J., WEN, L., GLYNN, B. P. & WITTERS, L. A. (1986). Protein kinase C-stimulated phosphorylation *in vitro* of a M_r 80 000 protein phosphorylated in response to phorbol esters and growth factors in intact fibroblasts. Distinction from protein kinase C and prominence in brain. *J. biol. Chem.* **261**, 1459–1469.

BONNEY, R. J., NARUNS, P., DAVIES, P. & HUMES, J. L. (1979). Antigen–antibody complexes stimulate the synthesis and release of prostaglandins by mouse peritoneal macrophages. *Prostaglandins* **18**, 605–614.

BONNEY, R. J., WIGHTMAN, P. D., DAHLGREN, M. E., DAVIES, P., KUEHL, F. A. & HUMES, J. L. (1978). Regulation of prostaglandin synthesis and of selective release of lysosomal hydrolases by mouse peritoneal macrophages. *Biochem. J.* **176**, 433–444.

BONNEY, R. J., WIGHTMAN, P. D., DAHLGREN, M. E., DAVIES, P., KUEHL, F. A. JR & HUMES, J. L. (1980). Effect of RNA and protein synthesis inhibitors on the release of inflammatory mediators by macrophages responding to phorbol myristate acetate. *Biochim. biophys. Acta* **633**, 410–421.

BUSS, J. E., KAMPS, M. P. & SEFTON, B. M. (1984). Myristic acid is attached to the transforming protein of Rous sarcoma virus during or immediately after synthesis and is present in both soluble and membrane-bound forms of the protein. *Molec. cell. Biol.* **4**, 2697–2704.

BUSS, J. E., MUMBY, S. M., CASEY, P. J., GILMAN, A. G. & SEFTON, B. M. (1987). Myristylated alpha subunits of guanine nucleotide-binding regulatory proteins. *Proc. natn. Acad. Sci. U.S.A.* **84**, 7493–7497.

BUSS, J. E. & SEFTON, B. M. (1985). Myristic acid, a rare fatty acid, is the lipid attached to the transforming protein of Rous sarcoma virus and its cellular homolog. *J. Virol.* **53**, 7–12.

CARR, S. A., BIEMAN, K., SHOJI, S., PARMELEE, D. C. & TITANI, K. (1982). n-Tetradecanoyl is the NH_2-terminal blocking group of the catalytic subunit of cyclic AMP-dependent protein kinase from bovine cardiac muscle. *Proc. natn. Acad. Sci. U.S.A.* **79**, 6128–6131.

CROSS, F. R., GARBER, E. A., PELLMAN, D. & HANAFUSA, H. (1984). A short sequence in the p60src N terminus is required for p60src myristylation and membrane association and for cell transformation. *Molec. cell. Biol.* **4**, 1834–1842.

DAVIES, P., BAILEY, P. J., GOLDENBERG, M. M. & FORD-HUTCHINSON, A. W. (1984). The role of arachidonic acid oxygenation products in pain and inflammation. *A. Rev. Immun.* **2**, 335–357.

DI VIRGILIO, F., LEW, D. P. & POZZAN, T. (1984). Protein kinase C activation of physiological processes in human neutrophils at vanishingly small cytosolic Ca^{2+} levels. *Nature, Lond.* **310**, 691–693.

GUTHRIE, L. A., McPHAIL, L. C., HENSON, P. M. & JOHNSTON, R. B. JR (1984). Priming of neutrophils for enhanced release of oxygen metabolites by bacterial lipopolysaccharide. Evidence for increased activity of the superoxide-producing enzyme. *J. exp. Med.* **160**, 1656–1671.

HAMAGUCHI, M. & HANAFUSA, H. (1987). Association of p60src with Triton X100-resistant cellular structure correlates with morphological transformation. *Proc. natn. Acad. Sci. U.S.A.* **84**, 2312–2316.

HAMILTON, T. A., JANSEN, M. M., SOMERS, S. D. & ADAMS, D. O. (1986). Effects of bacterial lipopolysaccharide on protein synthesis in murine peritoneal macrophages: relationship to activation for macrophage tumoricidal function. *J. cell Physiol.* **128**, 9–17.

HEYWORTH, P. G. & SEGAL, A. W. (1986). Further evidence for the involvement of a phosphoprotein in the respiratory burst oxidase of human neutrophils. *Biochem. J.* 239, 723–731.

HOMMA, J. Y., KANEGASAKI, S., LUDERITZ, O., SHIBA, T. & WESTPHAL, O. (1984). *Bacterial endotoxin: Chemical, biological and clinical aspects.* Weinheim: Verlag Chemie.

HUMES, J. L., SADOWSKI, S., GALAVAGE, M., GOLDENBERG, M., SUBERS, E., BONNEY, R. J. & KUEHL, F. A. JR (1982). Evidence for two sources of arachidonic acid for oxidative metabolism by mouse peritoneal macrophages. *J. biol. Chem.* **257**, 1591–1594.

KAMPS, M. P., BUSS, J. E. & SEFTON, B. M. (1985). Mutation of NH_2-terminal glycine of p60src prevents both myristoylation and morphological transformation. *Proc. natn. Acad. Sci. U.S.A.* **82**, 4625–4628.

MARCHILDON, G. A., CASNELLIE, J. E., WALSH, K. A. & KREBS, E. G. (1984). Covalently bound myristate in a lymphoma tyrosine protein kinase. *Proc. natn. Acad. Sci. U.S.A.* **81**, 7679–7682.

MAZZEI, G. J., KATOH, N. & KUO, J. F. (1982). Polymyxin B is a more selective inhibitor for phospholipid-sensitive Ca^{2+}-dependent protein kinase than for calmodulin-sensitive Ca^{2+}-dependent protein kinase. *Biochem. biophys. Res. Commun.* **109**, 1129–1133.

MORRISON, D. C. & ULEVITCH, R. J. (1978). The effects of bacterial endotoxins on host mediation systems. *Am. J. Path.* **93**, 527–617.

NATHAN, C. F., MURRAY, H. W., WIEBE, M. E. & RUBIN, B. Y. (1983). Identification of interferon-gamma as the lymphokine that activates human macrophage oxidative metabolism and antimicrobial activity. *J. exp. Med.* **158**, 670–689.

NEIDEL, J. E. & BLACKSHEAR, P. J. (1986). Protein kinase C. In *Phosphoinositides and receptor mechanisms, vol. 7* (ed. J. Putney), pp. 47–88. New York: Alan R. Liss.

NISHIZUKA, Y. (1986). Studies and perspectives of protein kinase C. *Science* **233**, 305–312.

OGMUNDSDOTTIR, H. M. & WEIR, D. M. (1979). Stimulation of phosphatidylinositol turnover in the macrophage plasma membrane: a possible mechanism for signal transmission. *Immunology* **37**, 689–696.

OLSON, E. N., TOWLER, D. A. & GLASER, L. (1985). Specificity of fatty acid acylation of cellular proteins. *J. biol. Chem.* **260**, 3784–3790.

OMARY, M. B. & TROWBRIDGE, I. S. (1981). Biosynthesis of the human transferrin receptor in cultured cells. *J. biol. Chem.* **256**, 12888–12892.

OZOLS, J., CARR, S. A. & STRITTMATTER, P. (1984). Identification of the NH_2-terminal blocking group of NADH–cytochrome b_5 reductase as myristic acid and the complete amino acid sequence of the membrane-binding domain. *J. biol. Chem.* **259**, 13349–13354.

PABST, M. J. & JOHNSTON, R. B. (1980). Increased production of superoxide anion by macrophages exposed *in vitro* to muramyl dipeptide or lipopolysaccharide. *J. exp. Med.* **151**, 101–114.

PAUL, A. V., SCHULTZ, A., PINCUS, S. E., OROSZLAN, S. & WIMMER, E. (1987). Capsid protein VP4 of poliovirus is *N*-myristoylated. *Proc. natn. Acad. Sci. U.S.A.* **84**, 7827–7831.

PAWLOWSKI, N. A., KAPLAN, G., HAMILL, A. L., COHN, Z. A. & SCOTT, W. A. (1983). Arachidonic acid metabolism by human monocytes. Studies with platelet-depleted cultures. *J. exp. Med.* **158**, 393–412.

PELLMAN, D., GARBER, E. A., CROSS, F. R. & HANAFUSA, H. (1985). An N-terminal peptide from p60src can direct myristylation and plasma membrane localization when fused to heterologous proteins. *Nature, Lond.* **314**, 374–377.

REIN, A., McCLURE, M. R., RICE, N. R., LUFTIG, R. B. & SCHULTZ, A. M. (1986). Myristylation site in Pr65gag is essential for virus particle formation by Moloney murine leukemia virus. *Proc. natn. Acad. Sci. U.S.A.* **83**, 7246–7250.

ROUZER, C. A. & SAMUELSSON, B. (1987). Reversible, calcium-dependent membrane association of human leukocyte 5-lipoxygenase. *Proc. natn. Acad. Sci. U.S.A.* **84**, 7393–7397.

ROUZER, C. A., SCOTT, W. A., COHN, Z. A., BLACKBURN, P. & MANNING, J. M. (1980). Mouse peritoneal macrophages release leukotriene C in response to a phagocytic stimulus. *Proc. natn. Acad. Sci. U.S.A.* **77**, 4928–4932.

ROUZER, C. A., SCOTT, W. A., HAMILL, A. L. & COHN, Z. A. (1982). Synthesis of leukotriene C and other arachidonic acid metabolites by mouse pulmonary macrophages. *J. exp. Med.* **155**, 720–733.

ROZENGURT, E., RODRIGUEZ-PENA, M. & SMITH, K. A. (1983). Phorbol esters, phospholipase C, and growth factors rapidly stimulate the phosphorylation of a M_r 80 000 protein in intact quiescent 3T3 cells. *Proc. natn. Acad. Sci. U.S.A.* **80**, 7244–7248.

SCHREIBER, R. D., PACE, J. L., RUSSELL, S. W., ALTMAN, A. & KATZ, D. H. (1983). Macrophage-activating factor produced by a T cell hybridoma: physiochemical and biosynthetic resemblance to gamma-interferon. *J. Immun.* **131**, 826–832.

SCHULTZ, A. M., HENDERSON, L. E., OROSZLAN, S., GARBER, E. A. & HANAFUSA, H. (1985). Amino terminal myristylation of the protein kinase p60src, a retroviral transforming protein. *Science* **227**, 427–429.

SCOTT, W. A., PAWLOWSKI, N. A., MURRAY, H. W., ANDREACH, M., ZRIKE, J. & COHN, Z. A. (1982). Regulation of arachidonic acid metabolism by macrophage activation. *J. exp. Med.* **155**, 1148–1160.

SCOTT, W. A., ZRIKE, J. M., HAMILL, A. L., KEMPE, J. & COHN, Z. A. (1980). Regulation of arachidonic acid metabolites in macrophages. *J. exp. Med.* **152**, 324–333.

SEFTON, B. M. & BUSS, J. E. (1987). The covalent modification of eukaryotic proteins with lipid. *J. Cell Biol.* **104**, 1449–1453.

TOWLER, D. A., ADAMS, S. P., EUBANKS, S. R., TOWERY, D. S., JACKSON-MACHELSKI, E., GLASER, L. & GORDON, J. I. (1987b). Purification and characterization of yeast myristoyl CoA:protein N-myristoyl transferase. *Proc. natn. Acad. Sci. U.S.A.* **84**, 2708–2712.

TOWLER, D. A., EUBANKS, S. R., TOWERY, D. S., ADAMS, S. P. & GLASER, L. (1978a) Amino-terminal processing of proteins by N-myristoylation: substrate specificity of N-myristoyl transferase. *J. biol. Chem.* **262**, 1030–1036.

TOWLER, D. & GLASER, L. (1986). Protein fatty acid acylation: enzymatic synthesis of an N-myristoylglycyl peptide. *Proc. natn. Acad. Sci. U.S.A.* **83**, 2812–2816.

TRIPP, C. S., MAHONEY, M. & NEEDLEMAN, P. (1985). Calcium ionophore enables soluble agonists to stimulate macrophage 5-lipoxygenase. *J. biol. Chem.* **260**, 5895–5898.

WEIEL, J. E., HAMILTON, T. A. & ADAMS, D. O. (1986). LPS induces altered phosphate labeling of proteins in murine peritoneal macrophages. *J. Immun.* **136**, 3012–3018.

WIGHTMAN, P. D., DAHLGREN, M. E., HALL, J. C., DAVIES, P. & BONNEY, R. J. (1981b). Identification and characterization of a phospholipase C activity in resident mouse peritoneal macrophages. Inhibition of the enzyme by phenothiazines. *Biochem. J.* **197**, 523–526.

WIGHTMAN, P. D., HUMES, J. L., DAVIES, P. & BONNEY, R. J. (1981a). Identification and characterization of two phospholipase A2 activities in resident mouse peritoneal macrophages. *Biochem. J.* **195**, 427–433.

WIGHTMAN, P. D. & RAETZ, C. R. (1984). The activation of protein kinase by biologically active lipid moieties of lipopolysaccharide. *J. biol. Chem.* **259**, 10 048–10 052.

WILCOX, C., HU, J. S. & OLSON, E. N. (1987). Acylation of proteins with myristic acid occurs cotranslationally. *Science* **238**, 1275–1278.

WOODGETT, J. R., HUNTER, T. & GOULD, K. L. (1987). In *Cell membranes: methods and reviews, vol. 3* (ed. E. L. Elson, W. A. Frazier & L. Glazer), pp. 215–340. New York: Plenum.

WU, W. S., WALAAS, S. I., NAIRN, A. C. & GREENGARD, P. (1982). Calcium/phospholipid regulates phosphorylation of a M_r "87k" substrate protein in brain synaptosomes. *Proc. natn. Acad. Sci. U.S.A.* **79**, 5249–5253.

YOUNG, J. D-E., KO, S. S. & COHN, Z. A. (1984). The increase in intracellular free calcium associated with IgG2b/1 Fc receptor–ligand interactions: role in phagocytosis. *Proc. natn. Acad. Aci. U.S.A.* **81**, 5430–5434.

J. Cell Sci. Suppl. 9, 169–184 (1988)
Printed in Great Britain © The Company of Biologists Limited 1988

The structure of the macrophage actin skeleton

H. L. YIN AND J. H. HARTWIG

Hematology-Oncology Unit, Massachusetts General Hospital and Harvard Medical School, Boston, MA, USA

Summary

The actin skeleton of the macrophage consists of a three-dimensional network of actin filaments and associated proteins. The organization of this multiprotein structure is regulated at several levels in cells. Receptor stimulation induces a massive actin polymerization at the cell cortex, changes in cell shape and active cellular movements. Gelsolin may have a pivotal role in restructuring the actin skeleton in response to agonist stimulation, as the activity of this potent actin-modulating protein is regulated by both Ca^{2+} and polyphosphoinositides. Micromolar concentrations of Ca^{2+} activate gelsolin to bind to the sides of actin filaments, sever, and cap the filament end. Polyphosphoinositides, in particular PIP and PIP_2, release gelsolin from the filament ends. A structure–function analysis of gelsolin indicates that its N-terminal half is primarily responsible for severing actin filaments, and elucidates mechanisms by which Ca^{2+} and phospholipid may regulate gelsolin functions. The ultrastructure of actin filaments in the macrophage cortical cytoplasm is regulated, to a large extent, by the actin cross-linking protein, actin-binding protein (ABP) which defines filament orthogonality.

Introduction

Actin, one of the most abundant and highly conserved proteins in nature, is a major determinant of cell shape and movement. In the cytoplasm, actin moves between pools of monomeric subunits (G actin) and double helical filaments (F actin). Filaments, in turn, can be further organized into a variety of interactive structures, ranging from anisotropic parallel bundles to isotropic orthogonal networks. The formation of these assemblies, and their diversity, which can subserve many different functions, depend on the actions of a large repertoire of cytoplasmic actin-binding proteins (Stossel *et al.* 1985; Pollard & Cooper, 1986). Since the actin structures are dynamic, they may continuously assemble, disassemble and re-orient within the cell. In this paper, we will briefly review the structure of the macrophage actin cytoskeleton, present evidence that it changes in response to agonist stimulation, and describe how the properties of several actin-modulating proteins provide a model for the dynamic regulation of actin structures in these highly motile cells.

The organization of actin filaments in macrophage cytoplasm

The organization of actin filaments in macrophage cytoplasm has been studied by removal of the plasma membrane either by detergent solubilization or 'peeling' of the apical (non-attached cell surface) plasma membrane of cells attached to glass. Fig. 1 shows a branching filament network in the edge of a macrophage, which was allowed to adhere to a coverslip, and was extracted with detergent. Labelling with the S1 subfragment of myosin reveals that >95% of these filaments are actin (Fig. 2).

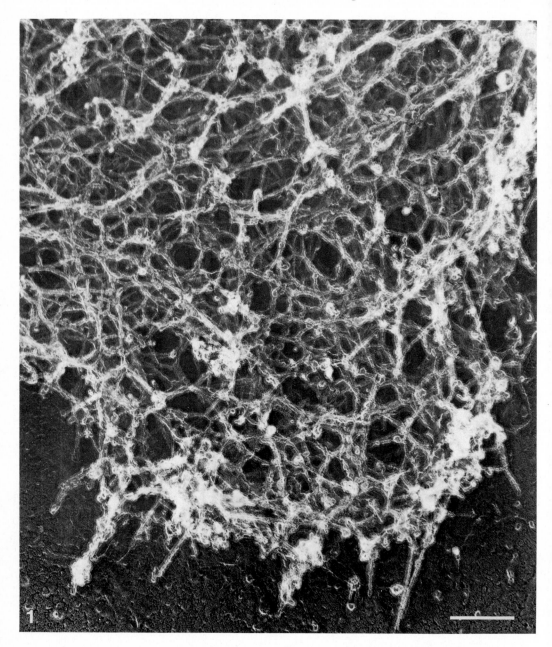

Fig. 1. Electron micrograph showing the organization of filaments at the periphery of Triton-X100 insoluble cytoskeleton of an adherent rabbit alveolar macrophage. The proteins were fixed with 1 % glutaraldehyde, rapidly frozen and freeze dried (Heuser & Kirschner, 1980). Bar, 0·2 μm.

Unlike actin filaments polymerized *in vitro* from purified actin, filaments in the cell cortex are short (about 0·5 μm in length) and frequently intersect along their lengths with striking perpendicularity. The frequency of intersections defines the pore size of

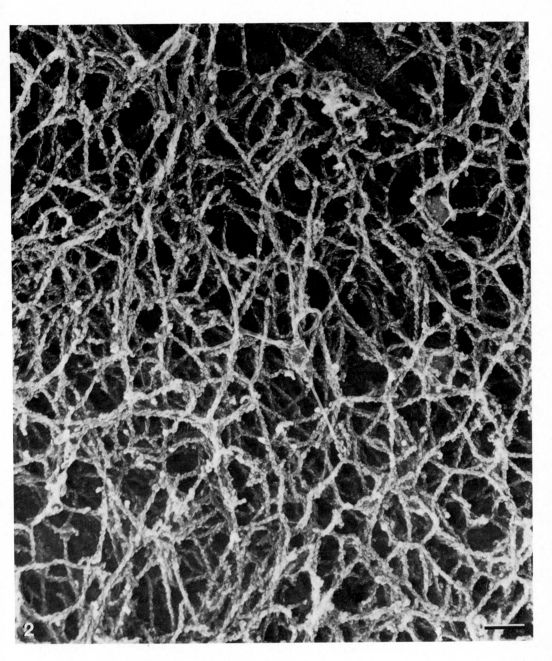

Fig. 2. Identification of cortical 10-nm filaments as actin. A macrophage cytoskeleton was incubated with $1\,\text{mg}\,\text{ml}^{-1}$ skeletal muscle myosin subfragment 1 before fixation. Actin filaments decorated with myosin S1 have a twisted cable-like appearance. The polarity of the filaments is most apparent near their ends where they connect to the sides of other filaments. Bar, $0.2\,\mu\text{m}$.

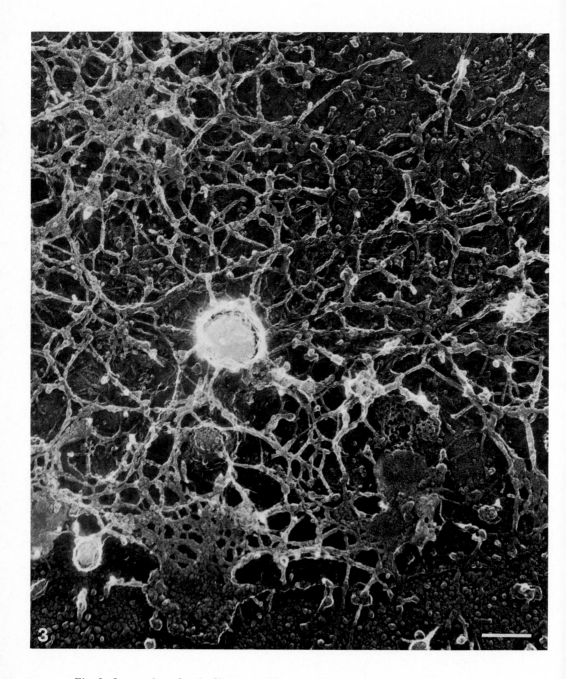

Fig. 3. Interaction of actin filaments with macrophage plasma membrane. The plasma membrane–cytoplasm interface of a cell spread on a glass coverslip was revealed after tearing the cell in half by adhering a polylysine-coated coverslip to its top surface and removing the coverslip. The bulk of 10-nm fibres attaching to the membrane (lower margin of the micrograph) is part of the three-dimensional filamentous network of the cell. Note that there are many regions of membrane that contain little filamentous material. Many clathrin-coated regions of the membrane are also apparent. Bar, 0·2 μm.

Table 1. *The macrophage cortical actin network*

Filament concentration	240–300 μM (monomers in filaments)
Average filament length	0·5–0·6 μm
Intersection length (pore size of the network)	0·1 μm
Free filament ends	Rare
Major type of filament intersection	Orthogonal branch: T- and Y-shaped filament junctions
Membrane–actin connections	'Barbed' end and lateral connections are common. 'Pointed' connections also found
Location and spacing of ABP	1 ABP: 0·35 μm of actin filament. Located at filament junctions
Predicted spacing from the molar ratio of ABP to actin in the cell cortex	1:0·21 μm of filament

the network, a value we have measured, and determined to be about 0·1 μm. There are no free filament ends within the body of the network. Actin filaments always attach their 'barbed' and 'pointed' ends (with respect to the binding of myosin S1) on the sides of other actin filaments, forming T- and Y-shaped branches. Actin filaments are concentrated in the periphery of the cell, and the relationship between the three-dimensional actin skeleton and cell plasma membrane, as well as other membrane-bounded compartments within the cell, can be examined by selectively peeling portions of apical plasma membrane from adherent cells (Fig. 3). Careful examination of such replicas in the electron microscope shows that actin filaments interact with the membrane in two ways: through lateral interactions, and through end-on interactions, predominantly with attachment at the 'fast' polymerizing (barbed) end of the filament but occasionally (10% of the time) at the 'slow' or pointed end of the filament (Fig. 4, Table 1).

A perpendicular network structure of the actin filaments could be the basis for the gel-like consistency of cytoplasm if the filaments were indeed cross-linked at their intersections. *In vitro*, actin filaments can be induced to form a network closely resembling that observed in the macrophage cortex by addition of the filament cross-linking protein actin-binding protein (ABP) (also called filamin) (Davies *et al.* 1982). ABP is a homodimer of 270K (K = $10^3 M_r$) subunits, and electron microscopy of the protein shows that each subunit is a flexible 80-nm long strand (Hartwig & Stossel, 1981). The actin-binding site is on one end and the self-association site is on the opposite end of the subunit strand. Three sets of observations indicate that ABP is primarily responsible for the orthogonal structure of actin filaments in the cell. First, ABP accounts for the bulk of actin cross-linking activity in macrophage extracts. Second, as mentioned above, actin assembled in the presence of ABP *in vitro* forms a rigid gel composed of perpendicular filament branches (Hartwig *et al.* 1980; Niederman *et al.* 1983). Third, ultrastructural studies by immunogold labelling with anti-ABP immunoglobulin G (IgG) show that ABP is located at points of filament

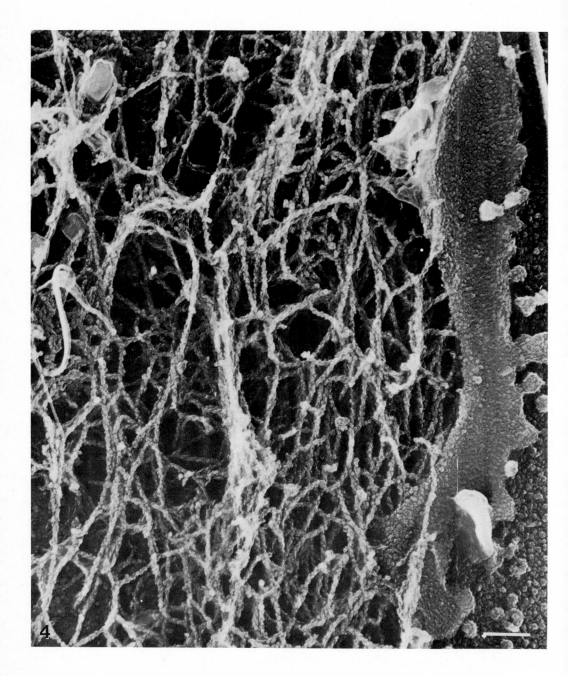

Fig. 4. Polarity of membrane-attached actin filaments. The apical membrane was peeled
from an adherent macrophage as described in Fig. 3. Using myosin subfragment-1 10-nm
filaments were identified as actin. Filaments can be seen to connect to membrane (on
right-hand margin of micrograph) with both their barbed and pointed ends. Bar, 0·2 μm.

intersection in the cell cortex (Hartwig & Shevlin, 1986), directly demonstrating that actin filaments in the cortex are cross-linked into a gel. At present, there is no evidence for a direct regulation of ABP–actin interaction by known intracellular messengers. The actin–ABP interaction can, however, be regulated indirectly by proteins that can control actin's polymerization state (Yin *et al.* 1980).

Regulation of actin filament assembly

Under physiological salt conditions, actin monomers polymerize into filaments. Assembly of actin *in vitro* occurs in at least three steps. First, monomers must become activated, a process that appears to involve a conformational change forming 'F monomers'. Two or three actin monomers then slowing aggregate to form stable complexes called nuclei. This is the rate limiting step in the assembly process. The last step, elongation, is more rapid, and involves addition of actin monomers onto the ends of the nuclei. Monomer addition occurs preferentially at the barbed end of filaments decorated with heavy meromyosin arrowheads. The concentrations of free monomers required to maintain the steady state (known as the critical monomer concentration) are, under physiological salt conditions, $0·1$ μM at the barbed end and $1·5$ μM at the pointed end. Therefore, filaments formed in purified actin solutions exist in equilibrium with about 1 μM-monomeric actin reflecting an average contribution of the two ends.

Given that the rate of actin assembly is dependent on the nucleation step and the extent of polymerization from the two ends of the filaments, actin assembly can be regulated by proteins that alter these parameters. There is ample evidence that receptor–ligand interactions, such as binding to the chemotactic peptide, f-Met–Leu–Phe (fMLP), induce a rapid and transient polymerization of cytoplasmic actin in human leukocytes and a reorganization of the cytoskeleton (Howard & Meyer, 1984; Howard & Oresajo, 1985). This net increase in cytoplasmic actin polymerization occurs selectively at the barbed ends of the filaments because it is blocked by the barbed end capping cytochalasins (Hartwig & Stossel, 1979; Maclean-Fletcher & Pollard, 1980). The intracellular signal(s) that initiates and regulates actin polymerization are still unknown. fMLP induces hydrolysis of polyphosphati-dylinositides, release of intracellular Ca^{2+}, activation of protein kinase C, and metabolism of arachidonic acid. The fMLP-induced rapid actin polymerization is mediated through a guanine-nucleotide-binding protein, because it is inhibited by pertussis toxin (Sha'afi & Molski, 1987). Both protein kinase C activation and the rise in intracellular Ca^{2+} to micromolar concentration occur coincidentally with the initiation of actin polymerization and precede the time of maximal F actin content in neutrophils. However, several recent studies using Quin 2 to buffer Ca^{2+} transients in cells have shown that the increase in intracellular Ca^{2+} is not necessary for actin polymerization, but does have an accelerating effect on the net rate of actin polymerization after fMLP exposure (Sha'afi *et al.* 1986; Sheterline *et al.* 1986). Howard & Wang (1987), using human neutrophils, show that A23187, a Ca^{2+} ionophore, causes a significant increase in F actin content but requires free Ca^{2+}

concentrations higher than that measured in fMLP-activated cells. Phorbol myristate acetate (PMA), a protein kinase C activator, induces a slow and smaller rise in F actin content. Therefore, it appears that neither a rise in intracellular Ca^{2+} concentration nor activation of protein kinase C alone, or in combination, are sufficient to explain the fMLP-induced changes in cytoskeletal organization.

The mechanism(s) mediating these transient F actin increases is also not known. To increase F actin content, cells must either add monomers onto the ends of existing filaments, or create new filaments, or do both. For addition to occur on the ends of pre-existing filaments, their barbed ends which are normally blocked in unactivated cells must become unblocked. New actin nuclei could also be added to the system, either through the fragmentation of existing filaments or by the activation of protein(s) functioning as actin nuclei. Furthermore, there is also a need to access actin monomers for polymerization.

Gelsolin (Yin, 1988) and profilin (Korn, 1982) are two well-characterized actin-modulating proteins, which are present in large quantities in macrophages. The interaction of each protein with actin is modulated by polyphosphoinositides (Janmey & Stossel, 1987; Janmey *et al*. 1987; Lassing & Lindberg, 1985), and that of gelsolin is further regulated by Ca^{2+} (Yin & Stossel, 1980). Since Ca^{2+} and polyphosphoinositide levels change transiently following agonist stimulation, these proteins may have a pivotal role in modulating cytoskeletal changes.

Gelsolin

Gelsolin is a potent actin-modulating protein first identified in rabbit lung macrophages (Yin & Stossel, 1979) and subsequently found in many mammalian cells. The name derives from its ability to mediate the transition of cytosolic extracts from a gel phase to a sol phase, through a reduction in the actin filament length distribution. Cytoplasmic gelsolin consists of a single $80\,000\,M_r$ polypeptide (Kwiatkowski *et al*. 1985). The interactions of gelsolin with actin are multiple and complex (Bryan & Hwo, 1986; Janmey *et al*. 1985; Chaponnier *et al*. 1986; Yin *et al*. 1988). Gelsolin has three main effects on actin. First, it breaks the non-covalent bond between actin–actin monomers within an actin filament, severing the filament. Second, gelsolin binds to a barbed filament end. This has the effect of raising the critical concentration for actin association into filaments, thus causing net actin depolymerization. Third, gelsolin nucleates actin assembly, again promoting formation of short actin filaments. Elongation from gelsolin–actin nuclei is on the slow growing end and therefore not likely to be important in cells.

The immediate effect of actin filament shortening is a decrease in their ability to be cross-linked into a gel network, by dramatically increasing the amount of a cross-linking protein required to join filamentous elements into a network, inhibiting actin gelation and solating pre-formed gels (Yin *et al*. 1980). In addition, filaments severed are capped by gelsolin. These could serve as a potential source of actin nuclei, provided that gelsolin can be removed from the barbed ends of the filaments. Our *in vitro* data would suggest that gelsolin is activated by Ca^{2+} to interact with actin and create short actin nuclei, while uncapping is effected not simply by removal of Ca^{2+}, but also by polyphosphoinositides. Actin monomers required for explosive growth of filaments will be provided by dissociation of profilin–actin complexes by polyphosphoinositides. Profilin is an actin monomer binding protein, which, on binding actin, impairs its ability to assemble into filaments (Korn, 1982; DiNuble & Southwick, 1985). Profilin can therefore decrease the steady-state F actin concentrations, and may explain why close to 50% of the actin in the cell extract of unactivated cells is not polymerized in spite of conditions favouring polymerization.

Several pieces of *in vivo* evidence suggest that gelsolin may indeed be involved in regulating actin assembly–disassembly in cells:

(1) Gelsolin is present in cells at high concentrations. There is one molecule of gelsolin per 100 actin monomers in macrophages. It is the major Ca^{2+}-dependent actin-severing protein, and also accounts for the bulk of actin nucleating and filament end capping activity in the cell cytoplasm.

(2) *In vitro* studies have shown that although gelsolin requires micromolar Ca^{2+} to bind actin, forming a 2 actin:1 gelsolin complex, subsequent chelation of Ca^{2+} with EGTA releases only one actin. The resultant EGTA-resistant 1:1 complexes (GA_1) do not fragment actin filaments but cap their ends even at submicromolar Ca^{2+} concentrations. Therefore, once gelsolin blocks the barbed end of a filament *in vitro*, it can no longer be dissociated from actin by removal of Ca^{2+}.

(3) Dissociation of the GA_1 complex can also be demonstrated in a number of cell types. Freshly isolated macrophages contain very little GA_1. Ionomycin increases GA_1 complex formation, while fMLP causes dissociation of GA_1 complexes. Therefore, while gelsolin–actin interaction in cells can be induced by Ca^{2+}, other factors, activated by fMLP, can dissociate GA_1 complexes (Chaponnier *et al.* 1987). Likewise, thrombin, which promotes actin polymerization in platelets, induces GA_1 complex formation and subsequent dissociation (Lind *et al.* 1987). Furthermore, it has been shown by immunogold labelling of ultrathin sections that gelsolin reversibly translocates to the plasma membrane of platelets with the same time course as that observed for formation and dissolution of GA_1 complexes (K. Chambers & J. H. Hartwig, unpublished results).

Taken together, these results suggest that cells possess a mechanism not directly involving Ca^{2+} for dissociating EGTA-resistant actin–gelsolin complexes subsequent to agonist stimulation. Since polyphosphoinositide 4,5-bisphosphate and monophosphate (PIP_2 and PIP, respectively) can functionally uncap actin filaments and dissociate GA_1 complexes *in vitro*, they are likely candidates as second regulators of gelsolin function. Besides having an effect on gelsolin, PIP_2 can also promote actin assembly by dissociating actin–profilin complexes.

As a working hypothesis, we propose that explosive polymerization of actin filaments can occur through the effect of PIP_2 on gelsolin and profilin (Fig. 5). In cells at rest, gelsolin is a soluble protein and is not bound to actin. When cells are activated, the concentration of PIP_2 in the plasma membrane falls as it is converted to diacylglycerol and inositol 1,4,5 triphosphate by activated phospholipase C. The latter product, in turn, mobilizes Ca^{2+} from internal stores and begins a 'gelsolin

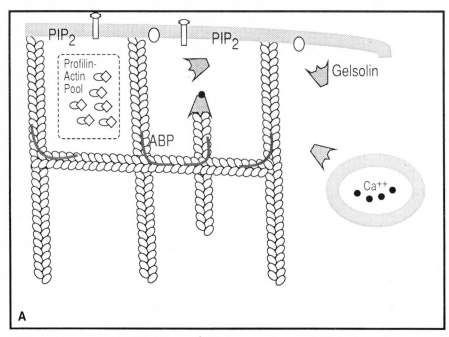

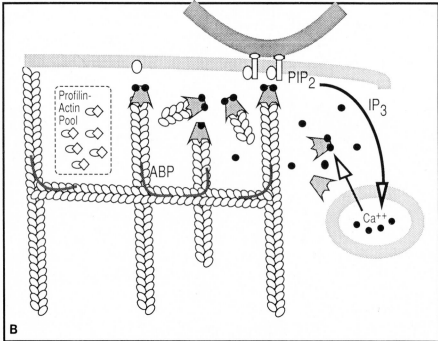

Fig. 5. For legend see p. 180

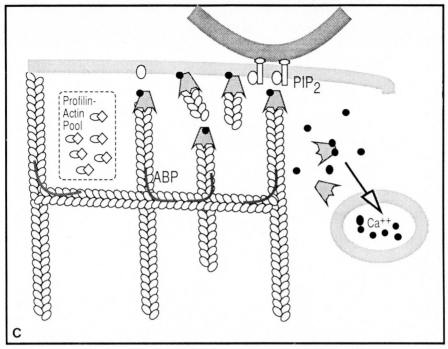

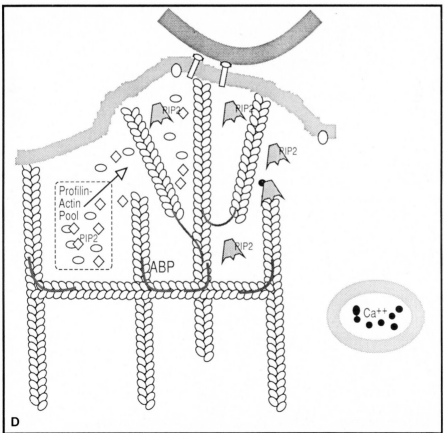

Fig. 5. For legend see p. 180

activation cascade'. Gelsolin–Ca^{2+} binds to the side of filaments, severing the cortical actin filament network, and rapidly produces numerous gelsolin-capped actin oligomers. Because these oligomers are short, they can diffuse freely within the cytoplasm. Oligomers can therefore move towards the plasma membrane and contact PIP and PIP_2, as their concentrations are restored following an initial fall. This leads to dissociation of gelsolin from actin oligomers, exposing nuclei with free barbed ends. Simultaneously, PIP_2 releases actin monomers from profilin–actin complexes (Lassing & Lindberg, 1985; Lind *et al.* 1987). The increased availability of both polymerization-competent actin monomers and the number of nuclei with free barbed ends result in rapid polymerization. Ca^{2+} potentiates the response by allowing gelsolin to sever actin prior to a rise in PIP_2 concentration, creating a large number of nuclei, and a large pool of actin monomers.

The domain structure of gelsolin

The multifunctionality of gelsolin, and its differential regulation by Ca^{2+} and polyphosphoinositides, suggest that there are distinct functional and regulatory domains in gelsolin. The domain structure of gelsolin has been analysed by limited proteolysis (Bryan & Hwo, 1986; Chaponnier *et al.* 1986; Kwiatkowski *et al.* 1985), and the picture that emerges is that gelsolin contains at least three actin binding sites located on the peptides CT14N, CT28N, and CT38C (Fig. 6). CT14N and CT38C, located on opposite halves of gelsolin and each containing an actin binding site, bind actin monomers to form 2 actin:1 gelsolin complexes. The third site, CT28N, located in the N-terminal half binds to F actin but not actin monomers. Since the N-terminal half of gelsolin (containing CT14N and CT28N) can sever actin filaments as effectively as intact gelsolin, but its subfragments do not, there must be a high degree of interaction between CT14N and CT28N. Recently, we have demonstrated that CT28N binds stoichiometrically to the side of actin filaments. Binding is inhibited by polyphosphoinositides with a dose response similar to that observed for the inhibition of severing, suggesting that CT28N initiates severing by allowing gelsolin to bind to filament sides (Yin *et al.* 1988). Severing by the N-terminal half is no longer Ca^{2+}-regulated, in contrast to that of intact gelsolin. Instead, the C-terminal

Fig. 5. Hypothetical model for the regulation of actin filament assembly by gelsolin and profilin. A. Actin filaments in the cortical cytoplasm of a resting cell are organized into a three-dimensional space-filling network by ABP. The bulk of the gelsolin is soluble and not bound to actin. B. Activation of the cells by receptor stimulation causes in the plasma membrane PIP_2 to be converted to inositol 1,4,5 triphosphate (IP_3) and diacyclglycerol (DAG). IP_3 is soluble and mobilizes Ca^{2+} from an internal compartment to begin the 'gelsolin activation cascade'. Gelsolin–Ca^{2+} in cortical cytoplasm binds to the sides of filaments composing the actin filament, severing them. This detaches the membrane from the actin skeleton and produces numerous gelsolin-capped actin oligomers. C. Gelsolin–actin oligomers diffuse to the plasma membrane. Cytosolic free calcium is re-sequestered into an intracellular compartment. D. Here they contact PIP_2, the concentration of which has been restored after its initial fall (conversion to IP_3). PIP_2 would dissociate gelsolin from these actin oligomers, exposing nuclei, and stimulating actin assembly. PIP_2 would also dissociate actin from profilin, providing the actin monomers for net filament assembly.

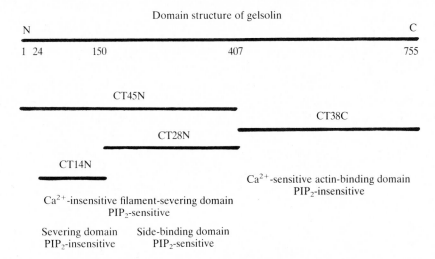

Fig. 6. Regulation of gelsolin:actin interaction by Ca^{2+} and PIP_2. Model of the primary structure of human plasma gelsolin. The major peptides generated by chymotrypsin (CT) cleavage in the presence of Ca^{2+} are indicated. The amino acid residues, deduced from cDNA sequence of plasma gelsolin, are indicated. The chymotryptic peptides are designated CT, followed by their molecular weight, and either N or C, to denote their origin from the N- or C-terminal half of the molecule. In this model, the N-terminal half of gelsolin is the actin-severing domain. It contains two distinct actin-binding peptides, CT14N and CT28N, which do not sever filaments efficiently as separate entities. Therefore, efficient severing requires an interaction between these two domains. We propose that CT28N allows gelsolin to bind to the side of actin filaments, optimizing subsequent binding of CT14N and severing. The C-terminal half peptide can bind actin monomers reversibly in response to changes in Ca^{2+} concentration. PIP_2 inhibits binding of CT28N to actin filaments, and has relatively less effect on the interaction of the other peptides with actin.

half of gelsolin contains a Ca^{2+}-regulated actin-binding domain. Therefore, the stringent Ca^{2+} requirement for actin severing found in intact gelsolin is not due to a direct effect of Ca^{2+} on the severing domain, but indirectly through an effect on domains in the C-terminal half of the molecule. Ca^{2+} induces a conformational change in gelsolin, causing it to assume a more elliptical shape (Soua *et al.* 1985) and to expose a protease-sensitive site in the middle of the molecule (Chaponnier *et al.* 1986; Bryan & Hwo, 1986; Rouayrenc *et al.* 1986). Therefore, a reasonable model is that the C-terminal half of gelsolin covers up the N-terminal severing sites, and this block is relieved by Ca^{2+} through a documented conformational change in the C-terminal half (Kwiatkowski *et al.* 1985; Hwo & Bryan, 1986).

Less is known about how polyphosphoinositides regulate gelsolin severing. Because polyphosphoinositides also inhibit severing by the N-terminal half of gelsolin and CT28N binding to F actin, it probably binds to CT28N. Gelsolin binds phenyl-Sepharose in the presence of micromolar Ca^{2+}, but is eluted by EGTA (Soua *et al.* 1985). Therefore, a hydrophobic domain on gelsolin may also be inaccesssible in EGTA. In this way, gelsolin resembles other proteins such as calpactin (Glenney *et al.* 1987), which requires Ca^{2+} to bind phospholipids. In fact, gelsolin contains putative phospholipid-binding consensus sequences identified for the calpactin-like family of proteins (Geisow & Walker, 1986).

The primary structure of gelsolin, deduced from human gelsolin cDNA clones (Kwiatkowski *et al*. 1986, 1988) supports the existence of duplicated actin-binding domains in the two halves of the molecule, because there is a corresponding strong tandem repeat in their amino acid sequence. Within each half, there is an additional threefold repeat. These repeated domains may have arisen from a gene duplication event, and diverged subsequently to adopt their respective unique functions. The site on actin to which gelsolin binds has been localized by chemical cross-linking studies to the first 12 amino acids of actin (Doi *et al*. 1987) and it will be interesting to determine whether the various actin binding domains have identical binding sites on actin.

This work was supported by USPHS Grants GM36507 and HL29113, NSF Grant DCB8517973 and Grants from the Council for Tobacco Research, USA, the Edwin S. Webster Foundation and the Whittaker Health Sciences Fund. H. L. Yin is an Established Investigator of the American Heart Association.

References

BRYAN, J. & HWO, S. (1986). Definition of an N-terminal actin-binding domain and a C-terminal Ca^{2+}-regulatory domain in human brevin. *J. Cell Biol*. **101**, 1236–1243.

CHAPONNIER, C., JANMEY, P. A. & YIN, H. L. (1986). The actin filament-severing domain of plasma gelsolin. *J. Cell Biol*. **103**, 1473–1481.

CHAPONNIER, C., YIN, H. L. & STOSSEL, T. P. (1987). Reversibility of gelsolin/actin interaction in macrophages. Evidence of Ca^{2+}-dependent and Ca^{2+}-independent pathways. *J. exp. Med*. **165**, 97–106.

DAVIES, P. J. A., SHIZUTA, Y. & PASTAN, I. (1982). Purification and properties of avian and mammalian filamins. In *Methods in Enzymology* (ed. D. W. Frederiksen & L. W. Cunningham), pp. 322–328. New York: Academic Press.

DINUBLE, M. J. & SOUTHWICK, F. S. (1985). Effects of macrophage profilin on actin in the presence of acumentin and gelsolin. *J. biol. Chem*. **260**, 7402–7409.

DOI, Y., HIGASHIDA, M. & KIDO, A. (1987). Plasma gelsolin binding sites on the actin sequence. *Eur. J. Biochem*. **164**, 89–94.

GEISOW, M. J. & WALKER, J. H. (1986). New proteins involved in cell regulation by Ca^{2+} and phospholipids. *Trends Biochem. Sci*. **11**, 420–423.

GLENNEY, J. R., TACK, B. & POWELL, M. A. (1987). Calpactins: two distinct Ca^{2+}-regulated phospholipid- and actin-binding proteins isolated from lung and placenta. *J. Cell Biol*. **104**, 503–511.

HARTWIG, J. H. & SHEVLIN, P. (1986). The architecture of actin filaments and the ultrastructural location of actin-binding protein in the periphery of lung macrophages. *J. Cell Biol*. **103**, 1007–1020.

HARTWIG, J. H. & STOSSEL, T. P. (1979). Cytochalasin B and the structure of actin gels. *J. molec. Biol*. **134**, 539–554.

HARTWIG, J. H. & STOSSEL, T. P. (1981). The structure of actin-binding protein molecules in solution and interacting with actin filaments. *J. molec. Biol*. **145**, 563–581.

HARTWIG, J. H., TYLER, J. & STOSSEL, T. P. (1980). Actin-binding protein promotes the bipolar and perpendicular branching of actin filaments. *J. Cell Biol*. **87**, 841–848.

HEUSER, J. E. & KIRSCHNER, M. W. (1980). Filament organization revealed in platinum replicas of freeze-dried cytoskeletons. *J. Cell Biol*. **86**, 212–234.

HOWARD, T. H. & MEYER, W. (1984). Chemotactic peptide modulation of actin assembly and locomotion in neutrophils. *J. Cell Biol*. **98**, 1265–1271.

HOWARD, T. H. & ORESAJO, C. O. (1985). The kinetics of chemotactic peptide-induced change in F-actin content, F-actin distribution, and the shape of neutrophils. *J. Cell Biol.* **101**, 1078–1085.

HOWARD, T. H. & WANG, D. (1987). Calcium ionophore, phorbol ester, and chemotactic peptide-induced cytoskeleton reorganization in human neutrophils. *J. clin. Invest.* **79**, 1359–1364.

HWO, S. & BRYAN, J. (1986). Immuno-identification of Ca^{2+}-induced conformational changes in human gelsolin and brevin. *J. Cell Biol.* **102**, 227–236.

JANMEY, P. A. & STOSSEL, T. P. (1987). Modulation of gelsolin function by phosphatidylinositol 4,5-bisphosphate. *Nature, Lond.* **325**, 362–364.

JANMEY, P. A., CHAPONNIER, C., LIND, S. E., ZANER, K. S., STOSSEL, T. P. & YIN, H. L. (1985). Interactions of gelsolin and gelsolin actin complexes with actin. Effects of calcium on actin nucleation, filament severing and end blocking. *Biochemistry* **24**, 3714–3723.

JANMEY, P. A., KAZUKO, I., YIN, H. L. & STOSSEL, T. P. (1987). Polyphosphoinositide micelles and polyphosphoinositide-containing vesicles dissociate endogenous gelsolin-actin complexes and promote actin assembly from the fast-growing end of actin filaments blocked by gelsolin. *J. biol. Chem.* **262**, 1228–1236.

KORN, E. D. (1982). Actin polymerization and its regulation by proteins from nonmuscle cells. *Physiol. Rev.* **62**, 672–737.

KWIATKOWSKI, D. J., JANMEY, P. A., MOLE, J. E. & YIN, H. L. (1985). Isolation and properties of two actin-binding domains in gelsolin. *J. biol. Chem.* **260**, 15 232–15 238.

KWIATKOWSKI, D. J., MEHL, R. & YIN. H. L. (1988). Genomic organization and biosynthesis of secreted and cytoplasmic forms of gelsolin. *J. Cell Biol.* (in press).

KWIATKOWSKI, D. J., STOSSEL, T. P., ORKIN, S. H., MOLE, J. E., COLTEN, H. E. & YIN, H. L. (1986). Plasma and cytoplasmic gelsolins are encoded by a single gene and contain a duplicated actin-binding domain. *Nature, Lond.* **323**, 455–458.

LASSING, I. & LINDBURG, U. (1985). Specific interaction between phosphatidylinositol 4,5-bisphosphate and profilactin. *Nature, Lond.* **318**, 472–474.

LIND, S. E., JANMEY, P. A., CHAPONNIER, C., HERBERT, T. J. & STOSSEL, T. P. (1987). Reversible binding of actin to gelsolin and profilin in human platelets. *J. Cell Biol.* **105**, 833–842.

MACLEAN-FLETCHER, S. & POLLARD, T. D. (1980). Mechanism of action of cytochalasin b on actin. *Cell* **20**, 329–341.

NIEDERMAN, R., AMREIN, P. & HARTWIG, J. H. (1983). The three dimensional structure of actin filaments in solution and an actin gel made with actin-binding protein. *J. Cell Biol.* **96**, 1400–1413.

POLLARD, T. D. & COOPER, J. A. (1986). Actin and actin-binding proteins. A critical evaluation of mechanisms and functions. *A. Rev. Biochem.* **55**, 987–1035.

ROUAYRENC, J. F., FATTOUM, A., MEJEAN, C. & KASSAB, R. (1986). Characterization of the Ca^{2+}-induced conformational changes in gelsolin and identification of interaction regions between actin and gelsolin. *Biochemistry* **25**, 3859–3867.

SHA'AFI, R. I. & MOLSKI, T. F. P. (1987). Signalling for increased cytoskeletal actin in neutrophils. *Biochem. biophys. Res. Commun.* **145**, 934–941.

SHA'AFI, R. I., SHEFCYK, J., YASSIN, R., MOLSKI, T. F. P., NACCACHE, P. H., WHITE, J. R., FEINSTEIN, M. B. & BECKER, E. L. (1986). Is a rise in intracellular concentration of free calcium necessary or sufficient for stimulated cytoskeletal-association actin? *J. Cell Biol.* **102**, 1459–1463.

SHETERLINE, P., RICKARD, J. E., BOOTHROYD, B. & RICHARDS, R. C. (1986). Phorbol ester induces rapid actin assembly in neutrophil leucocytes independently of changes in $[Ca^{2+}]_i$ and pH_i. *J. Muscle Res. Cell Motility* **7**, 405–412.

SOUA, Z., PORTE, F., HARRICANE, M. C., FEINBERG, J. & CAPONY, J. (1985). Bovine serum brevin. Purification by hydrophobic chromatography and properties. *Eur. J. Biochem.* **153**, 275–287.

STOSSEL, T. P., CHAPONNIER, C., EZZELL, R. M., HARTWIG, J. H., JANMEY, P. A., KWIAT-KOWSKI, D. J., LIND, S. E., SMITH, D., SOUTHWICK, F. S., YIN, H. L. & ZANER, K. S. (1985). Nonmuscle actin-binding proteins. *A. Rev. Cell Biol.* **1**, 353–402.

YIN, H. L. (1988). Gelsolin: Calcium- and polyphosphoinositide-regulated actin-modulating protein. *BioEssays* **7**, 176–178.

YIN, H. L., IIDA, K. & JANMEY, P. A. (1988). Identification of a polyphosphoinositide-modulated domain in gelsolin which binds to the sides of actin filaments. *J. Cell Biol.* **106**, 805–812.

YIN, H. L. & STOSSEL, T. P. (1979). Control of cytoplasmic actin gel-sol transformation by gelsolin, a calcium-dependent regulatory protein. *Nature, Lond.* **281**, 583–586.

YIN, H. L. & STOSSEL, T. P. (1980). Purification and structural properties of gelsolin, a Ca^{2+}-activated regulatory protein of macrophages. *J. biol. Chem.* **255**, 9490–9493.

YIN, H. L., ZANER, K. S. & STOSSEL, T. P. (1980). Ca^{2+} control of actin gelation. *J. biol. Chem.* **255**, 9494–9500.

J. Cell Sci. Suppl. 9, 185–206 (1988)
Printed in Great Britain © The Company of Biologists Limited 1988

Novel cell surface adhesion receptors involved in interactions between stromal macrophages and haematopoietic cells

PAUL R. CROCKER, LYNN MORRIS AND SIAMON GORDON

Sir William Dunn School of Pathology, Oxford University, South Parks Road, Oxford, OX1 3RE, UK

Summary

Immunocytochemical staining of tissues with the mouse macrophage-specific monoclonal anti-body, F4/80, has shown that large numbers of stromal macrophages are present in adult and foetal haematopoietic tissues. Macrophage plasma membrane processes are seen to establish extensive associations with myeloid and erythroid cells in adult bone marrow and with developing erythroblasts in foetal liver, suggestive of local trophic interactions. To explore the nature of these interactions, methods were developed for isolation of resident bone marrow macrophages (RBMM) and foetal liver macrophages (FLM). Following collagenase digestion of bone marrow or foetal liver, clusters were obtained which were composed of one or more central macrophages surrounded by proliferating haematopoietic cells. After attachment of clusters to glass coverslips, adherent macrophages could be stripped free of haematopoietic cells by pipetting in the absence of divalent cations. The purified RBMM, but not FLM, expressed a novel haemagglutinin, which mediated binding, without ingestion, of large numbers of unopsonized sheep erythrocytes by a divalent cation-independent mechanism. In view of the possibility that this sheep erythrocyte receptor (SER) could interact with a homologous ligand on mouse bone marrow cells, its properties were examined. SER was found to be a lectin-like protein which recognized protease-resistant sialylated glycoconjugates on sheep erythrocytes. The expression of SER was restricted to certain stromal tissue macrophages and was low or absent on monocytes and macrophages obtained from serous cavities. High levels of SER could be induced on elicited peritoneal macrophages by cultivation in mouse serum and the induced receptor was found to mediate low-avidity binding of murine bone marrow cells with characteristics indistinguishable from those seen for binding of sheep erythrocytes. However, maximal binding of bone marrow cells to RBMM depended on a distinct, divalent cation-dependent adhesion system. Using erythroblasts as a ligand, FLM were selected to explore the properties and expression of this adhesion receptor, the erythroblast receptor (EbR). Similar to SER, EbR did not mediate ingestion, and was restricted in its expression to foetal and adult stromal tissue macrophages. Unlike SER, EbR activity was not affected by neuraminidase treatment of the ligand and the receptor was not induced on peritoneal macrophages cultured in mouse serum. EbR appears to be a novel cell adhesion receptor because it was unaffected by inhibitors of several previously described cell adhesion molecules, including the fibronectin receptor. Future studies will attempt to explore the functional significance of these two receptors in macrophage-haematopoietic cell interactions.

Introduction

In mammals, the physical association of resident bone marrow macrophages (RBMM) with developing red blood cells to form erythroblastic islets has been recognized for many years (Undritz, 1950; Bessis, 1958). Several investigators have proposed that this macrophage population may play a dual role in erythroid homoeostasis, by removing effete nuclei and cellular debris and by providing an appropriate trophic microenvironment for proliferation and differentiation of haematopoietic cells (Bessis et al. 1978; Yoffey & Yaffe, 1980; Zakharov & Prenant, 1983). Recently, studies in our laboratory have demonstrated that, in mice, RBMM plasma membrane processes are also associated with myelomonocytic cells, suggesting that the potential range of trophic interactions is more diverse than previously thought (Hume et al. 1984; Crocker & Gordon, 1985). Here we consider the possible roles of RBMM and foetal liver macrophages (FLM) in haematopoietic regulation and describe our recent studies on macrophage receptors that interact with haematopoietic cells in foetal and adult mice.

The haematopoietic stroma

The haematopoietic stroma consists of a network of diverse cell types and extracellular matrix components which together provide a mechanical framework required for sustained haematopoiesis (for reviews see Dexter, 1982; Ploemacher et al. 1984; Weiss & Sakai, 1984). The stroma may therefore be essential in regulating such events as the self-renewal, commitment and differentiation of pluripotential stem cells and the orderly migration of maturing progeny from endosteal regions towards and across the sinusoidal endothelium.

The existence of distinct erythroid and granulocytic microenvironments was clearly shown in the studies of Wolf & Trentin (1968) who found that following lethal irradiation and bone marrow reconstitution of mice, colonies developing in the spleen were predominantly erythroid whereas those in bone marrow were more granulocytic. Transplantation of bone marrow fragments to spleen resulted in transfer of the 'myeloid' microenvironment, thus supporting the concept of the "haematopoietic inductive microenvironment" (Trentin, 1971) rather than the idea of "haematopoiesis engendered randomly", favoured by others (Till et al. 1964).

It is generally agreed that the stromal cell types in bone marrow include epithelial and endothelial cells, poorly defined fibroblast-like reticular cells and macrophages. Studies by Bainton and her colleagues (Westen & Bainton, 1979; Bainton, 1985) have demonstrated in histocytochemical studies that two types of 'reticulum cell' can be distinguished in rodent and human bone marrow: (1) a fibroblast-like cell which can be localized by reactivity for alkaline phosphatase on its plasma membrane and found concentrated near the endosteal regions of the bony trabeculae in close association with granulocytic precursors; (2) a macrophage-type reticulum cell which is evenly distributed throughout the marrow and characterized by its abundance of lysosomal acid phosphatase and associations mainly with erythroid precursors. Both reticulum cells were shown to extend long cytoplasmic processes between adjacent cells and these were frequently associated with extracellular fibrillar material (Bainton, 1985).

An intriguing property of the fibroblast-like cells is their ability to transfer the haematopoietic microenvironment when grown in culture and then transplanted to ectopic sites such as the kidney (Friedenstein et al. 1974). In addition, transplantation of stromal fibroblasts cultured from red (active) or yellow (inactive) marrow results in the formation of red and yellow marrow respectively (Patt et al. 1982). Further studies (Bainton et al. 1986) have demonstrated that stromal fibroblasts from yellow marrow express a much greater level of α-naphthylbutyrate esterase than those from red marrow, but fine structure and biosynthesis of collagen types were indistinguishable. Subtle changes in the phenotype of these cells may therefore have a major effect on haematopoiesis, but little is known of the specific mechanisms involved.

Resident macrophages in haematopoietic tissues

The widespread distribution of macrophages in bone marrow has been noted by a number of investigators in several mammalian species (Bessis, 1958; Ben-Ishay & Yoffey, 1971; Weiss, 1976; Berman, 1976). The resident population is quite distinct from the immature members of the mononuclear phagocyte system present in bone marrow, which comprise monoblasts, promonocytes and monocytes. In the mouse, these latter cells outnumber the RBMM by around 5:1 (P.R. Crocker, unpublished observations) and represent a rapidly proliferating pool of developmentally imma-ture macrophages, which enter the blood stream as monocytes and develop into tissue macrophages throughout the body (Van Furth & Cohn, 1968). In contrast, RBMM are thought to be 'fixed' in the marrow where they constitute part of the reticuloendothelial system (Florey & Gowans, 1962). Although there is no infor-mation on the life-span of RBMM, it is likely to be in the order of weeks or months. This has been clearly demonstrated for splenic marginal zone macrophages, which resemble RBMM both in their stellate morphology and close plasma membrane associations with surrounding cells (Humphrey & Sundaram, 1985). In addition, RBMM appear to be non-replicating or end-cells, since we have so far not observed mitotic figures or nuclear uptake of tritiated thymidine by these cells following isolation (Crocker & Gordon, 1985 and unpublished observations). Their repopu-lation therefore probably depends on monocytes, but it is not known if these are derived from circulating blood monocytes that re-enter the marrow, or whether RBMM are derived from monocytes that have differentiated locally.

In general, RBMM have been identified *in situ* by various criteria such as morphology and ultrastructure, the presence of phagocytic inclusions, reactivity for the lysosomal marker acid phosphatase and, recently, by immunocytochemistry with specific antibodies. By all approaches, RBMM are seen to be evenly distributed throughout the marrow. Some are present within vascular sinusoids where they contribute to clearance of effete erythrocytes (Bessis & Breton-Gorius, 1962), but the majority are found within the haematopoietic compartments (Fig. 1A; Hume *et al.* 1984). By routine histological techniques, a subpopulation of RBMM can be quite readily recognized by their associations with developing erythroblasts to form erythroblastic islets. These become especially prominent during episodes of stimu-lated erythropoiesis when they can even be found within sinusoids (Ben-Ishay & Yoffey, 1971; De Jong *et al.* 1987).

It is clear that in mice, RBMM also form associations with developing myelomono-cytic cells. This has been observed by morphology during heightened eosinophilo-poiesis following infection with *Ascaris suum* (Sakai *et al.* 1981) and can also be seen in normal mouse bone marrow by immunocytochemistry using the mouse macro-phage-specific monoclonal antibody, F4/80, developed by Austyn in our laboratory (Fig. 1A; Austyn & Gordon, 1981; Hume *et al*. 1984). This antibody recognizes an antigenic epitope on the macrophage plasma membrane and it is therefore possible to visualize the extensive plasma membrane processes that make contact with develop-ing haematopoietic cells (Fig. 1A). These processes are not easily detected using certain histochemical markers, such as acid phosphatase, which tend to give a more perinuclear staining pattern (Fig. 2B). In long-term bone marrow cultures, there is a clear-cut association of myeloid precursors with macrophages within the multicellu-lar adherent stromal layer (Allen & Dexter, 1984). Upon addition of an erythropoi-etic stimulus these cultures also form erythroblastic islets which are indistinguishable from their *in vivo* counterparts (Allen & Dexter, 1982).

During foetal development, the liver is the major site of blood cell production. Immunocytochemistry with F4/80 has shown that macrophages first appear in foetal liver on day 10 with active erythropoiesis being obvious from day 11 (L. Morris, unpublished results). These macrophages display long stellate plasma membrane processes, which are closely associated with erythroid cells (Fig. 1B). A striking feature of haematopoiesis in foetal liver is the low level of granulocyte production, despite the presence of progenitors (Johnson & Metcalf, 1978). This may be due in part to the lack of a suitable microenvironment for granulocyte development. Compared with bone marrow, less is known about the nature of the cellular components that comprise the haematopoietic stroma in foetal liver (Medlock & Haar, 1983), but it is interesting that alkaline-phosphatase-positive reticulum cells can be detected by day 16, but not at day 9 (Ahmad & Bainton, 1986).

Possible functions of macrophages in haematopoietic regulation

The extensive membrane associations of RBMM and FLM with developing haematopoietic cells provide an ideal opportunity for close-range regulation of cell growth, differentiation and movement. To date, however, there is no evidence that this macrophage population serves any role beyond phagocytosis of damaged cells and effete red cell nuclei and presumed turnover of the iron and other metabolites that arise from their breakdown. It has been estimated that a single macrophage in an

---

Fig. 1. Immunocytochemical analysis with F4/80 of RBMM and FLM *in situ* (A,B) and after isolation by collagenase digestion and adherence to glass coverslips (C–F). Counterstain Mayer's haematoxylin. A. 5-μm section of adult mouse bone marrow after perfusion fixation with paraformaldehyde–lysine–periodate and stained with F4/80. Occasional RBMM are present in sinusoids (arrow head), but the majority are found in haematopoietic compartments (arrows). Weakly F4/80$^+$ monocytes also seen closely associated with RBMM (asterisk). B. 5-μm section of day 14 mouse foetal liver after fixation with paraformaldehyde and staining with F4/80, shows associations of FLM with developing erythroid cells. C. Autoradiograph of [^{3}H]thymidine incorporation into clustering cells, pulsed for 2 h *in vitro*. Underlying RBMM stained with F4/80. D. Foetal liver clusters after 4 h adherence. Large well-spread F4/80$^+$ FLM (arrowhead) are present beneath attached erythroblasts. Unclustered fibroblasts were F4/80$^-$ (arrow). E. Reconstitution of stripped RBMM with bone marrow cells in presence of divalent cations. F. Reconstitution of stripped FLM with foetal liver erythroblasts in presence of divalent cations. ×450.

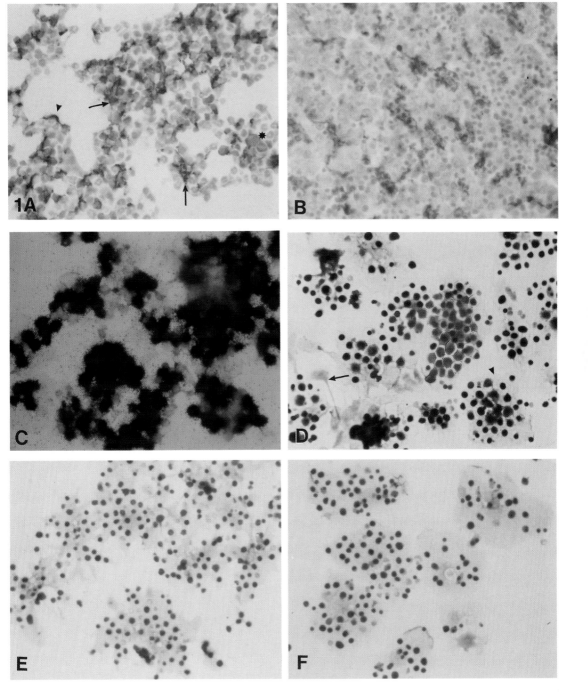

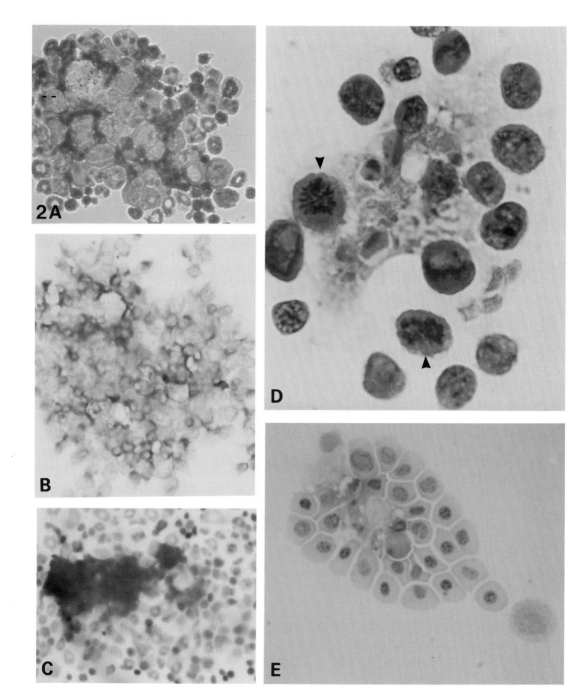

Fig. 3. Isolation of resident bone marrow macrophages and foetal liver macrophages for rosetting assays

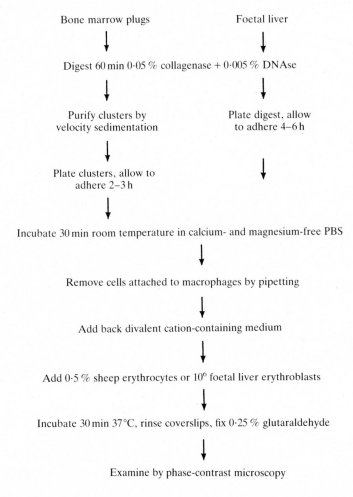

erythroblastic islet may phagocytose up to 40 nuclei per day (Yoffey & Yaffe, 1980). Indirect evidence that this cannot be the only function of RBMM has come from our unpublished observations that erythroblastic islets can be isolated from chicken bone marrow (Fig. 2E). These consist of one or more central acid-phosphatase-positive macrophages surrounded by developing erythroblasts, which, in the chicken, do not undergo enucleation.

Fig. 2. Morphology and histochemistry of purified mouse (A–D) or chicken (E) bone-marrow clusters in cytocentrifuge smears (A,B,C,E) or after adherence (D). A. May–Grunwald–Giemsa stain showing mixed myeloid and erythroid nature of clusters. B. Cluster stained for acid phosphatase, which reveals the presence of several intensely staining RBMM within clusters. C. Cluster stained with alkaline phosphatase to reveal presence of fibroblastic reticulum cells. D. Adherent cluster stained with acid phosphatase, showing the predominantly myeloid nature of cells associated with RBMM. Note mitotic figures (arrowheads). E. Chicken erythroblastic islet stained with acid phosphatase to show central macrophage. A–C, ×450; D, ×1500; E, ×1000.

Since the survival, growth and differentiation of haematopoietic cells *in vitro* depends on the continuous presence of specific colony stimulating factors (reviewed in Metcalf, 1984), it is interesting to speculate whether RBMM and FLM are important sources of these trophic factors *in vivo*, under steady-state conditions. There is some evidence that FLM and adult Kupffer cells are able to produce erythropoietin-like activity *in vitro* (Gruber *et al.* 1977; Paul *et al.* 1984) but there is no information on other growth factors. A major difficulty in exploring the biosynthetic capacities of these tissue macrophage populations is that sufficient numbers of purified cells cannot be obtained easily for analysis of growth factor production, either at the level of mRNA or protein synthesis (P.R. Crocker, unpublished observations). However, studies with mouse peritoneal macrophages and cultured human monocytes, which can be obtained pure and in large numbers ($>10^6$), have demonstrated the capacity of these cells to synthesize and secrete several of the haematopoietic growth factors. These include erythropoietin, GM-CSF, G-CSF and M-CSF (CSF-1) (Metcalf, 1984; Metcalf & Nicola, 1985; Rich, 1986; Horiguchi *et al.* 1987; Rambaldi *et al.* 1987; Thorens *et al.* 1987). In addition, macrophages are an important source of interleukin (IL)-1α, shown to be identical with haemopoietin-1 (Bartelmez & Stanley, 1985; Mochizuki *et al.* 1987). This molecule, which has a broad range of biological activities (Kampschmidt, 1984), is able to synergize with haematopoietic growth factors to promote the growth of developmentally very early progenitor cells (Stanley *et al.* 1986). *In vitro*, IL-1 and the macrophage product, tumour necrosis factor (TNF)α, can promote myelomono-cytic growth indirectly by stimulating the production of GM-CSF, G-CSF and M-CSF from fibroblasts and endothelial cells (Zucali *et al.* 1986; Broudy *et al.* 1987; Seelentag *et al.* 1987). Finally, IL-1 can also act negatively by inhibiting the growth of erythroid progenitors in response to erythropoietin (Schooley *et al.* 1987).

In addition to the above factors, macrophages are able to secrete a broad variety of other substances (Nathan, 1987), several of which could influence haematopoietic cell growth and differentiation. Well-characterized macrophage factors with inhibi-tory activity include α/β interferons, transforming growth factor (TGF)β and prostaglandins. In addition, bone marrow cells with macrophage-like properties are sources of two distinct but poorly characterized activities, one that stimulates and one that inhibits stem cell proliferation (Wright *et al.* 1980, 1982). However, at present it is unclear whether these latter activities are derived from RBMM or from the more numerous immature monocytes present in bone marrow cell suspensions. Although both cell types belong to the same lineage, they are likely to display widely differing secretory activities. This would be consistent with our single-cell analysis of RBMM, which showed that their expression of various surface antigens and receptors differed both quantitatively and qualitatively from those expressed by monocytes and peritoneal macrophages (Crocker & Gordon, 1985).

From the above discussion it is probable that macrophages participate in a complex regulatory network involving a variety of cell types, cytokines and haematopoietic growth factors. It is clear from *in vitro* and *in vivo* studies that the production of haematopoietic growth factors and IL-1 by peritoneal macrophages or

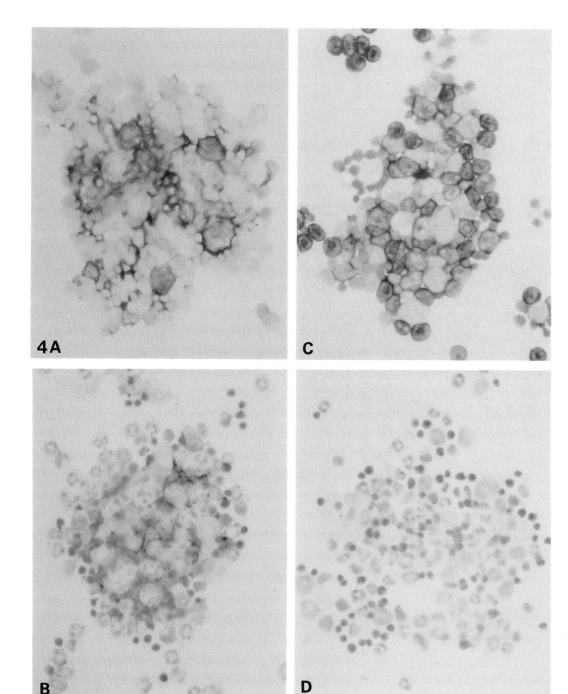

monocytes is not usually constitutive, but requires addition of either inflammatory stimulants, such as endotoxin, or certain haematopoietic growth factors (Metcalf, 1984; Metcalf & Nicola, 1985; Horiguchi *et al.* 1987). In the case of GM-CSF, even such non-specific stimuli as adhesion or phagocytosis were found to induce its synthesis and secretion by mouse peritoneal macrophages (Thorens *et al.* 1987). These observations, together with the suggestion that mRNA for several of the colony stimulating factors cannot be detected in long-term bone marrow cultures despite the presence of large numbers of macrophages (Allen & Dexter, 1984; Dexter & Spooncer, 1987), raise the possibility that production of these factors by macrophages may be more important during inflammatory responses than during steady-state haematopoiesis. Further studies are clearly needed to determine the range of synthetic and secretory activities of RBMM and FLM *in situ*.

Isolation of haematopoietic cell clusters

To gain insight into the possible functions of RBMM, it has been important to develop methods for their isolation rather than to use more accessible populations such as peritoneal macrophages (mouse) or blood monocytes (human) whose phenotypes differ from that of RBMM in either species (Crocker & Gordon, 1985; S-H. Lee, personal communication). Several investigators have shown that erythroblastic islets can be isolated from rodent bone marrow and spleen following gentle mechanical disruption (Le Charpentier & Prenant, 1975; Yoffey & Yaffe, 1980; Macario *et al.* 1981; Zakharov & Prenant, 1982). In all cases, the erythroblastic islets or 'nests' consisted of a single central macrophage surrounded by a cohort of erythroblasts at similar developmental stages. More recently, however, we found that gentle enzymic dispersion of murine bone marrow plugs with collagenase allowed the recovery of not only erythroblastic islets, but also more numerous clusters of haematopoietic cells, which contained large numbers (often up to 100 or more) of both immature myeloid and erythroid cells together with one or more macrophages (Figs 2–5; Crocker & Gordon, 1985). It is likely that these clusters are derived from much larger 'cell aggregates' by enzymic digestion of collagen and other matrix components that are responsible for maintaining the integrity of the marrow plug *in situ*. Dispersion of these cell aggregates into single-cell suspensions by purely mechanical means, such as vigorous pipetting, results in the virtual loss of RBMM. This is not surprising given the extensive network of delicate RBMM plasma membrane processes in clusters (Figs 1A, 4A,B).

Fig. 4. Immunocytochemical analysis of purified mouse bone marrow clusters in cytocentrifuge smears. Counterstain Mayer's haematoxylin. A. Cluster stained with F4/80 revealing several RBMM and their plasma membrane processes with weaker staining of small, rounded monocytes. B. Cluster stained with SER-4, showing specific staining of RBMM and their extensive plasma membrane associations with haematopoietic cells. C. Cluster stained with 7/4, an antibody specific for myelomonocytic cells, reveals the presence of developing myeloid cells. D. Negative control cluster, stained without first antibody. ×450.

With foetal liver, digestion with collagenase also allowed the recovery of erythroblastic islets together with multicellular aggregates containing a variety of poorly defined cells such as epithelioid pre-hepatocytes and other cells of mesenchymal and endodermal origin (Figs 1D, 5B; Morris *et al.* 1988).

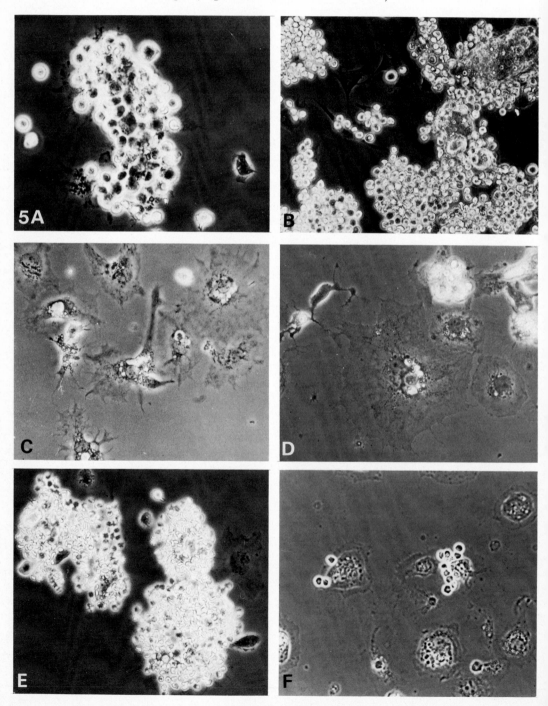

Characterization of haematopoietic cell clusters

An important question regarding the bone marrow clusters was whether they were composed of a subpopulation of haematopoietic cells. In other words, do RBMM establish selective associations that could be important regarding their potential role in haematopoietic regulation? To explore this question, clusters were purified from the excess of single cells in the digests by unit gravity velocity sedimentation on 30% foetal calf serum columns (Crocker & Gordon, 1985). In these preparations, erythroblastic islets are normally outnumbered by the larger clusters, which are usually composed of several macrophages and a mixture of erythroid and myeloid cells (Figs 2, 4). Within the clusters, it is sometimes possible to see a subset of the macrophages tightly surrounded by a concentric cohort of developing red cells. More commonly, however, macrophage plasma membrane processes within the clusters appear to be associated with a mixture of erythroid and myeloid cells.

By several criteria, our results to date have shown that RBMM interact selectively with haematopoietic cells. By morphology, it was found that purified clusters were enriched for immature myeloid and erythroid elements compared with the non-clustered fraction. However, the most striking demonstration of the selective nature of macrophage–haematopoietic cell interactions was seen when clustered and non-clustered fractions were compared for their uptake of tritiated thymidine. Cells in clusters incorporated up to fivefold more thymidine and autoradiography demonstrated that the majority of cells directly attached to RBMM were proliferating (Fig. 1C; Crocker & Gordon, 1985). In contrast to the enrichment for dividing cells, purified clusters were found to be selectively depleted of early granulocyte-macrophage progenitors (Crocker & Gordon, 1985). Early progenitors may be prevented from associating with RBMM as a result of sequestration by extracellular matrix components or by lectin-like interactions with other stromal elements (Aizawa & Tavassoli, 1987). At some point during differentiation, late progenitors such as CFU-E and myeloid cluster-forming cells presumably establish contact with RBMM or FLM membrane processes. They may then remain attached to macrophages within clusters throughout their last cycles of growth and differentiation. In this way, 'oligoclones' would develop around individual macrophages before their exit into the circulation. Experimental evidence for this possibility has been obtained in studies of postnatal liver, using mouse chimeras (Rossant *et al.* 1984), and has been inferred by the observation that erythroblasts often appear to be synchronized in erythroblastic

Fig. 5. Phase contrast micrographs of bone marrow and foetal liver clusters and macrophages after adhesion to glass coverslips. A. Intact bone marrow cluster showing spreading of macrophage plasma membrane underneath attached haematopoietic cells. B. Foetal liver clusters with refractile erythroid cells attached to underlying FLM. Occasional large aggregates of lipid-containing prehepatocytes and free fibroblasts are also present. C. Stripped bone marrow clusters revealing well-spread RBMM which contain prominent perinuclear pinocytic vesicles and varying amounts of phagocytic inclusions. D. Stripped foetal liver clusters showing very large, well-spread FLM with phagocytic inclusions. E. Rosette formation of RBMM with SE. Large numbers of SE bind but are not ingested. F. Lack of rosette formation of FLM with SE, showing that unlike RBMM, they express low levels of SER. ×450.

islets isolated from regenerating adult haematopoietic tissues and foetal liver (Bessis *et al.* 1978; Morris *et al.* 1988). Similarly, with the mouse thymus, Kyewski & co-workers (1982) demonstrated that 'rosettes' of thymocytes attached to a central macrophage could be isolated by enzymic dispersion. Using mixed bone marrow radiation chimeras, the thymocytes in rosettes were often enriched for a single genotype, suggesting they had undergone oligoclonal expansion whilst in contact with the central macrophage (Kyewski *et al.* 1984).

In vivo studies of murine bone marrow have demonstrated that the most intense division occurs subendosteally (Shackney *et al.* 1975). Myeloid progenitors have also been shown to exist in highest numbers close to this region (Lord *et al.* 1975). The higher frequency of proliferating cells in the subendosteum may be related to a correspondingly greater local production of colony stimulating factors compared with axial marrow (Chan & Metcalf, 1972). These may be derived in part from the fibroblastic reticulum cells since they are able to produce haematopoietic growth factors constitutively *in vitro* (Brockbank & Van Peer, 1983) and their subendosteal location correlates well with growth factor production and regional cell proliferation. It is likely that a proportion of the clusters liberated by collagenase digestion is derived from subendosteal regions of the bone marrow, since 10–30 % express the intense alkaline phosphatase reactivity of fibroblastic reticulum cells (Fig. 2C) and the majority contain developing myeloid cells, as revealed by morphology or immunocytochemical staining with the monoclonal antibody F7/4, which is specific for myelomonocytic cells (Figs 2A, 4C; Hirsch & Gordon, 1983; Crocker & Gordon, 1985).

Importance of cell–cell contact in haematopoiesis

One of the main aims of our work has been to explore the nature of molecules involved in cellular contacts between macrophages and haematopoietic cells. Several lines of evidence suggest that direct cellular interactions play important regulatory roles in haematopoiesis. In long-term bone marrow cultures, direct contact between the adherent stromal layer and haematopoietic stem cells is necessary for sustained growth (Bentley, 1981). Studies with murine IL-3-dependent stem-cell lines have shown that adhesion to irradiated stroma or to NIH 3T3 fibroblasts abrogates their IL-3 dependence and permits their complete differentiation to myeloid and erythroid lineages (Spooncer *et al.* 1986; Anklesaria *et al.* 1987). The effect of 3T3 cells appears to depend critically on adhesion rather than a metabolic response, because similar results were obtained following fixation of the 3T3 cells with glutaraldehyde (Roberts *et al.* 1987). The importance of adhesion has also been demonstrated in a blast colony assay in which the proliferation of human bone marrow progenitors depends on adhesion to a preformed stroma (Gordon *et al.* 1987*a*). At present, the nature of the adhesion between stroma and stem cells has not been defined, though glycosaminoglycans and lectin-like interactions have been implicated (Spooncer *et al.* 1983; Green *et al.* 1986; Aizawa & Tavassoli, 1987).

To date, the best defined substrate for haematopoietic cell adhesion is fibronectin. This was first demonstrated for erythroid cells (Patel & Lodish, 1984) and subsequently for myeloid cells (Giancotti *et al*. 1986) and is mediated *via* a well-characterized 140K ($K = 10^3 M_r$) receptor on immature haematopoietic cells, which is likely to belong to the integrin family of cell adhesion molecules (Hynes, 1987). Interestingly, studies in the mouse and human have shown that adhesion of erythroleukaemia cells or erythroblasts to fibronectin is able to promote haemoglobinization, terminal differentiation and enucleation in the presence of chemical inducers or erythropoietin (Patel & Lodish, 1987; Tsai *et al*. 1987). During the transition between erythroblast and erythrocyte, levels of fibronectin receptors (FnR) are greatly decreased and this correlates with the decreased adherence of the mature red cell to fibronectin (Patel *et al*. 1985). This finding has led to speculation that the interaction of immature haematopoietic cells with fibronectin prevents their premature release from bone marrow into the circulation (Patel *et al*. 1985). Other defined adhesion molecules for immature haematopoietic cells include a β-galactoside lectin on erythroblasts, which mediates agglutination (Harrison & Chesterton, 1980) and a recently described extracellular matrix glycoprotein, haemonectin, which appears to bind selectively to myeloid cells (Campbell *et al*. 1987).

RBMM express novel cell surface haemagglutinins: sheep erythrocyte receptor

In order to investigate the surface properties of RBMM and FLM, we devised a method for their purification based on adherence of cluster-containing macrophages to glass coverslips followed by removal of the attached haematopoietic cells (Figs 3, 5). In the case of RBMM, an extensive phenotypic cell analysis was carried out, comparing their surface properties with those of resident peritoneal macrophages (RPM) (Crocker & Gordon, 1985).

The most interesting and unexpected finding of this survey was the ability of most RBMM to bind large numbers of unopsonized sheep erythrocytes, a property which had previously not been described for murine macrophages (Fig. 5E). In view of the striking similarity between rosette formation with sheep erythrocytes and the natural ability of RBMM to cluster with haematopoietic cells, we considered the possibility that by chance, sheep erythrocytes were defining a macrophage receptor, whose natural ligand was present on the attached haematopoietic cells (Crocker & Gordon, 1986). Consistent with this hypothesis, RBMM showed virtually no ingestion of sheep erythrocytes over a period of several hours, an expected property of a putative cell interaction receptor.

Other characteristics of the sheep erythrocyte receptor (SER) are summarized in Table 1. The receptor is a macrophage-restricted, lectin-like protein, which recognizes sialylated glycoconjugates on the surface of sheep erythrocytes. The enhancement of binding observed after pretreatment of sheep erythrocytes with trypsin or protease and the potent inhibition mediated by the ganglioside GD1a (but not by a variety of heavily sialylated glycoproteins) raise the possibility that the sialic acid

Table 1. *Properties of the sheep erythrocyte receptor on resident bone marrow macrophages*

General

Mediates binding, not ingestion
Divalent cation-independent
Temperature-independent (0–37°C)
Unaffected by metabolic inhibitors
Expressed predominantly on Ia-negative subpopulation

Specific

SER trypsin-labile, neuraminidase-resistant
E ligand trypsin and protease-resistant, neuraminidase-labile
Binding inhibited by neuraminyllactose, 50% inhibition at 10 mM
No inhibition by lactose or neuraminic acid (100 mM)
Binding inhibited by ganglioside GD1a, 50% inhibition at 11 μM
No inhibition by ganglioside GM1 (650 μM), fetuin or orosomucoid (20 μM).

For further details see Crocker & Gordon (1986)

recognized on sheep erythrocytes is part of a ganglioside rather than a glycoprotein. In addition to RBMM, SER in adult mice was expressed at high levels on stromal lymph node macrophages, at intermediate levels on liver and stromal splenic macrophages, but it was low or undetectable on monocytes and peritoneal, pleural and bronchoalveolar macrophages (Fig. 6; Crocker & Gordon, 1986).

Regulation of SER expression

It was important to elucidate the mechanism(s) regulating expression of SER as this would allow us to develop an *in vitro* model of SER expression using an abundant macrophage population such as thioglycollate-elicited peritoneal macrophages (TPM). This would be essential in prospective cellular, biochemical and functional studies. One possibility was that the differential expression of SER observed *in vivo* was simply related to the maturity of different macrophage populations. This was

Fig. 6. Expression of SER on different macrophage populations. Cells were obtained by collagenase digestion (A–D, F) or lavage (E). Rosetting was carried out with cells adherent to glass coverslips (A–E) or in suspension followed by cytocentrifugation onto glass slides (F). Preparations were fixed were glutaraldehyde and stained by immunocytochemistry with anti-Ia to detect Ia antigens (A) or with F4/80 (B–F) and counterstained with Mayer's haematoxylin. A. Inverse expression of SER and Ia antigens on RBMM. One RBMM is stained strongly for Ia antigens but does not bind SE, whereas two RBMM bind large numbers of SE but are negative for Ia antigens (arrows). B. RBMM stained with F4/80. Unlike Ia antigens, F4/80 is uniformly expressed on both SER positive and negative RBMM. C. Kupffer cells stained with F4/80 showing moderate rosetting to SE. D. Adherent mesenteric lymph node cells showing a large 'stromal' F4/80 positive macrophage with attached SE. Small F4/80 positive monocyte-like cells and F4/80 negative cells do not form rosettes (arrows). E. Bronchoalveolar macrophages, obtained by lavage, and stained with F4/80 do not bind SE. F. Cytocentrifuge preparation of spleen cells after rosette formation in suspension and stained with F4/80. A single F4/80 positive macrophage with plasma membrane processes binds several SE. Cells with lymphocyte morphology do not form rosettes (arrows). ×450.

clearly not the case, however, since cultivation of TPM in media supplemented with 10% foetal calf serum for periods of up to 2 weeks did not result in significant expression of SER. We therefore considered the possibility that an inducing activity was absent from the *in vitro* system. Accordingly, when the foetal calf serum was replaced with homologous murine plasma or serum, we observed a dose-dependent induction of SER on TPM, which reached maximal levels within 3 days. The

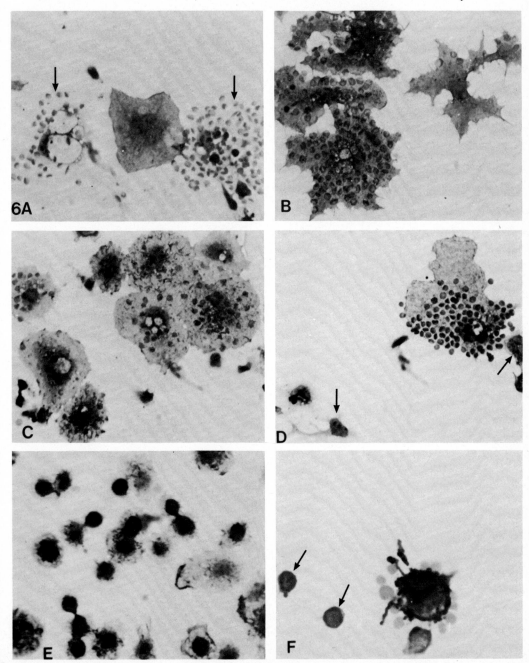

inducing activity of serum appeared to be species- but not strain-restricted, since relatively little induction of SER was observed in the presence of rat, guinea-pig, rabbit, horse or human sera, whereas equivalent induction was observed with sera from different inbred mouse strains (unpublished results).

The availability of TPM expressing high levels of SER has allowed us to raise a monoclonal antibody to the receptor. This was achieved by immunizing rats with induced TPM and screening hybridoma supernatants for inhibition of rosette formation. A hybridoma, called SER-4, was isolated using this strategy which was also able to inhibit binding of sheep erythrocytes to RBMM (unpublished results). Immunocytochemistry with this antibody on bone marrow clusters has confirmed the specificity of SER for RBMM and, unlike F4/80, it does not react with monocytes within clusters (Fig. 4B).

Murine haematopoietic cells express an appropriate ligand for SER

By the criteria described in Table 1, the induced SER was indistinguishable from SER expressed naturally on RBMM. Induction of SER on TPM was fully reversible, involved protein synthesis (inhibitable by cycloheximide) and required the continuous presence of mouse serum to maintain high levels. The levels of SER achieved *in vitro* were equivalent to, or even greater in some experiments, than those observed on isolated RBMM. It therefore provided us with a suitable system with which we could ask whether an appropriate sialylated ligand for SER was expressed on the surface of murine haematopoietic cells.

When single-cell suspensions from bone marrow were added to peritoneal macrophages cultured for 3 days in either 10% mouse serum or 10% foetal calf serum, significant attachment was only observed to the former, which also expressed high levels of SER. The characteristics of bone marrow cell binding to induced macrophages were very similar to those observed with sheep erythrocytes. These included the independence of divalent cations and apparent requirement for a protease-resistant sialylated structure(s). These observations are therefore consistent with the possibility that SER on RBMM can interact with an appropriate sialylated ligand on the attached haematopoietic cells.

A distinct haemagglutinin mediates binding of erythroblasts to FLM and RBMM

The finding that attachment of sheep erythrocytes to RBMM was independent of divalent cations suggested that SER was unlikely to be a dominant cell adhesion receptor, since, first, removal of divalent cations was an important step for detachment of haematopoietic cells from RBMM and FLM during their purification (Figs 3, 5) and, secondly, when bone marrow cells or foetal liver erythroblasts were added back to purified RBMM or FLM respectively, maximal adhesion was only obtained in the presence of divalent cations (Fig. 1E,F). In addition, FLM purified from erythroblastic islets expressed very low levels of SER (Fig. 5F). These

Table 2. *Comparison of properties of the sheep erythrocyte receptor (SER) and erythroblast receptor (EbR) in the mouse*

Property	SER	EbR
Stromal macrophage-restricted	+	+
Synthesized by macrophages	+	+
Binding without ingestion	+	+
Receptor protease-labile	+	+
Divalent cation dependent	−	+
Ligand protease-labile	−	−
Ligand neuraminidase-labile	+	−
Inhibitable by neuraminyllactose	+	−
Inhibitable by ganglioside GD1a	+	−
Induced by mouse serum *in vitro*	+	−

Table 3. *Differential expression of sheep erythrocyte receptor (SER) and erythroblast receptor (EbR) on macrophage populations*

Macrophage population	SER	EbR
Resident bone marrow macrophages	High	High
Foetal liver macrophages	Low	High
Thioglycollate-elicited peritoneal macrophages (freshly harvested)	Low	Low
Thioglycollate-elicited peritoneal macrophages (3 days in 10 % mouse serum)	High	Low

observations suggested that one or more haemagglutinins distinct from SER are required for high-avidity binding of haematopoietic cells to RBMM and FLM.

To explore the nature of this divalent cation-dependent adhesion, FLM were used, since erythroblasts could be obtained as a relatively homogeneous ligand from foetal livers and they gave minimal background adherence to the glass coverslips during rosetting assays (Morris *et al.* 1988). These studies have confirmed and extended the evidence that the erythroblast receptor (EbR) and SER are distinct (Table 2). Despite the differences in ligand specificity and divalent cation require-ments of the two receptors, they share the properties of being non-phagocytic cell surface proteins which are synthesized and selectively expressed by stromal macrophage subpopulations. Similarly to SER, high levels of EbR have been found on RBMM and stromal lymph node macrophages, whereas low levels are expressed on peritoneal cavity macrophages. Unlike SER, however, we have not observed induction of EbR on peritoneal macrophages cultured in homologous serum, suggesting that expression of the two receptors is controlled by different regulatory pathways (unpublished observations). Consistent with this notion, it has been possible to obtain macrophage populations *in vitro* that express all four possible combinations of the two receptors (Table 3).

The nature of the ligand on erythroblasts recognized by EbR is not yet defined, but it is resistant to treatment with both proteases and neuraminidase. In a preliminary investigation into the cell types that express an appropriate ligand for

EbR, we have seen avid divalent cation-dependent binding by adult bone marrow cells and by erythroblasts from spleens of phenylhydrazine-treated adult mice, but circulating erythrocytes bind poorly. The EbR ligand is therefore expressed at high levels on immature erythroid and myeloid cells but at considerably reduced levels on circulating blood cells. Thus, one potentially important function of EbR may be to prevent premature release of bone marrow cells into the circulation, as has previously been proposed for the FnR (Patel *et al.* 1985). Indeed, the similarities between EbR and FnR led us to investigate the relationship between the two receptors. Known inhibitors of FnR, including RGD-containing peptides and specific antisera to rodent FnR and fibronectin, had no effect on EbR activity, suggesting that erythroblasts do not bind to FLM by this mechanism. Further experiments are needed to identify the nature of EbR, but our studies to date indicate that this is a novel cell adhesion receptor (Morris *et al.* 1988).

In conclusion, there appear to be two distinct haemagglutinins expressed differentially by stromal tissue macrophages which are involved in macrophage–haematopoietic cell interactions. First, SER, which was defined on the basis of binding sheep erythrocytes, can also mediate low-affinity interactions with a homologous ligand on adult bone marrow cells. Establishment of the SER–ligand complex in haematopoietic cell clusters may depend on the second haemagglutinin, EbR which mediates high-avidity adhesion between macrophages and haematopoietic cells.

Functional implications of macrophage–haematopoietic cell adhesion

While the earlier discussion illustrated the likely importance of cell adhesion in haematopoiesis, there has been little insight into the mechanisms involved. Regarding growth and differentiation, it is possible that one outcome of adhesion mediated by receptors such as EbR is the establishment of secondary, low-affinity interactions between other receptors and ligands, which result in a biological response. For example, recent studies have shown that with T lymphocytes, the plasma membrane glycoprotein LFA-1 mediates adhesion to appropriate targets. This can then lead to ligation of the T-cell–receptor complex with antigen which results in cellular activation (Springer *et al.* 1987). Direct cellular activation of lymphocytes has been demonstrated for the human T-cell sheep erythrocyte receptor, CD2 (distinct from the mouse SER), whose natural ligand, LFA-3, is expressed on a broad variety of human cells (reviewed in Springer *et al.* 1987). Similarly, in the haematopoietic system, receptors such as SER and EbR may be capable of mediating direct cellular signalling with haematopoietic cells. In this respect, it is interesting that gangliosides, which are potential ligands for SER, are thought to be important signalling molecules for growth and differentiation (Dixon *et al.* 1987).

Adhesion of progenitors to stroma may promote interactions between certain growth factors or inhibitors presented by the stroma and their corresponding receptors on the haematopoietic cells. For instance, bone marrow extracellular matrix has been shown to sequester colony stimulating factors (Gordon *et al*. 1987*b*) and stromal cells may be able to present at their surface certain growth factors or inhibitors. In the mouse, a plasma membrane association of haematopoietic growth factors has been demonstrated for M-CSF (Cifone & Defendi, 1974; Rettenmier *et al*. 1987) and has been implicated for GM-CSF by the fact that one of the two possible mRNAs encodes a hydrophobic sequence, which could anchor the molecule within the plasma membrane (Gough *et al*. 1985). Recent studies have also shown that IL-1 can exist as a biologically active molecule on the plasma membrane of various cell types including macrophages (Kurt-Jones *et al*. 1985, 1987; Beuscher *et al*. 1987). The future availability of specific antisera should reveal whether molecules such as these are present on the plasma membrane of RBMM and FLM.

Adhesion between stroma and haematopoietic cells could play a role in close-range exchange of nutrients or other substances that influence growth and differentiation. This was proposed by Bessis & Breton-Gorius (1962) who considered the possibility that ferritin might be exchanged between macrophages and erythroblasts in erythroblastic islands. In ultrastructural studies of long-term bone marrow cultures Allen & Dexter (1982) noted occasional gap junctions and an increased number of vesicles at the points of contact between macrophages and erythroblasts. Although there has been no attempt to determine whether substances are exchanged between macrophages and haematopoietic cells, this has been demonstrated for lymphocytes, which are able to transfer lysosomal enzymes to fibroblasts in a contact-dependent fashion (Olsen *et al*. 1986).

Finally, adhesion molecules may be important in guiding the movement of progenitors and their differentiated progeny within the stromal matrix and across the endothelial barrier into the circulation. Control over these processes could be provided by the temporally regulated expression of ligands on haematopoietic cells and modulation of adhesion receptors by the fixed stromal elements. Receptors such as SER and EbR are excellent candidates for such functions.

Conclusions

We have identified two distinct and novel receptors which are selectively expressed at high levels on stromal macrophage populations. One of these, EbR, is present on RBMM and FLM and mediates high-avidity divalent cation-dependent binding between stromal tissue macrophages and immature haematopoietic cells and appears to represent a novel cell-adhesion system. In contrast, SER is present on RBMM but absent from FLM and is able to mediate low-avidity binding of haematopoietic cells when expressed at high levels *in vitro*. At present, the specific functions of these receptors are unknown but their distribution and properties indicate a fundamental role in communication between macrophages and haematopoietic cells. The future production of specific inhibitors to these receptors may shed light on the functional significance of macrophage–haematopoietic cell interactions.

Work in this laboratory was supported by grants from Medical Research Council and Leukaemia Research Fund, UK. P.R.C. is a Beit Memorial Fellow and a Junior Research Fellow of Wolfson

College, Oxford University. We thank Maxine Hill and Jim Kent for excellent technical assistance, Stan Buckingham for photography, Elwena Gregory for preparation of the manuscript and Dr Genevieve Milon for preparation and staining of bone marrow clusters and critical reading of the manuscript.

References

AHMAD, L. A. & BAINTON, D. F. (1986). Presence of alkaline-phosphatase-positive reticulum cells in fetal liver and bone marrow of mice and their absence in yolk sac. *Expl Hemat.* **14**, 705–709.

AIZAWA, S. & TAVASSOLI, M. (1987). *In vitro* homing of hemopoietic stem cells is mediated by a recognition system with galactosyl and mannosyl specificities. *Proc. natn. Acad. Sci. U.S.A.* **84**, 4485–4489.

ALLEN, T. D. & DEXTER, T. M. (1982). Ultrastructural aspects of erythropoietic differentiation in long-term bone marrow culture. *Differentiation* **21**, 86–94.

ALLEN, T. D. & DEXTER, T. M. (1984). The essential cells of the hemopoietic microenvironment. *Expl Hemat.* **12**, 517–521.

ANKLESARIA, P., KASE, K., GLOWACKI, J., HOLLAND, C. A., SAKAKEENY, M. A., WRIGHT, J. A., FITZGERALD, T. J., LEE, C-Y. & GREENBERGER, J. S. (1987). Engraftment of a clonal bone marrow stromal cell line *in vivo* stimulates hematopoietic recovery from total body irradiation. *Proc. natn. Acad. Sci. U.S.A.* **84**, 7681–7685.

AUSTYN, J. M. & GORDON, S. (1981). F4/80, a monoclonal antibody directed specifically against the mouse macrophage. *Eur. J. Immun.* **11**, 805–815.

BAINTON, D. F. (1985). Bone marrow stromal cells-fibroblasts and macrophages. In *Mononuclear Phagocytes. Characteristics, Physiology and Function* (ed. R. van Furth), pp. 125–136. Dordrecht: Martinus Nijhoff.

BAINTON, D. F., MALONEY, M. A., PATT, H. M. & STERN, R. (1986). Characterisation of rabbit stromal fibroblasts derived from red and yellow bone marrow. *J. exp. Med.* **163**, 400–413.

BARTELMEZ, S. H. & STANLEY, E. R. (1985). Synergism between hemopoietic growth factors (HGFs) detected by their effects on cells bearing receptors for a lineage specific HGF: Assay of hemopoietin-1. *J. cell. Physiol.* **122**, 370–378.

BEN-ISHAY, Z. & YOFFEY, J. M. (1971). Reticular cells of erythroid islands of rat bone marrow in hypoxia and rebound. *J. Reticuloendothel. Soc.* **10**, 482–494.

BENTLEY, S. A. (1981). Close range cell:cell interaction required for stem cell maintenance in continuous bone marrow culture. *Expl Hemat.* **9**, 308–312.

BERMAN, I. (1976). The ultrastructure of erythroblastic islands and reticular cells in mouse bone marrow. *J. Ultrastruct. Res.* **17**, 291–313.

BESSIS, M. (1958). L'ilot erythroblastique, unite fonctionelle de la moelle osseuse. *Rev. Hemtal.* **13**, 8–11.

BESSIS, M. & BRETON-GORIUS, J. (1962). Iron metabolism in the bone marrow as seen by electron microscopy: a critical review. *Blood* **19**, 635–663.

BESSIS, M., MIZE, C. & PRENANT, M. (1978). Erythropoiesis: Comparison of *in vivo* and *in vitro* amplification. *Blood Cells* **4**, 155–168.

BEUSCHER, H. U., FALLON, R. J. & COLTEN, H. R. (1987). Macrophage membrane interleukin 1 regulates the expression of acute phase proteins in human hepatoma Hep 3B cells. *J. Immun.* **139**, 1896–1901.

BROCKBANK, K. G. M. & VAN PEER, C. M. J. (1983). Colony-stimulating activity production by hemopoietic organ fibroblastoid cells *in vitro*. *Acta Haemat.* **69**, 369–375.

BROUDY, V. C., KAUSHANSKY, K., HARLAN, J. M. & ADAMSON, J. W. (1987). Interleukin 1 stimulates human endothelial cells to produce granulocyte-macrophage colony-stimulating factor and granulocyte colony-stimulating factor. *J. Immun.* **139**, 464–468.

CAMPBELL, A. D., LONG, M. W. & WICHA, M. S. (1987). Haemonectin, a bone marrow adhesion protein specific for cells of granulocyte lineage. *Nature, Lond.* **329**, 744–746.

CHAN, S. H. & METCALF, D. (1972). Local production of colony-stimulating factor within the bone marrow: Role of non-hematopoietic cells. *Blood* **40**, 646–653.

CIFONE, M. & DEFENDI, V. (1974). Cyclic expression of a growth conditioning factor (MGF) on the cell surface. *Nature, Lond.* **252**, 151–153.

CROCKER, P. R. & GORDON, S. (1985). Isolation and characterisation of resident stromal macrophages and hematopoietic cell clusters from mouse bone marrow. *J. exp. Med.* **162**, 993–1014.

CROCKER, P. R. & GORDON, S. (1986). Properties and distribution of a lectin like haemagglutinin differentially expressed by murine stromal tissue macrophages. *J. exp. Med.* **164**, 1862–1875.

DE JONG, J. P., NIKKELS, P. G. J., PIERSMA, A. H. & PLOEMACHER, R. E. (1987). Erythropoiesis and macrophage subsets in medullary and extramedullary sites. In *Molecular and Cellular Aspects of Erythropoietin and Erythropoiesis.* NATO ASI Series H, Cell Biology vol. 8. (ed. I. N. Rich), pp. 237–258. Berlin, Heidelberg: Springer-Verlag.

DEXTER, T. M. (1982). Stromal cell associated haemopoiesis. *J. cell. Physiol.* **Suppl. 1**, 87–94.

DEXTER, T. M. & SPOONCER, E. (1987). Growth and differentiation in the hemopoietic system. *A. Rev. Cell Biol.* **3**, 423–441.

DIXON, S. J., STEWART, D., GRINSTEIN, S. & SPIEGEL, S. (1987). Transmembrane signaling by the B subunit of cholera toxin: increased cytoplasmic free calcium in rat lymphocytes. *J. Cell Biol.* **105**, 1153–1160.

FLOREY, H. W. & GOWANS, J. L. (1962). In *General Pathology, Third Edition* (ed. H. Florey), pp. 128–138. London: Lloyd-Luke.

FRIEDENSTEIN, A. J., CHAILAKHYAN, R. K., LATSINIK, N. V., PANASYUK, A. F. & KEILISS-BOROK, (1974). Stromal cells responsible for transferring the microenvironment of the hemopoietic tissues: Cloning *in vitro* and retransplantation *in vivo. Transplantation* **17**, 331–340.

GIANCOTTI, F. G., COMOGLIO, P. M. & TARONE, G. (1986). Fibronectin-plasma membrane interaction in the adhesion of hemopoietic cells. *J. Cell Biol.* **103**, 429–437.

GORDON, M. Y., DOWDING, C. R., RILEY, G. P., GOLDMAN, J. M. & GREAVES, M. F. (1987*a*). Altered adhesive interactions with marrow stroma of haematopoietic progenitor cells in chronic myeloid leukaemia. *Nature, Lond.* **328**, 342–344.

GORDON, M. Y., RILEY, G. P., WATT, S. M. & GREAVES, M. F. (1987*b*). Compartmentalisation of a haematopoietic growth factor (GM-CSF) by glycosaminoglycans in the bone marrow microenvironment. *Nature, Lond.* **326**, 403–405.

GOUGH, N. M., METCALF, D., GOUGH, J., GRAIL, D. & DUNN, A. R. (1985). Structure and expression of the mRNA for murine granulocyte-macrophage colony stimulating factor. *EMBO J.* **4**, 645–653.

GREEN, E. S., DREXLER, H. G., HOFFBRAND, A. V. & FRANCIS, G. E. (1986). Haematopoietic cell-stromal cell interactions in freshly explanted bone marrow. *Br. J. Haemat.* **64**, 837.

GRUBER, D. F., ZUCALI, J. R. & MIRAND, E. A. (1977). Identification of erythropoietin producing cells in fetal mouse liver cultures. *Expl Hemat.* **5**, 392–398.

HARRISON, F. L. & CHESTERTON, C. J. (1980). Erythroid developmental agglutinin is a protein lectin mediating specific cell–cell adhesion between differentiating rabbit erythroblasts. *Nature, Lond.* **286**, 502–504.

HIRSCH, S. & GORDON, S. (1983). Polymorphic expression of a neutrophil differentiation antigen revealed by monoclonal antibody 7/4. *Immunogenetics* **18**, 229–239.

HORIGUCHI, J., WARREN, M. K., RALPH, P. & KUFE, D. (1987). Expression of the macrophage-specific colony-stimulating factor in human monocytes treated with granulocyte-macrophage colony-stimulating factor. *Blood* **69**, 1259–1261.

HUME, D. A., LOUTIT, J. F. & GORDON, S. (1984). The mononuclear phagocyte system of the mouse defined by immunohistochemical localization of antigen F4/80. Macrophages of bone and associated connective tissue. *J. Cell Sci.* **66**, 189–194.

HUMPHREY, J. H. & SUNDARAM, V. (1985). Origin and turnover of follicular dendritic cells and marginal zone macrophages in the mouse spleen. *Adv. exp. Med. Biol.* Vol. **186**, 167–170.

HYNES, R. O. (1987). Integrins: A family of cell surface receptors. *Cell* **48**, 549–554.

JOHNSON, G. R. & METCALF, D. (1978). Clonal analysis *in vitro* of fetal hepatic hematopoiesis. In *Differentiation of Normal and Neoplastic Hematopoietic Cells* (ed. Clarkson, Marks & Till), pp. 49–62. New York: Cold Spring Harbor Laboratory.

KAMPSCHMIDT, R. F. (1984). The numerous postulated biological manifestations of interleukin-1. *J. Leuk. Biol.* **36**, 341–355.

KURT-JONES, E. A., BELLER, D. I., MIZEL, S. B. & UNANUE, E. R. (1985). Identification of a cell surface associated interleukin 1. *Proc. natn. Acad. Sci. U.S.A.* **82**, 1204–1208.

KURT-JONES, E. A., FIERS, W. & POBER, J. S. (1987). Membrane interleukin 1 induction on human endothelial cells and dermal fibroblasts. *J. Immun.* **139**, 2317–2324.

KYEWSKI, B. A., ROUSE, R. V. & KAPLAN, H. S. (1982). Thymocyte rosettes: Multicellular complexes of lymphocytes and bone marrow-derived stromal cells in the mouse thymus. *Proc. natn. Acad. Sci. U.S.A.* **79**, 5646–5650.

KYEWSKI, B. A., TRAVIS, M. & KAPLAN, H. S. (1984). Intrathymic lymphopoiesis: stromal cell-associated proliferation of T cells is independent of lymphocyte genotype. *J. Immun.* **133**, 1111–1116.

LE CHARPENTIER, Y. & PRENANT, M. (1975). Isolement de l'ilot erythroblastique. Etude en microscopie optique et electronique a balayage. *Nouv. Rev. Fr. Hematol.* **15**, 119–140.

LORD, B. I., TESTA, N. G. & HENDRY, J. H. (1975). The relative spatial distribution of CFU-S and CFU-C in normal mouse femurs. *Blood* **46**, 65–72.

MACARIO, A. J. L., DUGAN, C., PEREZ-LLORET, I. L. & DE MACARIO, E. C. (1981). Purification of erythroblastic nests. *Blood* **57**, 922–927.

MEDLOCK, E. S. & HAAR, J. L. (1983). The liver hemopoietic environment: I. Developing hepatocytes and their role in fetal hemopoiesis. *Anat. Rec.* **207**, 31–41.

METCALF, D. (1984). *The Hemopoietic Colony Stimulating Factors*. Amsterdam: Elsevier.

METCALF, D. & NICOLA, A. (1985). Synthesis by mouse peritoneal cells of G-CSF, the differentiation inducer for myeloid leukaemia cells: stimulation by endotoxin, M-CSF and multi-CSF. *Leuk. Res.* **9**, 35–50.

MOCHIZUKI, D. Y., EISENMEN, J. R., CONLON, P. J., LARSEN, A. D. & TUSHINSKI, R. J. (1987). Interleukin 1 regulates hematopoietic activity, a role previously ascribed to hemopoietin-1. *Proc. natn. Acad. Sci. U.S.A.* **84**, 5267–5271.

MORRIS, L., CROCKER, P. R. & GORDON, S. (1988). Murine fetal liver macrophages bind developing erythroblasts by a divalent cation-dependent hemagglutinin. *J. Cell Biol.* **106**, 649–656.

NATHAN, C. F. (1987). Secretory products of macrophages. *J. clin. Invest.* **79**, 319–326.

OLSEN, I., OLIVER, T., MUIR, H., SMITH, R. & PARTRIDGE, T. (1986). Role of cell adhesion in contact-dependent transfer of a lysosomal enzyme from lymphocytes to fibroblasts. *J. Cell Sci.* **85**, 231–244.

PATEL, V. P., CIECHANOVER, A., PLATT, O. & LODISH, H. F. (1985). Mammalian reticulocytes lose adhesion to fibronectin during maturation to erythrocytes. *Proc. natn. Acad. Sci. U.S.A.* **82**, 440–444.

PATEL, V. P. & LODISH, H. F. (1984). Loss of adhesion of murine erythroleukaemia cells to fibronectin during erythroid differentiation. *Science* **224**, 996–998.

PATEL, V. P. & LODISH, H. F. (1987). A fibronectin matrix is required for differentiation of murine erythroleukaemia cells into reticulocytes. *J. Cell Biol.* **105**, 3107–3118.

PATT, H. M., MALONEY, M. A. & FLANNERY, M. L. (1982). Haematopoietic microenvironment transfer by stromal fibroblasts derived from bone marrow varying in cellularity. *Expl Hemat.* **10**, 738–742.

PAUL, P., ROTHMANN, S. A., McMAHON, J. T. & GORDON, A. S. (1984). Erythropoietin secretion by isolated rat Küpffer cells. *Expl Hemat.* **12**, 825–830.

PLOEMACHER, R. E., PIERSMA, A. H. & BROCKBANK, K. G. M. (1984). The nature and function of granulopoietic microenvironments. *Blood Cells* **10**, 341–367.

RAMBALDI, A., YOUNG, D. C. & GRIFFIN, J. D. (1987). Expression of the M-CSF (CSF-1) gene by human monocytes. *Blood* **69**, 1409–1413.

RETTENMIER, C. W., ROUSSEL, M. F., ASHMAN, R. A., RALPH, P., PRICE, K. & SHERR, C. J. (1987). Synthesis of membrane-bound colony-stimulating factors-1 (CSF-1) and down modulation of CSF-1 receptors in NIH 3T3 cells transformed by cotransfection of the human CSF-1 and c-*fms* (CSF-1 receptor) genes. *Molec. Cell Biol.* **7**, 2378–2387.

RICH, I. N. (1986). A role for the macrophage in normal hemopoiesis. I. Functional capacity of bone marrow-derived macrophages to release hemopoietic growth factors. *Expl Hemat.* **14**, 738–745.

ROSSANT, J., VIJH, K. M., GROSSI, C. E. & COOPER, M. D. (1984). Clonal origin of haematopoietic colonies in the postnatal mouse liver. *Nature, Lond.* **319**, 507–511.

ROBERTS, R. A., SPOONCER, E., PARKINSON, E. K., LORD, B. I., ALLEN, T. D. & DEXTER, T. M. (1987). Metabolically inactive 3T3 cells can substitute for marrow stromal cells to promote the proliferation and development of multipotent haemopoietic stem cells. *J. cell Physiol.* **132**, 203–214.

SAKAI, N., JOHNSTONE, C. & WEISS, L. (1981). Bone marrow cells associated with heightened eosinophilopoiesis: An electron microscope study of murine bone marrow stimulated by *Ascaris suum. Am. J. Anat.* **161**, 11–32.

SCHOOLEY, J. C., KULLGREN, B. & ALLISON, A. C. (1987). Inhibition by interleukin-1 of the action of erythropoietin on erythroid precursors and its possible role in the pathogenesis of hypoplastic anaemias. *Br. J. Haemat.* **67**, 11–17.

SEELENTAG, W. K., MERMOD, J.-J., MONTESANO, R. & VASSALLI, P. (1987). Additive effects of interleukin-1 and tumour necrosis factor-α on the accumulation of the three granulocyte and macrophage colony-stimulating factor mRNAs in human endothelial cells. *EMBO J.* **6**, 2261–2265.

SHACKNEY, S. E., FORD, S. S. & WITTIG, A. B. (1975). Kinetic–microarchitectural correlations in the bone marrow of the mouse. *Cell Tissue Kinet.* **8**, 505–516.

SPOONCER, E., GALLAGHER, J. T., KRIZA, F. & DEXTER, T. M. (1983). Regulation of haemopoiesis in long term bone marrow cultures. Glycosaminoglycan synthesis and the stimulation of haemopoiesis by β-O-xylosides. *J. Cell Biol.* **96**, 510–514.

SPOONCER, E., HEYWORTH, C. M., DUNN, A. & DEXTER, T. M. (1986). Self-renewal and differentiation of interleukin-3-dependent multipotent stem cells are modulated by stromal cells and serum factors. *Differentiation* **31**, 111–118.

SPRINGER, T. A., DUSTIN, M. L., KISHIMOTO, T. K. & MARLIN, S. D. (1987). The lymphocyte function-associated LFA-1, CD2, and LFA-3 molecules: Cell adhesion receptors of the immune system. *A. Rev. Immun.* **5**, 223–252.

STANLEY, E. R., BARTOCCI, A., PATINKIN, D., ROSENDAAL, M. & BRADLEY, T. R. (1986). Regulation of very primitive multipotent hemopoietic cells by hemopoietin-1. *Cell* **45**, 667–674.

THORENS, M. B., MERMOD, J.-J. & VASSALLI, P. (1987). Phagocytosis and inflammatory stimuli induce GM-CSF mRNA in macrophages through posttranscriptional regulation. *Cell* **48**, 671–679.

TILL, J. E., McCULLOCH, E. A. & SIMINOVITCH, L. (1964). A stochastic model of stem cell proliferation, based on the growth of spleen colony-forming cells. *Proc. natn. Acad. Sci. U.S.A.* **51**, 29–36.

TRENTIN, J. J. (1971). Determination of bone marrow stem cell differentiation by stromal hemopoietic inductive microenvironments (HIM). *Am. J. Path.* **65**, 621–627.

TSAI, S., PATEL, V. P., BEAUMONT, E., LODISH, H. F., NATHAN, D. G. & SIEFF, C. A. (1987). Differential binding of erythroid and myeloid progenitors to fibroblasts and fibronectin. *Blood* **69**, 1587–1594.

UNDRITZ, E. (1950). Die Regionaren Monocyten der Blutkorperchennester. *Folia Haematol.* **70**, 32–42.

VAN FURTH, R. & COHN, Z. A. (1968). The origin and kinetics of mononuclear phagocytes. *J. exp. med.* **128**, 415–436.

WEISS, L. (1976). The haematopoietic microenvironment of the bone marrow: An ultrastructural study of the stroma in rats. *Anat. Rec.* **186**, 161–184.

WEISS, L. & SAKAI, H. (1984). The hematopoietic stroma. *Am. J. Anat.* **170**, 447–463.

WESTEN, H. & BAINTON, D. F. (1979). Association of alkaline-phosphatase-positive reticulum cells in bone marrow with granulocytic precursors. *J. exp. Med.* **150**, 919–937.

WOLF, N. S. & TRENTIN, J. J. (1968). Haemopoietic colony studies. V. Effect of haemopoietic organ stroma on differentiation of pluripotent stem cells. *J. exp. Med.* **127**, 205–214.

WRIGHT, E. G., ALI, A. M., RICHES, A. C. & LORD, B. I. (1982). Stimulation of hemopoietic stem cell proliferation: characteristics of the stimulator producing cells. *Leuk. Res.* **6**, 531–539.

WRIGHT, E. G., GARLAND, J. M. & LORD, B. I. (1980). Specific inhibition of haemopoietic stem cell proliferation: characteristics of the inhibitor producing cells. *Leuk. Res.* **4**, 537–545.

YOFFEY, J. M. & YAFFE, P. (1980). The phagocytic central reticular cell of the erythroblastic island in rat bone marrow: Changes in hypoxia and rebound. *J. Reticuloendothel. Soc.* **28**, 37–47.

ZAKHAROV, Y. M. & PRENANT, M. (1982). Technique d'isolement et de culture des ilots erythroblastiques. Separation du macrophage central. *Nouv. Rev. Fr. Hematol.* **24**, 363–367.

ZAKHAROV, Y. & PRENANT, M. (1983). Influences des surnageants de culture de macrophages provenant des ilots erythroblastiques sur l'erythropoiese du rat. *Nouv. Rev. Fr. Hematol.* **25**, 17–22.

ZUCALI, J. R., DINARELLO, C. A., OBLON, D. J., GROSS, M. A., ANDERSON, L. & WEINER, R. S. (1986). Interleukin-1 stimulates fibroblasts to produce granulocyte-macrophage colony-stimulating activity and prostaglandin E_2. *J. clin. Invest.* **77**, 1857–1863.

INDEX

The Company of Biologists Limited is a non-profit-making organization whose directors are active professional biologists. The Company, which was founded in 1925, is the owner and publisher of this and *The Journal of Experimental Biology* and *Development* (formerly *Journal of Embryology and Experimental Morphology*).

Journal of Cell Science is devoted to the study of cell organization. Papers will be published dealing with the structure and function of plant and animal cells and their extracellular products, and with such topics as cell growth and division, cell movements and interactions, and cell genetics. Accounts of advances in the relevant techniques will also be published. Contributions concerned with morphogenesis at the cellular and sub-cellular level will be acceptable, as will studies of micro-organisms and viruses, in so far as they are relevant to an understanding of cell organization. Theoretical articles and occasional review articles will be published.

Subscriptions

Journal of Cell Science will be published 14 times in 1988 in the form of 3 volumes, each of 4 parts, and 2 Supplements. The subscription price of volumes 89, 90, 91 plus Supplements 9 and 10 is £325.00 (USA and Canada, US \$620.00; Japan, £355.00) post free. Supplements may be purchased individually – prices on application to the Biochemical Society Book Depot. Orders for 1988 may be sent to any bookseller or subscription agent, or to The Biochemical Society Book Depot, PO Box 32, Commerce Way, Colchester CO2 8HP, UK. Copies of the journal for subscribers in the USA and Canada are sent by air to New Jersey for delivery with the minimum delay.

Back numbers of the *Journal of Cell Science* may be ordered through The Biochemical Society Book Depot. This journal is the successor to the *Quarterly Journal of Microscopical Science*, back numbers of which are obtainable from Messrs William Dawson & Sons, Cannon House, Park Farm Road, Folkestone, Kent CT19 5EE, UK.

Journal of Cell Science Supplements

1 *Higher Order Structure in the Nucleus*
Edited by P. R. Cook and R. A. Laskey (£12/US$23.00)

2 *The Cell Surface in Plant Growth and Development*
Edited by K. Roberts, A. W. B. Johnston, C. W. Lloyd, P. Shaw and
H. W. Woolhouse (£15/US$30.00)

3 *Growth Factors: Structure and Function*
Edited by C. R. Hopkins and R. C. Hughes (£15/US$30.00)

4 *Prospects in Cell Biology*
Edited by A. V. Grimstone, Henry Harris and R. T. Johnson (£15/US$30.00)

5 *The Cytoskeleton: Cell Function and Organization*
Edited by C. W. Lloyd, J. S. Hyams and R. M. Warn (£15/US$30.00)

6 *Molecular Biology of DNA Repair*
Edited by A. R. S. Collins, R. T. Johnson and J. M. Boyle (£40/US$70.00)

7 *Virus Replication and Genome Interactions*
Edited by J. W. Davies *et al.* (£40/US$70.00)

8 *Cell Behaviour: Shape, Adhesion and Motility*
Edited by J. Heaysman, A. Middleton and F. Watt (£35/US$60.00)

These are provided free to subscribers to *Journal of Cell Science*. They may be
purchased separately from:

> The Biochemical Society Book Depot
> PO Box 32
> Commerce Way
> Colchester CO2 8HP
> UK